D1293528

MAN AND HIS UNIVERSE

"O man, look at man! For man has in himself heavens and earth and in him all things are latent." The visions of Hildegarde give us an idea of the medieval, scientific picture of the universe. (See p. 82.)

MAN
AND HIS UNIVERSE

BY

JOHN LANGDON-DAVIES

Author of
"A Short History of Women"
"The New Age of Faith"
"Dancing Catalans"
Etc.

Harper & Brothers Publishers
NEW YORK AND LONDON
1930

MAN
AND HIS UNIVERSE

Copyright, 1930, by John Langdon-Davies

Printed in the U. S. A.

FIRST EDITION

C-E

To

ROBERT B. GERSTENZANG

SYNOPSIS OF CONTENTS

INTRODUCTION   1

§1. How certain ants use their young as living shuttles to weave a
roof to their house. And how such a fact affects the modern man's
outlook on life as a whole, that is, his religion. How a book on
ants is part of a poem, part of a human biography, part of a bible.
§2. What the reader would have thought of these statements if
he had lived in the Middle Ages. §3. How science is poetry in
spite of the popular idea of a scientist. §4. How science is biography
and even ants our relatives. §5. How science is a search after
God. §6. The God of science versus the God of the fundamentalists, with some introduction to the contents of the modern man's
Bible. §7. Why has the human imagination willingly used up so
much energy over scientific research? How a man's overbelief or
religion must be based on his knowledge of the universe and how
anyone who has no time to learn about the universe should have
no time to believe.

CHAPTER I: *The Universe Makes Man*   17

§1. In the beginning the universe made man. One episode in
the story of this making tells how noses became less important
and eyes more so. By taking to the trees man's pre-ape ancestors
rose out of the realm of smell into that of vision, and the impetus
this gave to their brain development enabled them to outdistance
their rivals. §2. A consideration of the enormous knowledge of a
new-born infant and of whence it comes. How you, when you
were still one of your savage ancestors first saw fire, and what
this adventure of the imagination meant for you. How you tamed
the mysterious thing, and thought about it, and made false assumptions about it. §3. How you in your savage days speculated about
the sun, and worshipped it. The tragic wrongness of early human

thought and the misery it caused. §4. How these thoughts, wrong as they were, meant that you, living in the body of your ancestors, had ceased to be an animal and had become a man. Instead of the universe making man, man had begun to remake the universe. The wisdom and the folly of the savage outlook on life. §5. Man's outlook on life as a whole, his religion, depends on his knowledge of the universe. An example of this: the Thonga, natives of South Africa, their science and its resultant philosophy. §6. How are we different from the Thonga? We have wider scientific knowledge. Also we know a little better which of our desires are reasonable and which are not.

CHAPTER II: *The Medieval Picture of the Universe*   47

§1. As we have seen, the way in which we judge life must depend on our knowledge of the universe. Our ancestors have been animals and savage humans; from both we derive something of our total attitude towards life. After them came the period when we, living in the bodies of our ancestors, were medieval men. We cannot understand our minds today without knowing something of them when they were medieval. We must consider how for more than a thousand years Aristotle dominated men's intellects even more than Jesus of Nazareth dominated their emotions. §2. Aristotle's picture of the universe was of a number of transparent spheres one within another. He assumed that the earth was at the centre and that stars and planets moved round it in circles, for religious reasons. Aristotle's idea of the universe seemed right to him because it fitted the facts as he knew them, from which we learn that a scientific explanation may seem right but be wrong. Moreover we see that in his scientific picture of the universe were buried certain "overbeliefs" or religious feelings, from which we learn that scientific theories are often mixed with metaphysics, often without the scientist realising it. §3. Ptolemy's mathematical solution of the position of the stars; and the medieval attitude to what science can tell about the universe. §4. The medieval fundamentalists who got their astronomy from the Bible and insisted that the earth was flat, or the universe shaped like a bathroom. Lactantius proves from the

Bible that Australia cannot exist, and Cosmas proves from the Bible that there is an ocean overhead. §5. A comparison of the points of view about the universe of Aristotle, Ptolemy and the medieval fundamentalists: all were wrong, but which was the right method of approach? §6. Some examples of how Aristotle's ideas of animals were heartily accepted as late as Shakespeare's day. What this blind worship of authority meant to the human spirit in its search for God and truth. §7. The medieval outlook on the universe was that it was meant for man and that every part of it affected his life. Examples of this from Albertus Magnus' supposed treatise, "On the Secrets of Women." The effect of the stars on the unborn child. Hildegarde's visions of the powers and virtues of the stars over the human body. §8. An example of the medieval picture of the universe and its effect on the human outlook on life is to be found in the witchcraft superstition. The arguments for the existence of witches as they are to be found in the Inquisition text-book on the subject. §9. Summary of the medieval outlook, its logic, its unity.

CHAPTER III: *The First Renaissance*   99

§1. The modern man is asked to imagine he is alive in 1543. He is reading a book by Vesalius and another by Copernicus. The nature of the new theories and the effect they had upon the reader. How Copernicus' book played for safety and pretended to be the solution of a mathematical puzzle and not a picture of the universe, or a statement of reality. How Vesalius doubted Galen's medical and anatomical authority and the awfulness of such an offence. How Copernicus showed that God might have made the universe less clumsily than Ptolemy said he had. §2. How you, as your medieval ancestor in 1543, felt uneasy about Copernicus and how you tried to get rid of your uneasiness by writing a refutation. A summary of your refutation: your reasons practical, scientific, philosophic and theological. But at the end you still had a doubt lest Copernicus had not discovered a better idea of God than the old one of Ptolemy and Aristotle. §3. Why the medieval mind did not accept Copernicus: its picture of the universe a unity wherein the change of one part would mean the collapse of the whole. An example of this unity of structure is the solemn way in which a great lawyer advocated the prosecution and legal punishment of animals. How Chassenée defended the rats accused of trespassing and stealing corn. §4. Kepler the sunworshipper and his search for God. All early science is a branch of theology and its object the knowing of God as much as the knowing of his work. How Kepler thought that God could only invent six planets and therefore decided that the sun was the centre of the solar system. How Kepler was worried because God could not keep the planets going at uniform speed and how he saved God's reputation in this matter. §5. How Galileo went up the leaning tower of Pisa and dropped two weights and how the learned professors refused to believe their eyes but went home and read Aristotle. Galileo's telescope and the shocking things it revealed; sunspots, Jupiter's moons, lunar mountains. The objections of the professors. §6. What had Galileo done to the human imagination? How had he laid the way for the modern man's idea of life, God and the universe? The end of authority and of Aristotle and the beginning of looking in front of your nose. Galileo and the Inquisition. §7. The modern man is asked to imagine himself alive in 1643 and to compare his outlook on life with that which he had a hundred years earlier as described at the beginning of the chapter. He writes out his thoughts under the heading, "God, the Universe and my soul" and notes what science has so far done to the medieval outlook. He sees how Galileo was not condemned simply for saying the earth moved, but for upsetting a whole philosophy of God and the universe.

Chapter IV: *Newton* 143

§1. The boy on the sea-shore playing with bright pebbles. Newton's varied enthusiasms and how what they led to gave the modern man his religion. His mind turned the increasing chaos brought by science into a new unity. How Newton discovered the law of gravitation; how first he lost the clue and later found it. The spirit of his age and the things which the Royal Society loved to discuss, to the amusement of Pepys and the scorn of Swift. §2. What Newton's work did to our knowledge of the universe; how it bound together in one mathematical formula every piece of matter in creation and explained their motions. How instead of new discoveries complicating things as they did in Aristotle's, Ptolemy's, Copernicus', Galileo's days they merely verified what Newton had said. §3. What Newton's discovery did to God. How the God of the Middle Ages and the God of Newtonian science were bound to be different. How the medievalist saw in things qualities such as goodness, badness, perfection, imperfection, while Newton only saw measurable things such as mass and motion. How this altered the human outlook on life, and necessitated new religions. Newton's own idea of God as the perfect mechanical engineer, who had made the universe go like a well-regulated watch. How Newton provided for God's continued necessity by showing certain ways in which this watch might run down without his repairing skill. Natural Theology, the childish attempt of science to keep God busy. §4. How Newton's picture of the universe, being unsatisfactory to human emotions, produced a reaction in many minds. What William Blake thought of Newton and science. How most human beings have a Newton-part and a Blake-part in their minds, always in conflict and disagreement, and how we can sum up the effect of science on the human mind as the destruction of medieval unity and the substitution for it of this unlucky conflict. Eddington's example of the sliding elephant as an illustration of man's intellectual dilemma.

CHAPTER V: *Dalton's Dust*   187

§1. How men have always wanted to possess eternal life and to be rich; and how these desires led them to study matter and to build up the science of chemistry. Aristotle taught that all matter was of four kinds and Hippocrates taught that there were four bodily "humors." Why we say men are "bilious," "jaundiced," "sanguine," "melancholy." The obscure recipes of alchemists and man's effort to follow them. The Italian who turned tin into gold. The curious properties of some precious stones. §2. The story of Philippus Aureolus Theophrastus Paracelsus Bombast ab Hohenheim. The medicine which Paracelsus concocted and his impor-

tance as a pioneer in chemistry. How his character suitably symbolises chemistry's sowing of its wild oats. §3. The Quaker, John
Dalton, and a pair of silk stockings. How Dalton's life differed
from that of Paracelsus and symbolised chemistry's settling down
to serious things. How Dalton fell in love over a conversation
about dephlogisticated marine acid. The contribution of steady-
going people to the riches of our imaginative life. §4. How Boyle
had destroyed the old ideas about the four elements. How phlogiston, the fire-soul in matter, dominated people's ideas until Lavoisier
came. How Lavoisier altered men's outlook on life as a whole
by burning phosphorus. How Dalton weighed the elements one
against the other and how in consequence we know now that
the universe is made of ninety-two substances, all very dusty, and
all, according to Lavoisier, indestructible; and how depressing
people have found this. The awful word "materialism."

CHAPTER VI: *Darwin and Evolution* 214

§1. Science the leveller and measurer lays its hand on man, and
man in a fury of snobbism turns and bites the hand of science.
Charles Darwin, the man about whom the tempest raged. How
he was offered a voyage round the world out of which came the
knowledge which revealed the theory of evolution, and how his
acceptance of that offer depended on a thirty-mile drive and was
nearly nullified by the shape of his nose. §2. How an element of
pure accident seems to enter into great scientific discoveries. What
evolution and the doctrine of change did to Newton's picture of
the universe and to Newton's God. Evolution not merely a matter of man coming from ape-like ancestors, but of geology and
the birth of planets from suns; stars from nebulæ. §3. Darwin's
own description of how the idea of evolution came to him during
the voyage of the *Beagle*. The story of the growth of an idea as
an example of how scientists work. §4. How the idea came
along similar paths to the mind of another scientist, Alfred
Russell Wallace. His description of the birth in his mind of the
idea of evolution and his explanation of why he and Darwin both
discovered it separately yet at the same time. §5. Why the spirit
and needs of the age were hungry for evolution. How some

scientists resented it, not on scientific but on religious grounds, while others eagerly accepted it, but also on religious grounds. How evolution touched the human emotions and gave young men the basis of a religion and a live overbelief to take the place of the moribund orthodoxy of the nineteenth century. How the orthodox idea of God had ceased to satisfy human ideals and how Darwinism seemed to give a higher hope and higher ideals than orthodox Christianity. How such things made Darwinism seem at the same time "an ocean of new life and boundless possibilities" to some, and to others "a gospel of dirt." §6. What Darwin thought of the argument from design for God's existence. The story of the ichneumon fly and the caterpillar. How the ichneumon fly's argument for a benevolent God's existence from design could not appeal to the caterpillar. How the same is true of human ichneumon flies and human caterpillars. How a scientific picture of the universe requires that the times shall be ripe for its acceptance and then gives men a new God and a new religion. §7. We go back to the starting point and consider what all this means to the modern man in his search for a satisfactory outlook on life as a whole. As in 1543 and 1643 so in 1900 the reader is invited to consider the effect of the current scientific picture of the universe on his ideas of God, and his own life as a whole. Thirteen ways in which these ideas have been changed by science. §8. How the picture of the universe given by science in 1900 gave man a feeling of claustrophobia. Man felt himself to be the puppet *Petroushka*, heartlessly made, hopelessly imprisoned.

CHAPTER VII: *The New Renaissance*   256

A. The Universe.

§1. How Darwin closes the Old Testament of the modern man's Bible, with a glance at the coming of the New Testament. How M. Becquerel put a photographic plate away in a drawer and the consequence to our ideas of Dalton's dust. How radium taught us to look within the atom and how we discovered there a great world of delight hidden to our senses. §2. How Max Planck showed that a hot body cooled in jerks. How an electron gets from one place to another in an atom in no time and without going through

the space between. How we may have to get rid of the idea
that space is continuous just as the medievalist had to get rid
of the idea of centrehood. The importance of something called *h*.
Is the universe meaningless? How scientists are beginning to
doubt if it can be explained at all. §3. How the planet Mercury is
always unpunctual and how this has upset the Newtonian picture
of the universe. How Lobatchevsky criticised Euclid's geometry
and undermined our faith in our ideas of space. How space is
not at all like our room and has different "dimensions." How Einstein by considering such things as Mercury's unpunctualities
has taken away our faith in our senses and made words like
"space" and "time" incomprehensible. How two people's watches
may be different but both have the correct time.

B. Man.
§1. How Darwinism leaves a great deal without explanation.
In order to understand the new ideas coming into biology we will
study at some length the loves of the orchids. The orthodox
Darwinian explanation of how a flower evolves. §2. How Darwin
showed that an orchid is an elaborate trap to attract insects. The
landing stage, the nectar spur, the pollen grains and their hinged
stalks. §3. And yet, no honey! Why should an insect bother to
come? A case of bachelors in a he-infested world sowing their
wild oats and embracing phantoms. §4. Can orthodox Darwinism
explain such facts? §5. What new ideas will be needed to complete
the explanation. What a living being *does* as important as what
it is. §6. How the bee behaves on arrival at the hive. How it dances
and thereby tells its companions about its discoveries. Can orthodox
Darwinism explain even this? Samuel Butler once more and the
new-born baby's surprising knowledge. §7. What the future
Einstein of biology will make of all this. §8. A passing glance at
Freud.

C. Man and his Universe.
§1. What will man make of this new picture of the universe?
What overbeliefs will he add to the scientific picture of the New
Renaissance? The magic of the word Relativity. Just as Evolution

was the watchword in 1900 so Relativity is the watchword in 1930. How our ideas about Human Nature have been changed by the reign of Relativity. "You cannot get away from human nature"—is this true? How the anthropologist brings evidence that it is not true. Some reasons why men work. Our attitude on morals and on crime is changed by our new feelings about the Relativity of Human Nature. §2. What does the new picture of the universe make us feel about immortality? Immortality must seem different according as we have the picture of the universe of Aristotle, or of Galileo or of Newton or of Darwin or of Einstein. How Galileo's new star upset ideas about immortality; how Newton provided for a future life; how the idea of a "four dimensional space-time continuum" affects the idea of immortality. Is the universe immortal? The new picture of the universe neither accepts nor rejects the idea of immortality, but does something far more revolutionary. The unnaturalness of wanting to live for ever and the foolishness of our ideas about time and space. §3. The foolishness of children's questions. Is the universe absurd? " 'Important, unimportant' said Alice!" What shall we do with the meaningless things of which we are made? How science nowadays says we must *not* believe our senses and the possible effect of this on our everyday life and overbeliefs. The need for a new language. §4. The modern man instead of being asked to imagine himself in his study in 1543, 1643 or 1900 is asked to walk out into the night under the stars and think things over. Some strayed revellers. How science has begun the greatest task of all, the abolition of fear from our lives.

NOTE

For anyone whose life permits him the leisure for such occupation, there can be no more urgent thing than to try and form an honest, reasonable, day to day philosophy. Perhaps the urge is strongest between the ages of thirty and forty, for then it is possible to gather a certain body of experience together, and it is not too late to profit by it.

This book in no sense offers such a philosophy, but it does

try to present some of the spade work which is required before anyone can begin to plant the seeds of a philosophy. It suggests in a fragmentary way the effect of science upon those beliefs the holding of which makes life worth living for each of us. It is not therefore exactly a history of science but a history of the human imagination as science has affected it and allowed it to grow. It is hardly likely to introduce order, peace, certainty into the mind of the reader, but it is my modest hope that it may in some cases succeed in widening the view. If we want to understand and love the countryside we must begin by constructing a room with a view, large windows through which light waves and sound waves will come to us as we sit at our desk. This book is a plea for making the windows large with some reasons in support of throwing stones even at glass houses!

Among the many books which have been of very great assistance to me, I would mention first of all, Professor E. A. Burtt's, *The Metaphysical Foundations of Modern Science*. For soundness and significance coupled with intelligibility few recent books can be compared with it; and readers who desire a less popular account of our subject from Copernicus to Newton can be certain of finding an able tutor in Dr. Burtt. Other writers who have been useful for various parts of the subject matter include Sir Oliver Lodge, *Pioneers of Science*; Sir David Brewster, *Life of Sir Isaac Newton*; J. L. E. Dreyer, *Planetary Systems from Thales to Kepler*; J. J. Fahie, "The Scientific Works of Galileo" in Charles Singer's *Studies in the History and Method of Science*; Thomas Thomson's *History of Chemistry*; Henry Roscoe, *Life of Dalton*; Lynn Thorndyke, *History of Magic and Experimental Science*; G. Elliot Smith, *Essays on the Evolution of Man*; W. K. Clifford, *Works*; H. A. Junod, *The Life of a South African Tribe*; J. H. Driberg, "The Savage as He Really Is"; T. H. Huxley, *Science and Christian Tradition*. Sprenger's *Malleus Maleficorum* trans. and ed. by M. Summers; Cajori, *History of Physics*; A. D. White, *Warfare of Science with Theology*; The Darwin Wallace Celebration of the Linnean Society; The standard Life of Charles Darwin; and for the last chapter various works of Eddington, Jeans,

SYNOPSIS OF CONTENTS

Bertrand Russell, Whitehead and Soddy. This list is inadequate and is written as the names occur to me, but in most cases the influence from these and unnamed authors has been indirect, unless expressly acknowledged in the Text.

In preparing the illustrations I have received invaluable assistance from Miss Emily P. Watts, for which I desire to express gratitude; as also to the officials of the New York Public Library and the Library of Columbia University, who provided her with facilities. The frontispiece and the illustration of Dante's universe are reproduced with kind permission of the publishers from Dr. Charles Singer's *Studies in the History and Method of Science* (Oxford University Press), and the portrait of Einstein is from *Relativity: the Special and General Theory,* translated by Robert W. Lawson (Henry Holt & Co.).

For personal help and encouragement I have only one person to thank—my wife—who as usual has benefited the work by much weeding, hoeing, and watering.

JOHN LANGDON-DAVIES

Cott House
    Dartington
       Totnes
          Devon.
    November 1929.

ILLUSTRATIONS

"O man, look at man! For man has in himself heavens and earth and in him all things are latent." The visions of Hildegarde give us an idea of the medieval, scientific picture of the universe. ....*Frontispiece*

Facing page

Ptolemy's Universe: ". . . it explained what could be seen by human eyes, that is, it was scientific; and it agreed in shape and motions with what men conceived to be the necessary attributes of God's handiwork, that is, it was theologically satisfactory." 10

The Universe according to Cosmas. "Moses expressly states that the Tabernacle set up in the wilderness was a model of the universe . . . so that instead of wasting time taking measurements and doing sums the fundamentalist learns his astronomy from reading the description of Moses' Tabernacle." 26

Dante's Universe. "Nothing gives a clearer introduction to medieval thought than the realization that to all the most learned men of the time the universe actually was very much as it is described in the *Divine Comedy*." 74

From the days of Aristotle and Pliny until after Shakespeare, people never learned about animals by looking at them but always by reading the descriptions written by Aristotle or Pliny. 90

". . . the universe was in its parts and as a whole made for man; more even than that, the universe was a sort of symbol, an allegory which, when understood, explained man's being and his destiny. Except for its value as a symbol it had no reality whatever." 114

Abomination des Sorciers. "Nor is it easy to see how any modern fundamentalist who refuses to believe in evolution because he believes in Genesis can consistently fail to believe in witches." 154

Vesalius, "an impious madman, who is poisoning the air of all Europe with his vapourings." He is demonstrating a dissection which contradicts a text of Galen. By destroying respect for authority he helped to bring in a new age......... 170

"Tycho Brahe spent most of his life recording the exact position in the sky of the planets and the stars, hour by hour, night after night; indeed he did very little else; and yet Tycho was one of the men who are directly responsible, though he had no idea of it himself, for building up the modern man's idea of God." 202

After a design by Blake. "The search which in the early days with Kepler had accepted the sun as the centre of the universe because it fitted so well the idea of God as a morning-bright Apollo, culminated with Newton seeing him as a super-professor of mechanics, almost worse still . . . a super-annuated mechanic." 218

Blake's "Portrait of Sir Isaac Newton." "Newton measured the stars and regretted his inability to measure a flower or to state the human will in terms of mathematical forces. This was sheer idiocy to Blake . . ." 250

A chemical experiment conducted with due attention to the influence of the stars. "Some stars sulphurised the atmosphere, while others made it arsenical, saline or mercurial." 266

⌒xx⌒

ILLUSTRATIONS

Charles Darwin, by the Hon. John Collier. " 'An ocean of new life and boundless possibilities'—'the gospel of dirt'—one and the same piece of patient scientific research seemed both these things according to the human mind by which it was absorbed. Darwin at once became Anti-christ or the giver of a new religion; however much he would have preferred it, never for a moment could he remain a mere entomologist and biologist. No one indeed was more surprised than himself." 298

A. Einstein. "Thus it comes about, fantastic though it may sound, that men lie with their neighbours' wives denuded of the last shred of a guilty conscience because observations of Mercury's perihelion enabled Einstein to alter our ideas about space-time!" 314

INTRODUCTION

>>>>>>>>>>>>>>>>>>>>>>>><<<<<<<<<<<<<<<<<<<<<<<<

§ 1

"It has long been known that certain ants, such as Œcophylla, dwell in nests of finely woven silk. At one time I thought that Œcophylla wove their silk for themselves as our spiders do. This however was an error. The truth——" And Auguste Forel goes on to tell us the following remarkable truth about the ants called Œcophylla.

They live in houses of leaves sewn together with silk, but unlike most insects who live in such homes they cannot themselves secrete silk. They cannot attach a gummy substance to a leaf and then, moving away, unwind out of their innards yards upon yards of tough delicate thread. They have no silk-producing glands or organs. What then do they do?

The infant Œcophylla, before it becomes a grown-up six-footed ant, is of course a little grub-like larva which is fed for an allotted time, and then, weaving around itself a cocoon of soft thread, sleeps its way into adult shape and anthood. It is fully provided with a factory for the produce of silk for its own pubescent purposes. *The adult Œcophylla, wishing to build a nest, use their young as shuttles to weave the leaves together.*

Half a dozen ants go to a place where two leaves hang close, and pull the edges nearer by hanging onto one with their jaws and onto the other with their six legs: if they cannot reach across the intervening space until it has been further reduced, they form chains of interlocked ants, and, having thus bridged the gap, tug till it has lessened sufficiently for their purpose.

Meanwhile a second squad of ants arrives on the scene, each member of it with an ant larva in its mouth; they climb along the opposite side of the leaves and, while their fellows hold the edges together, make the larvæ attach themselves to one edge with the end of a thread; then by passing the living shuttle from edge to edge, unwinding the thread as they go, they weave with their own children a textile roof for the nest. The work done, the shuttles are taken back to the nursery. "We have here," says Forel, "a fact almost unique in nature, except in man, the use of one living creature by another as a working tool."

When Forel tells us astounding facts such as this in his monumental treatise on ants, what is he doing? In the first place, he is of course writing a chapter of the natural history of the family Formicidæ of the order Hymenoptera of the class Arthropoda: a word, this last, which is "a name denoting the possession by certain animals of jointed limbs, now applied to one of the three sub-phyla into which one of the great phyla (or primary branches) of coelomocoelous animals—the Appendiculata—is divided."

But, if that were all, we should not be detaining the reader with an isolated, irrelevant fact about child labour among the Œcophylla. The reader is not an Arthropod, nor even a student of Arthropods, and probably looks upon books describing them with some little impatience.

Forel is however doing something much more important to the ordinary modern man than may appear at first sight: indeed he is doing three things of the very greatest importance to all thoughtful human beings.

In the first place, he is composing a few stanzas in an epic poem far more exciting than the *Odyssey*; because the adventures of the imagination latent in his news about Œcophylla are deeper and wilder than outworn fights and ended journeys of dead heroes can ever be.

In the second place he is writing a chapter in the biography of himself and his readers; for the weaving of the Œcophylla is something which happened, if not to Forel or the reader in person, certainly to a member of their very large family. But for a minute accident which decreed that we should belong to another branch of the family you or I might very well have been an Œcophylla instead of merely reading about it. At least we had a common ancestor with the ants, which Forel has described, and, as all men are born ancestor worshippers, a little imagination will give a book on ants all the attractiveness of family biography. We may go further: for reasons which will appear later the biography of an ancestor is really only a partly disguised biography of oneself. Forel writing about ants is being an autobiographer.

§ 2

"Yes," the reader would say, if he happened to live in the Middle Ages, "yes, I perfectly understand you. You mean that ants have a human interest, because they have been created to teach us lessons." You would remind me of the Bible, "go to the ant, thou sluggard," you would quote "consider her ways and be wise: which having no guide, overseer or ruler provideth her meat in the summer, and gathereth her food in the harvest": an exceedingly apt quotation, as it happens, since certain ants do actually cultivate gardens of fungus and other crops in the most exemplary and painstaking fashion, as Forel tells us elsewhere in his book. This attitude towards nature, familiar to all of us since nursery days because of Æsop's fables, prevailed in the human spirit for a thousand years and more, and in consequence, like everything else that has a long history, lingers on in every mind as a survival even today: an attitude which regards the contents of the universe as nicely coloured pictures, with moral lessons to be read in them, all prettily bound up in the azure sky and the green earth and presented gratis to every naked new-born baby, a possession to be thumbed and dog's-eared, or kept with the Bible on the shelf devoted to unopened but respectable literature. Of course Solomon's advice is excellent, as far as any moral advice is likely to be, but too often the leaders of thought in the Middle Ages went much further and adopted an attitude towards nature which is wholly indefensible. They assumed that the ant existed for the sole purpose of reforming the human sluggard.

The modern man's attitude is very different; to him comes the astounding realisation that the ant actually exists for its own sake, that indeed everything else in the world exists for its own sake, and that nothing has ever, so to speak, even heard of man's existence. Only in so far as a man has allowed this to sink into his mind and to colour his whole outlook on life, his religion, can he claim to be modern. How important it is to comprehend that the world would get on perfectly well if some catastrophe added the human to the innumerable forms already extinct we shall see fully later; for certainly our attitude towards life and God depends largely upon it.

Knowledge of the ant is not important to us then for its salutary moral effect nor is it to be regarded as important because it is the sort of wonder which may excite our imagination. The facts of science should never be treated as "wonders" to be greeted with little shrieks of surprise in drawing-rooms after dinner, or to be used as "fillers" at the bottom of a column devoted to the latest murder in the daily tabloid journal. This is not what is meant by saying that Forel's book has a humanistic interest: yet how often is this the only attitude to be found in popular scientific writing! For example: it is believed that certain insects, whose young live on caterpillars, sting the caterpillars in their nerve centres in such a way that they do not die, but merely become paralysed; so that the young insects have fresh, living meat every day of their lives. Such a fact does stimulate the imagination merely as a peculiarly horrible fact: the young lady in the deck-chair crossing the Atlantic shudders and exclaims "ugh! the brutes"; the convinced rationalist mutters "and then people believe in a benevolent creator"; the old colonel exclaims "worse than Bolshevism," and all three go on to read that an express train going at sixty miles an hour would take years and years to get to the sun, or Jupiter, or the nebula in Andromeda, as the case may be. It is significant that the daily paper supplied on Atlantic liners for the delight of men and women recovering from seasickness is full of such paragraphs as these.

The real importance of such facts about these insects is that apart from any momentary emotional thrill they may afford, they inevitably penetrate into the human mind and take their place among all the elements out of which is made a picture of the universe and an attitude to life. In short, they supply part of the raw material of religion.

§ 3

That science is poetry is carefully concealed from the knowledge of most people by the text-books out of which science is taught in schools and colleges.

Moreover, the picture of the scientific research worker, that has been insinuated into the public mind, is largely responsible for the idea that science is poles removed from art and literature. Whereas art, literature and music are the elements of culture, science and the scientist are thought of as things apart; the people who are ashamed of being found not to have read the latest poem, seen the latest play and heard the latest violinist are not in the least ashamed of knowing the name of no scientist since Darwin. These same people usually suppose the scientist to be devoid of human feelings; even if he does not actually leave his wife, he scarcely notices her existence; he never has a love affair; he never listens to music, nor notices that trees in autumn are beautiful; at least not if he is a *really good* scientist; then he is cold, mechanical and altogether inhuman.

And yet the truth is that the urge which makes a man give himself to science is precisely the same as that which produces the poet or the composer—a passion for beauty and a desire to enjoy æsthetic pleasure. "The intense pleasure I have received from this discovery can never be told in words. I regretted no more the time wasted; I tired of no labour; I shunned no toil of reckoning, days and nights spent in calculation, until I could see whether my hypothesis would agree with the orbits of Copernicus or whether my joy was to vanish into air." It is Kepler the astronomer writing and his discovery was of certain harmonies and proportions obeyed by the planets, a poetical and musical behaviour on the part of certain stars, the next best thing to the "music of the spheres." It so happens, as we shall see later, that Kepler was wrong, childishly wrong, we would think now, in the particular matter about which he speaks with such enthusiasm; but the episode is an example of how the chief incentive to all the earlier astronomers was to show that the stars obeyed æsthetic laws, that their motions were beautiful. Indeed beauty, nice conduct, harmonious movement, are what every scientist looks for in nature and only when he finds them does he believe that he has found something which is true.

Since the urge to discover a scientific fact or to perfect a scientific theory is precisely the same as the urge to write a poem, and since the pleasure to be derived from understanding some one else's theory is precisely the same as the pleasure to be derived from reading some one else's poem, it is wrong to distinguish so vitally between science on the one hand and art on the other: both are children of the imagination, both of them ways of discovering and enjoying beauty, both a search for the poetry lurking round the corner throughout the universe.

∽7∾

The fact that so many of us never discover this is due to the bad way in which science is taught in schools and also to the general opinion among ignorant people that the object of science is utilitarian,—motor cars, gas pipes or a new patent medicine perhaps,—but if the modern man rightly understands science he will discover that it arouses in him the same exalted state of mind experienced as we listen to a beautiful piece of music, or read a sublime piece of prose. It leads him to the land beyond good and evil, where happiness and sorrow dissolve and become transformed into a mixture of reverence, awe and wistful peace.

§ 4

One of the things which comes out of reading this vast epic is a realisation that precisely the same forces which make you or me exalted with hopes or debased with fears are working to produce curious results in the ant or the wasp; that we, reader and writer, together with Mr. Ramsay MacDonald, Mr. Hoover, Gene Tunney and Mary Pickford, are really so many attempts to solve an unknown problem set by an unknown something; and that the ant, the tiger and the palm tree are other attempts. Human beings are not the solutions and the rest the failures, the palm tree may be as good a solution as Mr. Hoover; we do not know: all we can know is that a very exciting game is being played with ourselves as pieces and not the least exciting thing about it is that apparently we know as much about it when we are asleep as we do when we are awake.

Let us think for a moment of our part in this enormous game: this large complicated piece of machinery our body was not so many years ago squeezed down to the dimension of a single cell, itself the much contracted sum total of the two machines our parents; and if we could probe backwards into times long past we should see a succession of these contractions and expansions stretching back for ever, an unbroken chain of the same individual living and reliving its life as its parents, its grandparents, its ancestors, its animal ancestors; after each separate life contracting into one little cell until a time is reached when the expansions are so small that they cannot be distinguished from the contractions; until the single cell, instead of swelling into a larger being, remained a single cell always. Reverse the process back to its true sequence in time and you have your history and mine. When we and the world of living things were young together wc just broke in two and so had twins, both of our offspring being half ourselves. From that day to this the whole of our past history has consisted of an unbroken chain of individuals getting tired of life and dying; but first of all distilling into one cell all that seemed worth while of ourselves so that we might live again in our children. In this way we are our own ancestors, having passed from them through the bottle neck of the germ plasm, millions and millions of times until we became ourselves, and, were it not that in the process of this distilling ourselves into one cell we have always thrown out conscious memory as being of little value, we would remember what we did when we were our ancestors.

We shall see later that some particularly bold scientists assert that although conscious memory was thrown out, unconscious memory persisted; and that that is why a new-born baby knows how to breathe, to drink milk from its mother's breast, to digest it—because it remembers doing it before; clearly then, once we have a glimmering of the truth about these things, the difficulty of seeing that science is autobiography vanishes. And if science is autobiography, how much more interesting it is than we were led to expect in schools!

But we must warn the reader that it is of course only a really modern scientist who will admit this outlook even today, for, scientists have for a long time been terrified by the misunderstandings of the fundamentalists, mythologists, mumbo-jumbo worshippers and other half-baked thinkers into denying anything which might be misconstrued by them into being useful for their own low purposes. These people had created out of their dogged superstitions, for all that they phrased them in words of sweetness and light, such a frightful, painful, brutal outlook on life and the universe that the nineteenth century biologists reacting in disgust could not admit anything into their new outlook which could be made to look as if they thought life anything but mechanical and materialistic in the old-fashioned sense of these words. And even to this day fundamentalists force scientists in self-protection to be more old-fashioned and "materialistic" than they desire to be at heart.

§ 5

Lastly, Forel, as we have said, in telling us about ants is writing some verses in a chapter of the modern man's Bible. The whole history of science has been a direct

Ptolemy's Universe: ". . . it explained what could be seen by human eyes, that is, it was scientific; and it agreed in shape and motions with what men conceived to be the necessary attributes of God's handiwork, that is, it was theologically satisfactory." (See p. 63.)

search for God; deliberate and conscious, until well into the eighteenth century, and since then unconscious, for the most part, because so much had been discovered about God by then that scientists began to think fit to change the name of the subject of their search. Copernicus, Kepler, Galileo, Newton, Leibnitz and the rest did not merely believe in God in an orthodox sort of way, they believed that their work told humanity more about God than had been known before. Their incentive in working at all was a desire to know God, and they regarded their discoveries as not only proving his existence, but as revealing more and more of his nature. If men had not wanted to know about God, it is highly doubtful if they would have worried to know about nature. When we come to read about these men we will see that the key to their lives and labours was their invariable thirst for religious truth. This was the first and greatest of the human thirsts; there were others, such as the thirst for eternal life, the thirst for perfect health, the thirst for knowledge of the future and the thirst for unlimited wealth. Whatever further incentive science required beyond the thirst after God, was found in the existence of these other thirsts.

We shall see how the philosopher's stone, the elixir of life, the prophetic virtues of astrology gave birth to the sciences and how, although not one single human thirst has been assuaged, the gallant attempt to do so has quite without forethought produced a power which is able to say to all men, "Whosoever drinketh of my cup shall never thirst again."

We die at seventy after much disease and long after youth has faded; we are poor and lonely and know not what is to come; but, if we can learn to understand the value of science pursued for itself alone, we can be perfectly content. Few people have been so happy as the scientists.

§ 6

The history of science is the history of the most intelligent search for God, the best attempt at constructing a noble religion, which civilised men have yet known. Were that history well and fully written down we should have the modern man's Bible. Just as Joshua, Judges, Kings and Chronicles, the historical books of the Old Testament trace the evolution of the Hebrews and of the Hebrew idea of a tribal god; so the lives and works of Copernicus, Galileo and Newton are episodes in the evolution of the modern man's God and the modern man's outlook on life. Without a clear idea of what such men have done no religious outlook today is really of much value.

What then, the reader may say, of the so-called conflict between science and religion? There is no such thing: there is only a conflict between two religious outlooks and two ideas of God. We shall see how true that is when we study how Copernicus, searching after God, discovered a more satisfactory idea of God than the orthodox one; and from Copernicus to the present day the whole of this conflict has been due to the irritation of orthodox religions with the new and better conceptions of the eternal truths revealed by science.

Do we mean that nature is God's created word and the Bible God's written word and that there is no conflict between them? Far from it: a very different God comes out of the scientific search for him from the one whom the fundamentalists have pressed flat, dry and lifeless between Genesis and Revelations. The conflict between science and fundamentalism is very real: only it began earlier than most fundamentalists realise; it began long before Darwin; before Copernicus even and perhaps the first important fundamentalist was the early church father Lactantius who proved from the Bible that the earth was not round. The fundamentalist idea of God was not withered by evolution, for Copernicus had killed it long before.

Indeed to those who have read the historical books of this great bible of science there is very little interest to be got out of the fundamentalist God: for science almost from its start was able to give mankind a loftier concept to put in its place, the concept of a great artificer, a first-rate mathematician, an artist to the "finger tips," instead of an irritable old gentleman believing in corporal punishment.

Moreover we shall see that this bible, like the Christian one, has an old and a new testament; the old ending in gloom and the mutterings of the minor prophets like Herbert Spencer: the new at once destroying and fulfilling the old.

§ 7

The history of science is then a poetic search for God carried out by rummaging among man's old family records, and as such it will be sketched here. Why has so much of human energy and imagination gone to the making of this search? Partly because of an honest love of adventure inherent in all energetic human beings to be satisfied by such a search to a far greater degree than by any other means. Money making, making love, sport, politics, all of them bore the truly energetic man; for even when he has squeezed them dry of interest, he will find himself with energy still unused. But all his energy is needed for the most exciting of all quests, the most exacting and exhausting of all hobbies, the search for truth.

But there is another reason besides honest love of adventure: it is that, whether rationalists like it or not, man is a believing animal and the really enlightened man is not the one who believes nothing, but the man who founds his belief on the firmest rock of reality. Such a man sees in the scientific picture of the universe which happens to be painted in his age the most perfect foundation for his beliefs; and to what is known, he adds an overbelief, something which cannot be proved, but which, on the other hand, cannot be disproved by the body of natural knowledge on which it is built. This overbelief is a man's religion; any overbelief that can be disproved by what science can show to be true is his superstition.

A man's overbelief then depends upon his knowledge of the universe; in so far as he is ignorant about the universe, that far is his religion likely to be valueless to himself and to everyone else. For the modern man to hold overbeliefs without a knowledge of the historic books of his Bible, of Copernicus, Galileo, Newton is as ridiculous as for a fundamentalist to doubt Darwin without having read Genesis.

We have got so used to the idea that our beliefs or faith consist in holding for true those things that we have neither time nor training nor courage to examine logically, that this idea of founding our overbelief, our religion on a knowledge of the universe derived from science may seem fantastic and impossible. We haven't the time to study the universe, we may complain; and yet we want to believe. That truly great Victorian, W. K. Clifford, imagines just such a man as this: " 'But,' says one, 'I am a busy man; I have no time for the long course of study which would be necessary to make me in any degree a competent judge of certain questions, or even able to understand the nature of the arguments.' *Then he should have no time to believe.*" The modern man refuses to take this lazy attitude: he has his religion, his total reaction to life, his myth, but he takes every pains to see that it squares with all that science can tell him.

And why does the modern man have a religion? Because the material facts of life are not sufficient for his happiness. Nothing is more certain than that for the majority of human beings alive today the future holds more that is unpleasant than that is pleasant. There are disappointments, disease, loss of friends, poverty, misunderstandings, thwartings in front of all of us and then the last enemy, death. When men were children they invented a loving father to whom they could fly as chickens do to a hen, and they invented another life with all the unsatisfactory features of this one left out. Science set out to find proofs of the existence of this loving father and of the perpetual holiday after death; and it must be confessed that it has failed completely in its quest.

Now science was made for man and not man for science, and if science failed to do what was required of it, we might expect men to abandon it as good for nothing. Let it remain for mundane things, man might say; although it has not quenched our thirst with the elixir of life it has healed our diseases and made bodily life more tolerable; it has multiplied our powers and our activities and made many things easier and more comfortable; but for its chief function, that of discoverer of God, the kind father, and of the Elysium which could alone justify him in creating us, it has proved ineffectual; let us forget it.

Curiously enough no man who has once learned to understand science as poetry and as religion ever feels like this. For in the search he discovers unexpected prizes, undreamed-of emotional satisfactions, which compensate him for any childish dreams he has to give up. Let us now see how this may come about; let us trace in outline the path along which the modern man may go in order to find at the end of it some little philosophy, not wholly unworthy of an honest mind.

CHAPTER ONE

>>>>>>>>>>>>>>>>>>>>>><<<<<<<<<<<<<<<<<<<<<<

The Universe Makes Man

§ 1

IN THE beginning the universe made man; and afterwards man began to remake the universe.

It is this second episode which will detain us longer, a story of how the human mind with its genius for patterns and form reduced chaos to order, an order dependent on the human mind, ready to fall back into chaos directly that mind ceases to function, ready to change to a different pattern directly mankind "changes its mind" and builds up different scientific conceptions. Human thought eats the raw materials of the universe, digests them and turns them into something new, something organised, something rhythmic and beautiful. This new, organised and beautiful thing is what we mean by a scientific explanation of the universe.

Of course in this process of digestion, human thought is restricted by the raw material at its command; there are some things which no mental manœuvring can distil out of the universe; but within limits there is scope for variety. That is why we can say that the picture drawn for us by the orthodox science of any special time in human history is only one of the pictures which could be drawn; a very great deal nearer "reality" perhaps than most of the other pictures actually drawn at the time, but probably less accurate than others as yet undrawn. The important point is that man, unlike other animals, is the creator, or recreator, of the universe; within limits he can make what he will of it. He is not a wretched atom tossed to and fro by cosmic gales; since provided he takes the trouble to learn the art of navigation he can ride out any storms.

How did such a masterly animal come into existence? Nobody knows how "life" began; that is, nobody knows how matter became organised into atoms and electrons able to move, grow, reproduce themselves, digest food, while all the other masses of solids, liquids and gases on the face of the earth, remained unable to do these things. But once matter had acquired the habits of living tissue, we can make a rough guess as to how its first living form succeeded in turning itself into ourselves; and the story of this guess will occupy considerable space in a later chapter of our history.

Here we can select but one episode in the long epic poem of life, an episode which loses nothing in imaginative value if we regard it as something which happened actually to ourselves; a romantic, irretrievable step in the dark taken by ourselves, when we were some of our very distant ancestors.

It was long before there were apes or even monkeys, those very close cousins of ours, whose ancestors are our great-great-great . . . uncles and not our grandfathers. In those days the most important thing in the universe from the point of view of living beings was scent; life smelled its way through the joys and dangers of existence. The little brain which had been accumulated so far was almost all nose. Opportunity, pleasure, pain, friendship, enmity lay "right in front of your nose" in a sense far more complete than the phrase could ever have today.

In those days our own direct ancestors were very unimportant people; in one way or another other mammals had achieved far greater successes; some had grown very big, others had learned to run very fast, others had put all their energies into burrowing into the ground, becoming ingeniously contrived excavating machines, others had taken to the water; specialists all, and very conservative, they learned to do one thing very well, and when changes of climate, or other natural conditions demanded that they should do something else, they could not adapt themselves to new needs and their dominance began to decay.

"But," says Professor Elliot Smith, "the race is not always to the swift. The lowly group of mammals that took advantage of its significance to develop its powers evenly and very gradually, without sacrificing in narrow specialisation any of its possibilities of future achievement, eventually gave birth to the most dominant and most intelligent of all living creatures." In fact, the little Tree Shrews, loudly affirming a faith that life was not all smell, refused to become all nose, and climbed up trees and remained therein in order to get away from the region where smells are commonest and most persistent.

Fortunately for those of us who like to draw family portraits of our really early ancestors, fortunately, that is, for the Biologists, there still exist almost unchanged some of these original Tree Shrews even today in Sarawak, where they share the forests along with their descendants, our more recent ancestors, the Orang Utans; so that if you go to Sarawak you can see yourself as you were before the Tertiary Period, rather like a squirrel, living on insects and fruit, sitting up on your haunches to eat and holding your food in your fore paws.

Understand clearly; at this time you had not become a Primate, that is one of the monkey group of mammals; you were an Insectivore; you belonged to the group which includes, today, the moles, the shrew mice and the hedgehogs. Your relatives adopted modes of life suitable for noses, they burrowed or ran along amid the undergrowth; you went up a tree. Their sense of smell grew stronger and stronger because those of them who happened to have an extra strong sense of smell used it to defeat the others in the struggle for existence and had offspring with a strong sense of smell also. Your sense of smell remained where it was, even grew less, because in the tree-tops you found eyes and ears more useful than noses. You put your money on eyes, so to speak, and you won; those who backed noses and lost remained hedgehogs and their descendants catch cockroaches to this day in the cellars of their luckier cousins.

In the same part of the world as the Tree Shrews, there is still to be found an animal with huge eyes called the Spectral Tarsier. You were once exceedingly like a Spectral Tarsier; a little animal which you could place together with its young on the palm of your human hand; with almost terrifyingly big eyes far larger than the Tree Shrew's. "The name *tarsier*," says the Encyclopaedia Britannica, "refers to the great elongation of two of the bones of the tarsus, or ankle, and *spectral* to the huge goggle-like eyes and attenuated form which constitute two of the most distinctive features of this weird little creature. Rather smaller than a squirrel, with dusky

20

brown fur, the tarsier has immense eyes, large ears, a long thin tail, tufted at the end, a greatly elongated tarsal portion of the foot, and disk-like adhesive surfaces on the fingers, which doubtless assist the animal in maintaining its position on the boughs. It feeds chiefly on insects and lizards, sleeps during the day, but is tolerably active at night, moving chiefly by jumping from place to place; an action for which the structure of its hindlegs seems particularly well adapted. It is rare, not more than two being generally found together, and only brings forth one young at a time."

How was it that you changed from being a Tree Shrew and became a Spectral Tarsier? It was part of the process by which the Universe, using severity far more often than kindness, working incessantly from the days before the stars existed, was licking you into the shape of a man. Every few years you, as a Tree Shrew, died, having first distilled into a single cell, or several single cells, all that was essential in you, not only a memory of the shape you found useful, but a memory of all the buffets and chances which came from that shape being hardly used by the universe around. In some way by no means altogether clear to us, these unconscious memories, while keeping you in mind of anything useful in your past experience, accumulated hints of even more useful possibilities and an ability to profit by them. The sum total of these changes was the first Spectral Tarsier.

Put more simply, the Spectral Tarsier was the Tree Shrew modified by the experience of life up a tree. What had that experience done? It had produced the first Primate, the first form distinctly belonging to the same class as the monkeys and man; which is only another way of saying that life up a tree had paved the way for your present-day stupendous brain! Or as Professor Elliot Smith puts it: "a noteworthy further reduction in the size of the olfactory parts of the brain, such as is seen in that of the Spectral Tarsier quite emancipated the creature from the dominating influence of olfactory impressions, the sway of which was already shaken, but not quite overcome when its Tree Shrew-like ancestor took to an arboreal life. This change was associated with an enormous development of the visual cortex in the neopallium, which not only increased in extent so far as to exceed that of the Tree Shrew but also became more highly specialised in structure. Thus in the Spectral Tarsier, vision entirely usurped the controlling place once occupied by smell; but the significance of this change is not to be measured merely as the substitution of one sense for another."

By what else can we measure the significance of this change? Why should it have been so important for human beings that simply by going up a tree a little animal began to trust to eyes rather than to nose? We shall see in a moment; but first let us ponder on the astonishing fact that the path to glory was over the disgrace of the sense of smell. We all know that Mr. G. K. Chesterton's dog, Quoodle, has a great contempt for us human beings for this very reason.

> They haven't got no noses,
> The fallen sons of Eve;
> Even the smell of roses
> Is not what they supposes;
> But more than mind discloses
> And more than men believe.

And Quoodle here discloses
All things that Quoodle can,
They haven't got no noses,
They haven't got no noses,
And goodness only knowses
The Noselessness of Man.

What did we gain to counterbalance this loss? "An enormous development of the visual cortex in the neopallium." And what was the use of this?

The neopallium, to put it shortly, is a sort of club house in the brain, where various senses meet to swap stories and make plans; the visual sense is a member of the club; the sense of smell is not—and so long therefore as the sense of smell was most important in the local politics of the human body, the club could not become powerful; directly power and usefulness passed to vision, a club member in good standing, the club could grow in might and the concerted, pooled energies and wisdom of all its members were able to go farther and to fare better than ever the sense of smell working out of touch with the other senses could. In fact getting out of the smell-zone into the tree-tops gave a chance for team work to show what it could do, the neopallium grew, expanded, became subtle in its reactions, and all was set for the coming of the human brain. "Thus arose an organ of attention," says Elliot Smith, "which co-ordinated with the activities of the whole neopallium so as the more efficiently to regulate the various centres controlling the muscles of the whole body. In this way not only is the guidance of all the senses secured, but the way opened for all the muscles of the body to act harmoniously so as to permit the concentration of their action for the performance of delicate and finely adjusted movement." And finally there grew out of all this the beginnings of those parts of the brain, the prefrontal area, which enable us to perform all our higher psychic functions of attention and reflection and self-consciousness.

It is a beautiful example of the sort of imaginative adventure which blazed the trail for the coming of man. Moved either by luck or by cunning, a lowly, modest animal climbed a tree; by so doing it altered the destiny of the whole universe; it set in motion a chain of circumstances which led to man. And when we remember that that animal was not merely one of our ancestors, but our very selves in an earlier life; that although we cannot remember consciously having been that animal, nevertheless unconsciously we do remember and act accordingly, then some of the poetry of science must surely move our emotions and stimulate our imagination.

It was very late in our story that we became conscious of all these facts; they had to meet all sorts of opposition, as we shall see; for example, the fact of how the Tree Shrew became a Spectral Tarsier, and the Tarsier an Ape-like animal, and the Ape-like animal a Man, flatly contradicts the story of the Fall of Man, suggesting that instead of falling, "on stepping stones of our dead selves, we rise to higher things"; and that upsets a great many people to this very day. All this we shall see later; here we are only glancing at one incident in the making of man by the universe, an example of a lower animal being turned into a higher one because a lucky chance gave it the right environment. The change from Tree Shrew

to Spectral Tarsier is typical of the way in which you and
I have become what we are.

§ 2

We had to climb a tree in order to rid ourselves of
our noses; then once denasalised, we had to climb down
the tree and learn to walk upright on the ground. This
is a later episode in the process whereby the Universe
made man; it is indeed almost the last episode before man
began to remake the universe. We cannot follow this part
of our autobiography any further, but we must remember one important thing: our life as we are able to lead
it today is based on unconscious memories of what we
did to change from Tree Shrew to Tarsier, from one form
to another, all the way from the first life form, through
all our ancestral selves, to the present day.

Consider the first day of our life as a human infant on
this earth: what innumerable things we were able to do
without being taught, without knowing that we did
them. We could suck, digest, breathe, see, hear, cry, contract and expand muscles, send our blood pulsing along,
without a single lesson. At school we were taught that
we did these "by instinct," which is not explanation but
word-invention. Actually we have to suppose that we
were able to do these things because we had done them
so often before and the more often we had done them
the easier they were to do.

One of the first to point this out was Samuel Butler
to whom scientists today are beginning to do honour,
"We are most conscious of, and have most control over,
such habits as speech, the upright position, the arts and

sciences which are acquisitions peculiar to the human race, always acquired after birth, and not common to ourselves and any ancestor who had not become entirely human. We are less conscious of, and have less control over, eating and drinking, swallowing, breathing, seeing and hearing, which were acquisitions of our prehuman ancestry, and for which we have provided ourselves with all the necessary apparatus before we saw light, but which are geologically speaking, recent, or comparatively recent. We are most unconscious of, and have least control over, our digestion and circulation, which belonged even to our invertebrate ancestry, and which are habits, geologically speaking, of extreme antiquity."

In short, the more practice we have had at doing things the simpler we find it to do them. Think of all the things you can do, divide them between those things you could already do when you were a Spectral Tarsier and those things you have learned to do since. You will find that the first group contain the things you find easiest to do, such as breathing, eating, seeing, digesting, and that you have to think more about the others. Some things of course you cannot do as well as the Tarsier, climb trees for example, and that is because you deliberately forgot how to live in a tree when you ceased to be an ape; your memories of tree climbing are conflicting, at one time in your past lives you did climb trees, at others you got out of practice, so that you have to practise the art afresh every time you are a boy so as to learn how not to fall. On the other hand, for millions of years before you were a Tarsier you had practised circulating your blood, and now not only do you not think about it, but you could not cure yourself of the habit, even if you desired to do so.

These are sketches from an MS. of Cosmas' Christian Topography. They show how an early fundamentalist proved that the universe was a certain shape by referring to texts in the Bible.

Thus Figure 2 shows the earth and heaven according to the early Christian fathers. The crossbar represents the firmament.

Figure 3 is a picture of the waters above the firmament.

Figure 4 is a representation of the conical mountain around which the sun went at nighttime.

Figure 5 is "a representation of the oblong rectangular figure of the earth which we inhabit, with its surrounding ocean, seat of Paradise and the abode of man before the flood. The four gulfs which penetrate into our earth from the ocean, and the rivers which flow into it from Paradise, are also depicted. Above the ocean in the outer earth is this inscription: 'the earth beyond the ocean where men dwelt before the flood.' "

Figure 7 is a picture of the earth with the walls which came down from heaven.

Figure 8 is "a picture of the conical mountain with three circling lines to show the paths of the sun as he moves around it at various altitudes, thus making the nights shorter or longer."

(These figures and many others are published in the Hakluyt Society's edition of Cosmas.)

These are sketches from an MS. of Cosmas' Christian Topography. They show how an early fundamentalist proved that the universe was a certain shape by referring to texts in the Bible.

Thus Figure 2 shows the earth and heaven according to the early Christian fathers. The crossbar represents the firmament.

Figure 3 is a picture of the waters above the firmament.

Figure 4 is a representation of the conical mountain around which the sun went at nighttime.

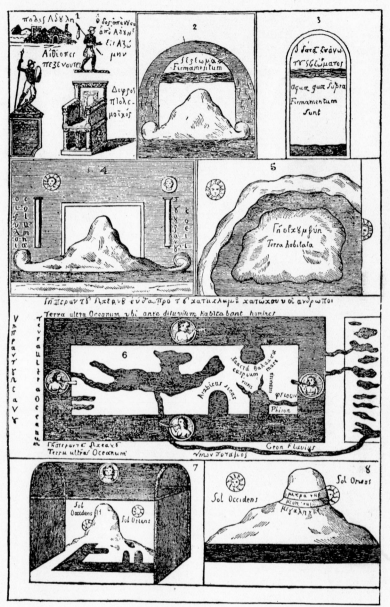

The Universe according to Cosmas. "*Moses expressly states that the Tabernacle set up in the wilderness was a model of the universe . . . so that instead of wasting time taking measurements and doing sums the fundamentalist learns his astronomy from reading the description of Moses' tabernacle.*" (See p. 68.)

Thus after millions of years the descendant of the Tarsier assumed manhood; an ape-like being straightened his back and observed the world about him; and at this point our autobiography starts on its second volume.

This time the Universe had produced a creature capable of a quite new form of activity. Hitherto all life had been able to do, was to take the opportunities afforded by the world around, now it began to make opportunities for itself. When you were an animal, you were clay in the hands of the potter, now you began to remould the potter, who made you. Let us consider one example of this altogether new capability. For millions of years you had changed your habits and your bodies because the world grew hotter or colder, then one day you decided that you would regulate the temperature to suit the body that you had: you found Fire.

One of the sad things about modern comfort and efficiency is that it has made us lose all the excitement of our earlier intercourse with the elements. Gas, electricity, matches, candles—they have made us take for granted that tamed and humbled thing, that domestic drudge sent through pipes or along wires, to warm us, cook for us, or light us to bed. But do you remember your emotions when you were just ceasing to be an ape-man, and saw the yellow flower far away at night, climbing nearer and nearer over the prairie stretching out long tendrils towards you and your hutments on the hillside? You do not remember because when your ancestor selves distilled all that was important down into that one cell, that particular memory was thrown out of your consciousness as of insufficient importance to your future existence, save that possibly a vague uneasiness, a sense of awe, was allowed to remain submerged in the lower reaches of your mind.

Fortunately by travelling we can recapture a little of these lost experiences and even today some such sight as a Texan prairie fire, when they split up cattle and drag them across the dry earth so as to wet it with blood in the hope of stopping the flames, can still arouse a shadow of more primitive emotional experiences.

An appalling manifestation of power it must have been to us savages when after the blind terror was over we wondered what the miles of black death could mean. Was it an animal which we had seen eating up the grass? At least it was very strong and quite relentless, and in our terror and humility we created out of it the image of our master, our god; and we worshipped and propitiated with prayer and sacrifice, what we knew we could not control by force. And then one day, an astonishing accident; a child, perhaps playing on the grass, rubbing two sticks together, made by its own efforts a smouldering flame. The wild beast which ate up everything had been domesticated. Instead of flying from it over the prairies or through the forest, we kept it in an earthenware pot, which we had baked in the sun. We found that it brought warmth instead of death. Our god had become our slave to warm us and feed us and comfort us by day and by night, it obeyed our will in everything and with it our first vague efforts to remake the universe could be redoubled; the arts and crafts grew rapidly, and our whole life centred round the carefully preserved embers, which we never permitted to die out. So useful, so necessary did fire become, that we felt that our whole life was bound up with its life; its death would be our death; so that we have never lost the habit of thinking of our life, the essential being, as a flame, even to this day.

Yet useful slave as it was, fire had been too long the most powerful of wild beasts for us ever to get quite used to it as a slave. We stood in awe of it, it was sacred, it was still god, even now that we could use it as we willed. We can still see among savages something of our own early worship of the Fire-god and of our belief in its magic and mystery.

Moreover we were not content with using it, we speculated about its origin, its nature, its attributes. Because it was born of two pieces of wood rubbed together, we decided that it was in the wood to begin with; we said that the whole world had once been a ball of fire, whence that element had entered the trees, whence it came again whenever we rubbed, or we said that a bird had been given it to give man, and had wandered from tree to tree pecking at them with its bill and hiding the force within them; or we invented and imagined a host of other possible origins.

Then we began to attribute all sorts of virtues to Fire; women lay down by the hearth and were impregnated by it; the souls of our ancestors dwelt within the fire upon the hearth; it was able at certain times and seasons to make cattle and women fruitful; by kindling flame we even hoped to hold the sun high in the sky when after midsummer it began its annual sinking towards the shortest day. We had ceased to be animals, for we had begun both to alter the universe and to explain it; and yet we remained animals at the same time, for our unconscious race memory prevented us then and at all later times from casting off altogether the vestiges of earlier stages. So today you can see in a Spanish village at midsummer, fires kindled at every street corner, reminiscent of days when the virtue of these fires would keep the sun from falling down the sky.

So too, in our thoughts, now that we live in a scientific age, there are hidden, as often as not, vestiges of savage superstition and even animal emotions as we shall see as our story progresses.

But first let us consider that greatest of fires which we sought as savages to influence by lesser fires, that fire above our head at noon, the Sun.

§ 3

Animals take the sun for granted: the Spectral Tarsier avoids it; dogs seek it out and bask in it. Having neither reason nor imagination, they are content to use it when they need it, and otherwise to forget it. Men are different. When you and I ceased to be ape-men and became human savages, we paid a great deal of attention to the sun; instead of accepting it, we speculated upon it; and it is that which marks the coming of our humanity.

But let us make no mistake; human beings are different from animals, not because they are wiser than animals, but because they are sometimes wiser and sometimes far more foolish. When you were a Spectral Tarsier you were never in any error at all about the sun; every dealing you had with it was absolutely correct; when you became a man you began to admire the sun, to reason about it, to imagine things about it, to feel emotions about it, and almost immediately you began to admire it for false properties which you attributed to it, to reason illogically, to use your imagination to create stupid, unnecessary fears and hopes, to allow your emotions to become entangled in ways which could only make a fool of you.

The Spectral Tarsier found that the sunlight made him blink, his huge eyes could not stand the glare, so he ducked behind the leaves or went into a hole in his tree trunk and that was the end of it; the savage would not leave the sun alone, he argued upon false premises this, that and the other about it, explained its origin, attributed all sorts of powers to it, thanked it for its services, convinced himself that by magic he could control it, and finally succeeded, as with fire, in worshipping it as a god. All of this you as a Tarsier had been saved, because you had not acquired reason, imagination, the higher gifts of the developed brain, without which you could not make a fool of yourself. It takes an animal that might be wise to make a fool since, if you cannot ask questions, you can never give the wrong answer. And it is here that we can find the source of all our woes, for humanity began by giving all the wrong answers.

To the savage the Sun is clearly not the same as it is to us; it has quite other properties which would never occur to our minds at all. The Arab boy throws his first teeth towards it and calls upon it for better ones and "the sun gives the lad from his own nursery-ground a tooth like a hailstone, white and polished." When the Sun burned high at midsummer all sorts of flowers and plants acquired special healing properties; by shooting at it on Midsummer day fern seed could be procured; it must shine upon women at their marriage in order to bring them good luck and fertility; hundreds of strange properties were attributed to it, hundreds of things besides the giving of light and warmth; and lest anyone should feel too much contempt for his own superstitions when he was a savage, let us remember that every other man and woman today seems to believe, too firmly to have their belief shaken, that sunlight puts out the fire in their grate. Then and now superstition and knowledge are mingled in every picture of the universe and of its parts.

But not only did the Sun perform miracles,—if we can speak of miracles in a world where nothing "natural" happens at all,—we savages could make the sun obey us; we were, in fact, responsible, so we thought, for the sun's well-being. When an eclipse came, we shot fire-tipped arrows into the air, so as to rekindle the flagging globe of fire; or we beat drums and screamed loudly to frighten off the monster devouring our heavenly lamp; we made up odd bundles containing plants and corals, two locks of our child's hair and the jawbone of an ancestor, and these we burned, saying, "Sun! I do this that you may be burning hot, and eat up all the clouds in the sky." In Africa where the sun usually burns from a cloudless sky, great sorrow and uneasiness is felt on a misty, overcast dawn. "All work," says Junod, "stands still, and all the food of the previous day is given to matrons or old women. They may eat it and may share it with the children they are nursing, but no one else may taste it. The people go down to the river and wash themselves all over. Each man throws into the river a stone taken from his domestic hearth, and replaces it with one picked up in the bed of the river. On their return to the village, the chief kindles a fire in his hut, and all his subjects come and get a light from it. A general dance follows." Thus and thus only is the sun saved from a cloudy morning; the clouds are put to flight, the sun, stimulated by its human friends, bursts forth and all is well. And if the sun was setting too fast and work remained to be done, it was not difficult to catch and delay him in a noose or a net of reeds.

And who or what was the sun? Innumerable ideas of the nature of the solar system grew up everywhere, most of them assuming that the Bright-shining One was a god, often the greatest of all gods. To the Greeks of Rhodes, he was a hero driving a chariot and four horses across the skies, so they sacrificed a chariot and four horses to him, flinging them into the sea; the gasping, suffocated animals went to replace those exhausted by the long journey and were harnessed by the charioteer when he plunged with his chariot beneath the western waves. American Indians provided him with a wife. Peruvians dedicated brides of god vowed to perpetual chastity, and, if they were unfaithful to their bridegroom in heaven, they were buried in the earth alive. Other Indian women, when they were first with child, would cry aloud to the sun beating down on them: "I am with child. When it is born I shall offer it to you. Have pity upon us." And when the child was born, they remembered their vows and by sacrificing their son, their first-born, they hoped to gain life and health for the rest of their family, which was to come after.

The Mexicans, having built up the greatest of ancient American civilisations, worshipped that which with its scorching beams called into being all the cruel monstrosity of their tropical dominion. They call it "He by whom men live" and they saw him pouring into them all the barbaric energy which conquered the tangle of their primeval forests. And so, lest the store of energy should be exhausted, they tore out the bleeding hearts of living men, and gave them to the Sun, who sucked up the life and energy they contained; and to have a sufficiency of living hearts they devastated their neighbours and themselves with interminable wars from which they could bring home to the sun-god's temples a holocaust of captives.

It is some relief from those horrible tragedies of the human imagination to compare with them the sacrifice which Romans made in spring of red-haired puppies to propitiate the Dog-star, or to read in the Rigveda that the sun was a golden swing in the sky; but we cannot forget that when man began to rise above the beast, and to use his imagination, his first achievement was to cause all nature to bleed. Nature, since the beginning, had always been red in tooth and claw, but for good reasons; now man's little finger was thicker than nature's loins and all because he was a fool delighting in his own folly. The Spectral Tarsier did not kill its young in order that a mass of incandescent gases, more than ninety million miles away, should give the later offspring a clean bill of health. The Tree Shrew did not make itself and all the other Tree Shrews miserable for the sake of an imaginary superman in the sky. An ape-like primate distilled all that was good and useful in its nature into one single cell so that a nobler self should live and call itself a man; and this self distilled all that was good and useful in its nature into one single cell so that a palpitating heart

34

should be torn out, and the pavement of the sun's temple be splashed with blood. How easily could a cynical hedge-hog have said that if that was what eyes led to, noses were the better for the world in general and for life as a whole!

§ 4

Fortunately these fantastic stumblings of early man were not inheritable: important though they were for the man who sacrificed his fellow men to the sun, they were not important enough to be stored within the chromosomes of the single cell: the guardian of Life shrugged his shoulders and threw them out on the rubbish heap.

But although customs themselves can never be passed on through the living body to burden later generations, the habit of thinking well of what is customary can be. The Tarsier, the ape-man, every living creature is pre-disposed to believe well of, to cling to, that which has been, because it was this that enabled it to subsist. We believe in breathing because breathing is a custom which has to be observed in order that we may live; we believe in speech for the same reason, and we believe that what is customary is good. And it always was good in the days when you were a Tarsier; it only ceased to be always good when you became a man, for then your imagination and your reason invented for the first time in the world's history customs and habits which were definitely bad. Alas, you had inherited at the same time the instinct to cling to whatever was customary. Just as you would have regarded as a dangerous lunatic a man who advocated the abandoning of the good custom of breathing, so you regarded as a dangerous lunatic the man who advocated the abandoning of any of the bad customs based on the tricks and deceits played against you by a deficient reason and a deceitful imagination. That is why the whole epic of man's spiritual and imaginative experience for thousands of years has been not the filling up of a clean page with truth, but the rubbing out of a page crossed and recrossed with close-written, contradictory, half-illegible idiocies. And we should realise even at this early stage of our story that the will to undertake this labour comes from what we call scientific imagination; that the scientist is the scavenger cleaning the human mind of all its false ideas, from which have hung innumerable sorrows and cruelties since the first ape-man speculated wildly about the universe around him.

But although we can hardly think about our mistakes as savages, the blood spilt, the fears invented, the sorrows unnecessarily bestowed, we must not forget the positive gain. Man had been made by the universe, but now in his own interest he must remake the universe or die. Hitherto the universe had been to all intents without form, for even if the planets had been circling round the sun in harmonious mathematical orbits for ages upon ages, this had been void of all significance so long as no living mind was there to realise what was happening. Now out of the battered experiences of countless generations this thing Life had been transformed into a power able to give form to the universe, able to arrange its forces, its shapes, its changes, into an intelligible pattern, a system co-ordinated and satisfying because of its æsthetic beauty and its essential unity. The very fact that man sacrificed his fellows to the sun was in a sense an advance: the sun pours out life to all the world, therefore it must be given life, because it will need to be replenished; that is how the savage explained his actions and, of course, the whole sentence is tragically wrong; but there are two words in it which are huge discoveries for Life to have made: they are "therefore" and "because"; words which can be forged into weapons, for the destruction of shadows, and for the making of night to shine with the light of imagination. "Because" and "therefore" had to be used falsely an infinite number of times, thereby adding to human sorrow and disappointment, so that in the end they might be used rightly and bring us to the palace of truth.

In many directions indeed man learned to use these words correctly at an astonishingly early stage, and they helped him to conquer his environment whenever he applied them to things about which he really knew what he thought he knew. Mr. J. H. Driberg in his excellent pamphlet "The Savage as He Really Is" combats the idea of the illogical, mystical savage which has been overdone by some eminent writers, and gives us some good examples of the sweet reasonableness of primitive men. "It is in their triumphs over environment," he says, "in their inventions rather than in their discoveries, that the genius of the savage is most easily discernible. Their intentions may be crude and primitive, but they show the savage taking command over his environment. What little knowledge he has he puts to the best possible use. With few material resources and without the facilities for scientific research which we possess he has nevertheless proceeded along sound scientific lines. By the process of trial and error, by observation and inference, he has been able to master his environment in several unexpected directions. Let us take the example of water. Over very large tracts of country at certain seasons of the year water is scarce and clean water unobtainable. Hunting parties may have to rely on a chance supply found in pockets of a dried-up marsh. Here the water is heavy with suspended particles of vegetable matter and covered with a green scum on which float water beetles and other insects, living and dead. But this is the only water available. The Lango of Uganda taught me how to drink this. A fine marsh grass is gathered and spread criss-cross over the water, completely obscuring it. This pad of fine grass forms a natural filter, and one can suck clear water through it, however impure the original source. The Bushmen of South Africa use a similar method of purifying water, and according to Passarge the Aikawe Bushmen have even improved on the device. 'Water is sucked,' he writes; 'the digging stick is thrust into the wet sand and twisted several times so as to form a funnel-shaped hole. Into this a tube is pushed, the end of which is covered with a spindle-shaped frame of grass; the opening of the hole is covered round the tube hermetically with sand, and then he sucks strongly and constantly. The vacuum formed in the hole draws the water from the sand, it rises into the mouth, from which it is conveyed by clever movements of the mouth, tongue and cheek into a straw in the corner of the sucker's mouth and by means of it into an ostrich egg shell standing near. By these means the father sucks water for the whole family.' "

Here we have the savage being as wise in his methods

as Edison could be; using his available information about the universe to get what he wants. "Because I need water," he says, "therefore I must purify this muddy liquid. Because I have noticed that a pad of grass holds back some of the dirt, therefore I will make an even better pad for myself and get even cleaner water. Because sand is an even better filter, therefore I will force the water through sand into my mouth." He is being wiser than any Spectral Tarsier, and he is in many ways more capable of looking after himself than a more civilised man would be: that is to say that a man used to a town water supply would not succeed as well if confronted with nothing to drink but a muddy pool.

§ 5

Man's outlook on the universe as a whole, that is his religion, is dependent upon his knowledge of the universe. If man, having emerged from the animal stage, had been able to say "I know nothing, the days of my knowledge lie in the future; when I have learned slowly to use these instruments called thinking and imagining as they should be used, I will gradually discover the meaning of life, the nature of God, the riddle of existence," mankind would have been saved generations of painful mistakes. Alas! as we have said, he started in no such spirit, he jumped to conclusions on everything and built up systems founded on ignorance which his children have had to pull down and alter. The things about which he knew least he thought he understood best and he was most violent in defending his own ideas of them. It will make our story clearer if we consider a typical savage system of the universe, a savage astronomy or body of knowledge upon which an attitude, philosophic and religious, has been based by a South African tribe. It is simply one of thousands which men adopted and had to unlearn later.

The Thonga, an agricultural tribe of Bantus, neither worship nor personify the sun; they may have done so once but they no longer do so now. They believe it to come out of the sea and they think that the glow on the waters is a reservoir of light out of which the sun is cut, that the sun then sticks to the heaven and moves round until it reaches the west. Next day a further portion of light is "cut out from the provision of fire." Others believe that the sun is the same every day and that it passes during the night along the flat bottom of the earth back to the east. Opponents of this theory say that the earth is bottomless and that therefore there is no space along which the sun can pass.

The earth is a great flat plain upon which there rests the solid blue vault of heaven like an upturned bowl. The extreme horizon is called the "place where women can lean their pestles against the vault" or the "place where women pound their mealies on their knees" since if they stood up the pestles would hit the sky.

The moon is a thing which, beginning very tender and delicate, grows stronger as the month advances. So fragile is it on the day of the new moon, that no work of any sort may be done in the fields lest it be injured. As with the sun, opinions differ as to whether it is another body each time it reappears, or the same. Some natives believe that "the sun and the moon have a race each month; the moon when it first appears is not yet firm like a new-born child, so its light is feeble; it is dominated by the sun; but it grows and fights. When it is full, the sun sees 'that now it is the moon!': it is something to be reckoned with. During the second half of the month, as it decreases, it lingers in the sky and the sun soon over-takes it again and compels it to pass behind. Then the moon is entirely vanquished."

The Thonga, unlike oriental peoples, are not interested in the stars and talk of no groups or constellations except the Pleiades. Nobody is allowed to count the stars and so difficult would this be if it had to be done that it is regarded as the very symbol of torment: a child is told, "you will feel hungry and not be able to go to sleep; you will be as unhappy as if you had to count the stars."

Planets are not distinguished from other stars, but Venus being very conspicuous is well known and used as a time-piece and announcer of the dawn. When Venus shines as a morning star it is the hour to start a journey or a warlike attack so that by the time daylight breaks, the men will be well on their way.

Apparently a Thonga does not busy himself overmuch about things which are of no great importance to him and his astronomical researches are restricted. Not so his meteorological researches: here he is dealing with things which are life and death to him, and knowledge is piled up about rain, lightning, thunder and the other natural phenomena associated with them.

About rain, for example, he has a great deal to say: it is the spirits of the ancestors which cause rain to fall, and if the rain fails the ancestors are to be propitiated, and anything which may have annoyed them inquired into and regulated. The chief natural causes which, according

to the Thonga, prevent rain from falling are "the miscarriage of women, the birth of twins, and the death of
children not yet initiated into the tribe, unless buried
in wet ground." Because twins have been born, therefore
there is no rain, say the Thonga, and we see how dangerous and two-edged the implements "because" and "therefore" may be. "When a woman has had a miscarriage,"
one Thonga explained, "when she has let her blood flow
secretly and has buried the abortive child in an unknown
place, it is enough to make the burning winds blow, and
to dry up all the land: the rain can no longer fall, because
the country is no longer right. Rain fears that spot. It
must stop at that very place and can go no further. This
woman has been very guilty. She has spoilt the country
of the chief, because she has hidden blood which had
not yet properly united to make a human being. What
she has done is forbidden, it causes starvation."

In order that the rain may be induced to fall once
more, it is necessary to purify the ground: the medicine
men "after having sent old women to the river to throw
away the contaminated earth, order them to make a
ball of that earth, and to bring it back to us in the early
morning. We grind it, we put it into a pot where it must
remain for five days and then we prepare the great drug
to sprinkle the land. The medicine is put into oxen
horns and they go to all the drifts; they must not however
cross rivers. Our neighbours do the same on their own
side. One of the girls digs the earth, the others dip a
stick into the horn and sprinkle the drug into the hole.
We also sprinkle the road on which these women have
trodden, when they had their blood; we remove the

misfortune caused by these women on the roads. The country is pure again. Rain can fall."

Much more could be said about rain-making, and it would all show that by the wrong use of "because" and "therefore," combined with too little knowledge of natural phenomena, the savage tries to control that which is really beyond his control, to explain that which cannot be explained without a deeper knowledge and a sounder logic. And beyond such vital things as rain and sunlight there are those even more serious problems, the origin of man and the meaning of death. About these the Thonga has thought constantly and has arrived at solutions in which he firmly believes. They are the main problems of his philosophy, the main quests of his religion: and his solutions are founded upon his knowledge of the universe. So too are our own.

§ 6

What light do these savage theories throw on our immediate quest in this book? We see, on the one hand, that the Thonga concerns himself in much the same way as we do with the universe around. For example, he sees the sun moving in its daily course and he produces a theory which, as the medieval philosophers said, "saves the phenomena." There was nothing known to him which contradicted the idea that a piece of light detached itself from the pool of light to be seen in the eastern waves and moved round to the west. There was nothing against the idea of the earth as a great flat plain. If we have today a different opinion of the sun, it is because we know several other things about it which make the

Thonga theory useless, we know phenomena which are not "saved" by believing that the earth is flat or the glow on the waves a pool of light. That is the only reason why we have altered our opinions. On the other hand, we see the Thonga busied with a desire to control nature and to get exactly what he wants out of it. He tries to get his desires fulfilled in accordance with his knowledge of the universe; what he knows and what he thinks he knows give him ideas about rain and drought. With us it is rather different: we can certainly do many things of which no Thonga ever dreamed, but we know too much even to try and do some of the things which he tries to do. The Thonga would think our meteorological reports very foolish because they are a confession that we must wait upon the rain rather than expect the rain to wait upon us; while he would highly approve of prayers for rain or for fine weather offered in some village church.

And so we find that the difference between us and the Thonga is in part an improvement in technical knowledge and in part a better discrimination between those of our desires which are possible and those which are impossible. We have discovered that human beings stand straddled like a Colossus, one foot in the world of reality, one in a world of dream invented by themselves, and we find that gradually the world of dream needs to be remade as our understanding of the world of reality increases; that in fact our religions, our philosophies, our emotions, our ideals are all of them dependent on our science.

We did not begin by building up the world of our dreams step by step with the world of our science: we built the first up to the gables before we had laid the foundations of the other and that has made the building of the world of science more difficult and the rebuilding of the world of dreams more painful.

Moreover we must remember with the utmost care that there has been a continuity in all the stages of our growth: just as we learned when we were Spectral Tarsiers to do many things which we have never had to relearn, so we learned things as savages which we find hard to forget. The trouble is that whereas what we learned as animals was good for us on the whole, what we learned as savages was almost wholly bad. Science has had to burn its way through an undergrowth of false doctrine, to pull down many carefully laid bricks and stones, so that the mansion of our dreams may some day be built in the same style as the mansion of reality.

The religion of the savage, his outlook on life as a whole, depended upon the picture of the universe which he possessed; with him, as with us, there were two possible ways of using the gift of imagination; humanity can either listen to its longings first and then imagine a picture of the universe which fits into those longings; or it can use its imagination to discover the truest possible picture of the universe and then develop out of this a reasonable set of longings. The trouble is that we have become accustomed to using the word "imaginary" exclusively for the first kind of picture, the kind made when imagination is the slave of everyday longings, and this makes us blind to the fact that the picture given us by science is also the gift of our imagination, but in this case of our imagination acting as the servant of a greater human longing still, namely, the longing to understand reality.

The history of the human intellect is the increasing ability to construct pictures of the universe which do not merely satisfy transient emotions but the permanent underlying emotion, love of reality. We cease to be savages in accordance with our progress along this road; we are still many days' journey from the end. Nor was it science as we understand it today that was our guide during the first stages of our journey; it was rather the great system which was eventually destroyed by science, a system which ruled men for a thousand years before it died out and which has left in consequence a good many traces of its existence in our minds today. We have all been animals, we have all been savages, we are all perhaps modern scientific men, but before we became that we were all of us something quite different for hundreds of years, namely, medieval men. Let us turn then from savages to the followers of Christ and Aristotle.

CHAPTER TWO

>>>>>>>>>>>>>>>>>>>>>>><<<<<<<<<<<<<<<<<<<<<<<

The Medieval Picture of the Universe

§ 1

"The character of the emotion with which men contemplate the world," said W. K. Clifford, "the temper in which they stand in the presence of the immensities and the eternities, must depend first of all on what they think the world is." The modern Man contemplates the world with mixed emotions because he is very muddled about what he thinks the world is. He is heir to the thoughts and knowledge of all his ancestors and he takes a curiously varied selection of them in order to paint his picture of the universe.

We have looked at two stages of living thought, the animal and the savage: we have learned to regard ourselves as leading a succession of lives from the present back to the amœba and to realise that each of them left its ineradicable mark upon us. As far as our animal existences are concerned the mark is chiefly in our bodies; at least it does not affect our attitude towards the universe as a whole, for the sufficient reason that when we were animals we did not care a rap for the universe as a whole, and had no attitude towards it. A cat lapping milk by a warm fire cares nothing for the pictures on the walls of the room, and so we, as animals, only interested ourselves in the essentials of food and drink and self-preservation. We never therefore became bad judges of pictures in those days, although we did get the possibly bad habit of believing that food and self-preservation are probably more important than pictures, an attitude which some folk rightly or wrongly deplore. But apart from a belief that first things come first, and that first things are meat and drink rather than poetry and fine thinking, we derive nothing of our picture of the universe as a whole from our animal existence.

From our savage existence we derive a great deal and especially the belief that whatever the universe may be our desires are certainly its mainspring; if we want to be immortal, then we imagine ourselves to be immortal; if we want rain, then we imagine we can make rain; if we want to feel more excellent than our neighbour, then we convince ourselves that we are more excellent. In short, instead of modelling the mansion of our dreams on the lines of the mansion of reality, we try to do the opposite and remodel reality to look like our dream. Instead of seeking God we make him as we wish him to be. Instead of finding out what life contains and learning to enjoy it, we try to pretend that we can invent the joys and then look to the universe to satisfy them.

Indeed, there is a skeleton in our intellectual cupboard, articulated of the fears, hopes, joys, sorrows, vanities of the savage mind.

Some people have thought that the modern man consists only of this skeleton and its dust, and a nice new broom, called reason or science, ready to sweep the dust and bones away. It is not so simple as that, however, because not only is there savage superstition and modern science, but a third element complicating them both, at once tinged with savage ideas and colouring science. This third element is the great attempt made to reduce the chaos of savage imagination to order by our cultural ancestors during two thousand years of history. From the time of Aristotle until about four hundred years ago the mind of man was busy remaking the universe according to a system which was not that of the savage nor that of the modern scientist but quite different from either. It was a gallant attempt, a stupendous adventure of the human imagination, and though in the end it failed, it has left many traces behind it in our minds today.

If the modern man is to understand anything of his picture of the universe and of his outlook on life, he must study the way in which the genius and authority of one man so dominated and overpowered the mind of humanity for close on two thousand years, that throughout that time there was scarcely any progress; while any attempt to cast doubt upon one word of this man's writings came to be regarded as blasphemous.

No man has ever influenced mankind to a degree in the least comparable with Aristotle. Yet Aristotle himself warned people against the very attitude which later they adopted: "I found no basis prepared," he said, "no models to copy. Mine is the first step, and therefore a small one, though worked out with much thought and hard labour. It must be looked at as a first step and judged with indulgence." What Aristotle called a first step became the last word for sixty generations of human beings. He it was whose knowledge of the universe defined humanity's emotional attitude to life for centuries; and, although nobody today is a complete Aristotelian, hardly any point of view of the modern man is not tinged by his influence. If the train of thought instituted by Aristotle had never come into the world you and I would have a totally different idea of God, existence, the universe. But of course such an "if" is meaningless, for Aristotle is only the concrete form of a state through which the human imagination was bound to pass sooner or later.

The world before Aristotle was, as we have seen, full of ideas about the universe as a whole, and about everything in the universe; but the basis of all these ideas was a firm belief that the universe was pretty much what the savage mind wished it to be. We, as savages, had fashioned the universe in the image of our own desires; when those desires were what we should now call reasonable, we succeeded in accomplishing them by making necessary alteration in the universe—thus the African Lango filtered muddy water and obtained a pure beverage; when however our desires were unreasonable, we devised elaborate self-deceptions and convinced ourselves that we could do the impossible—the Thonga unwilling to admit that they were at the mercy of the elements convinced themselves that they could make rain. In this way reality became more and more lost in an increasingly complicated scheme woven to suit human needs and emotions as they existed in the savage.

But it was not just a question of trying to satisfy isolated desires, this altering of the universe: it was far deeper than this, for behind the daily desires for food, comfort, protection, sexual satisfaction, there lies in every human being, however savage, the desire to make out of all life's experiences a consistent, harmonious pattern into which everything fits; a desire for unity and proportion;

⌢50⌢

a desire for a philosophy of life, without contradictions and without absurdities; and though daily hungers played their part in the savage distortion of reality, there was always present also this desire to satisfy a far deeper and nobler hunger still.

There are two ways in which any human being can go about to satisfy this hunger; either by so seeing reality that it does not contradict his desires, or by so disciplining his desires that they do not conflict with reality. The importance of Aristotle is that he is the chief master in the first school which got any distance in the second of these two directions. He can be regarded as the first great disciplinarian of the human mind. He created a pattern out of the universe which was consistent in its details, which did not require reality to be wrongly seen for the benefit of human emotions, which was not a savage pattern because it was based on a right use of "because" and "therefore." With him the human imagination began to hunger and thirst after righteousness and to discipline its tendency to cry for the moon.

By a strange coincidence a religion, which grew up around the interesting figure of Jesus of Nazareth and found favour with the greatest military force the world had seen, the Roman Empire, accepted for all essential purposes the word of Aristotle as inspired, to such an extent that many of the beliefs which orthodox Christians hold and held, on the assumption that they have to do with the teachings of Jesus, are really the result of the mental dominance of a pagan Greek philosopher. In short, the "medieval mind" which included all that was best in humanity for more than a thousand years was largely Aristotelian, certainly far more so than it was

ever "Christian" and the fact that Aristotle's works were
actually lost for a large part of that time, made
no difference because their influence lingered on in
out-of-the-way corners and never ceased to colour human
thought.

Now you are a modern man, not very interested in the
history of human thought, but deeply anxious to put all
the various adventures of the human imagination into an
order which shall help you to decide for yourself how
you are going to regard the great riddle of life. You do
not want to build up a clear picture of all the chances
and changes which took place during the Middle Ages,
but you do want to know what in your own day can
only be understood by understanding what medievalism
really was. We need not therefore do more than describe
in general terms the picture of the universe seen by our
medieval ancestors and show how that picture is vital
to all the later adventures of the human spirit and to
our own personal adventures not least. We shall not concern ourselves with how that picture differed in various
minds and at different periods, we need only the essence
common to all these variations. And the reason why we
need this essence is that all the rest of our story is based
upon its decay: Aristotle and medieval philosophy were
beautiful flowers in their day, and after making bright
the garden of the world for a time, they decayed and
became the fertiliser necessary for a different crop of
flowers. It is as absurd to regard them as a sort of enemy
to be attacked and conquered by modern science, as it
would be if this year's plants were regarded as the enemy
of those plants which next year will spring from mould
enriched by their dead and rotted leaves. Nor are they

dead, seeing that we carry their transmuted tissues in every tissue of our minds.

No man can have a reasonable religion today, that is, a reasonable reaction to life as a whole, unless he knows how the world seemed to cultured Europeans five hundred years ago for that knowledge is essential for his understanding of why he holds certain deep-seated beliefs, upon which much of his everyday philosophy rests.

§ 2

Let us begin by considering what Aristotle thought of the solar system and of the stars and then let us consider how such ideas affected everyday life so long as they were held.

We have seen that the South African Thonga, trusting to their eyes, regard the sky as a solid inverted cup against the rim of which a woman could lean her pestle; in the same way Aristotle believed that the universe was a sphere. Unlike the savages he had got past the idea that the earth was flat and he saw that the dome above was half the whole sky and was completed by a dome beneath the earth. This he knew simply because the Greeks knew rather more geography than the Thonga and having travelled farther had seen the horizon flee before them, new stars appear, and other phenomena unknown to the stay-at-home Bantu. No longer did the idea of a flat earth "save all the phenomena," and instead it was seen that if the earth was a sphere and the starry heavens a larger sphere, revolving rapidly round it, then everything known about the universe was explained. The stars were fixed to a huge sphere revolving on itself and were carried round by it in twenty-four hours, which explained their rising and setting perfectly. This much had been seen long before Aristotle; but what makes Aristotle's acceptance of it of supreme importance is his explanation of why this was so. In these days we hardly expect that astronomical ideas could upset religions and yet nearly two thousand years after he was dead another philosopher, Galileo, was to suffer because he denied the picture of the universe accepted by Aristotle and by so doing endangered all the most sacred beliefs of his age; we can only understand how this was so, if we understand the reason given by Aristotle for this picture.

The universe was in the shape of a sphere—that it was so seemed to follow from the observation of the senses—because the sphere is the *most perfect shape*! Why was the sphere the *most perfect shape*? Because if you turned it round it always occupied the same space, which is not true, of course, if you revolve a cube, or a pyramid, or a table, or a chair. Twist a tennis ball round and round and it will always occupy a space of its own original shape and dimensions; but a tennis racket will not: therefore in Aristotle's mind a tennis ball is of a more "perfect" shape than a tennis racket. And as "obviously" the universe is perfect its shape is the most perfect, that is a sphere: if it were not a sphere, then it would not be perfect and its creator would not be perfect, which is absurd.

The modern man is, of course, likely to be dumbfounded by such a line of argument and yet it is fundamental to medieval philosophy wherein again and again the belief in certain things being perfect and others imperfect reigns supreme. Take for example the creation of the world in six days according to Genesis: St. Augustine expressly says: "There are three classes of numbers—the more than perfect, the perfect, and the less than perfect, according as the sum of them is greater than, equal to, or less than the original number. Six is the first perfect number: wherefore we must not say that six is a perfect number because God finished all his works in six days, but that God finished all his works in six days because six is a perfect number." We need not worry about why St. Augustine calls six a perfect number, but it is vital to understand that in the Middle Ages the human mind thought of certain numbers, shapes, motions as "perfect," and assumed that it was the nature of the universe to exhibit these perfections at every turn, and the nature of God to use them for his handiwork. If God had made the world in any other number of days he would not have done perfectly, and this was of course simply blasphemous.

It was because of this belief that anyone who suggested that the universe was not a sphere immediately became suspect of impiety, for he was really suggesting that the works of God were not perfect, or that God himself was imperfect and in this way any scientific discovery might turn out to be blasphemous if it ran counter to orthodox teachings about what is perfect.

Aristotle then believed that the universe was a sphere, a hard material thing identical with the sky and revolving about the lesser sphere, the earth. It did not escape him, of course, that such a picture did not cover all astronomical facts: although the motions of the fixed stars were thus completely accounted for, the movements of the sun, the moon and the planets were not. The very name "planet" means a wandering star, one which is not fixed to the sphere of the fixed stars, but wanders about appearing now among one group of stars, now among another. The sun and moon are constantly to be seen against a different background of stars, while Mercury, Venus, Mars, Jupiter and Saturn instead of moving from east to west wander here and there among their apparent neighbours.

Now supposing all these bodies moved round the earth in circles, their motions could be accounted for in the following manner: The moon, for example, was attached to a hollow, transparent sphere revolving round the earth in twenty-seven days from west to east, and this sphere was in its turn attached to another sphere moving in another way and at another speed, and this to a third sphere revolving round like the fixed stars in twenty-four hours. In short, the moon's motion through the sky was accounted for by assuming the existence of three hollow, transparent spheres all revolving round the earth, all having the same centre as the earth, two of them having no body on them and the third holding the moon. It is moreover perfectly true that the moon's motion, as far as it could be observed by an ancient Greek is accurately accounted for by such a theory. The sun, which rises and sets and seems to march month by month through a background of varied stars, also needed three such spheres to account for its motion. The planets required an extra sphere each to account for their motions and later still other spheres were added until altogether by Aristotle's day thirty-three spheres were believed to account for all the motions of the solar system and of the fixed stars.

But Aristotle was not content with this: believing that these spheres actually existed as real material things he saw the difficulty that one sphere would by friction move the next sphere to it, so he introduced a sort of free-wheel system by adding twenty-two "unrolling" spheres in between the others like ball-bearings on a bicycle. Finally all these spheres, moving against one another harmoniously, produced the "music of the spheres," the perpetual pleasure of God and the angels.

It is a curious picture of the universe: but if you could carve out and insert fifty-five hollow, transparent balls one within the other and if these balls could all be twisted round on their own axes at different angles and speeds, you would be able to reproduce all the motions and positions of the stars, planets, the moon and the sun as accurately as Aristotle knew them and therefore your picture of the universe, with the earth in the middle, surrounded, like a Chinese toy, with fifty-five hollow spheres would be scientifically accurate. Until new facts came along not explained by such a system the system could not possibly be attacked, for it "saved the phenomena." Eudoxus who, as far as we know, invented the system, is, according to Dreyer, "the first to go beyond mere philosophical reasoning about the construction of the universe; he is the first to attempt systematically to account for the planetary motions. When he has done this the next question is how far this theory satisfies the observed phenomena, and Kalippus at once supplies the observational facts required to test the theory and modifies the latter until the theoretical and observed motions agree within the limit of accuracy attainable at the time. Philosophical speculation unsupported by steadily pursued observations is from henceforth abandoned; the science of astronomy has started on its career." Instead of laughing at this strange picture of the universe we will do well to realise what an advance it is upon the system, let us say, of the Thonga.

For our purpose there are two things particularly to be borne in mind: First, that such an idea of the universe, ridiculous as it seems to us, fitted in with everything that human beings had observed; true, we now know it to be wrong in every way, but to the Greek there was no way of seeing that it was wrong, since he had no telescopes, no accurate measuring instruments and no sufficiently large collection of observations of the stars and planets. All he could do was to watch the sky and think out how what he saw there could be reproduced in a mathematical drawing or a mechanical model.

Second, the idea rested on certain "overbeliefs," certain assumptions which had nothing at all to do with things seen or measured, but rather with the nature of God or truth or beauty or perfection. It was assumed that the earth was in the centre of all things and that the sphere of the fixed stars rotated round it in twenty-four hours and that all the heavenly bodies moved in circles. Though some of these things were the result of observation in the first place, they were also all the result of ideas about fitness and perfection. The circle was the perfect path and therefore the heavens moved in circles; to suggest that any other path could be taken by a planet—an oval, or an ellipse for example—was to suggest that the universe was less perfect than it might be. Indeed the phrase, used often by many people who may not understand its original meaning, "this sublunary world" or "existence" alludes to the fact that on the earth things move in straight lines and zigzags and all sorts of imperfect ways, whereas in the sphere of the moon and in the spheres above the moon all motion is perfect, that is, circular. Moreover the best sphere is the sphere with the most perfect, that is, the fastest motion, and clearly this sphere is the outermost one since being farthest from the earth it has the longest journey to complete in the twenty-four hours. This then means that the creative power, or God, dwells in the outermost sphere and its influence penetrates inwards until it reaches the earth in a greatly weakened condition: that is why things are imperfect, changing, mortal, muddled, here, whereas above the moon all is perfect, unchanging, immortal and harmonious. And of course the idea that the earth is the centre is simply a matter of common sense: where else should it be?

Now what do these two things mean to the modern man? First, they mean that a perfectly scientific picture of the universe, that is a picture which accounts for all the known facts, may be completely wrong; and second, that every picture, right or wrong, is mixed with non-scientific overbeliefs which very often are the real reason why men desire to paint that particular picture. Put in another way it means that there may be several scientifically possible pictures of the universe and of them the one which satisfies the overbelief of the particular epoch will prevail. Moreover when a given scientific picture has been accepted for a long time the overbeliefs of humanity come to depend more and more upon it so that at last one cannot exist without the other; that is why new scientific knowledge almost always irritates the human imagination before it is accepted.

If this is borne in mind we shall gain a far clearer idea of why Copernicus, Galileo and Kepler met with opposition and persecution. We shall also have to learn that the so-called conflict between Science and Religion is usually by no means the simple war between truth and fiction often imagined by the village atheist; for science, as we shall soon see, has been the seeking out of God just as much as theology or anything else has been and only when the idea of God discovered by science varies from the one accepted by the theology of the day has there been any conflict at all. However, since theology is always conservative and science always revolutionary clashes have been not infrequent.

§ 3

Aristotle actually believed that his fifty-five hollow, transparent, concentric spheres were a machine which went. That was the universe as far as he was concerned; an aeroplane could conceivably visit each sphere, though whether it could get through them is another matter; there they were as materially as the chair on which the reader is sitting; they were not a mere "explanation" of the way in which stars were seen to move through the night sky, they were the actuality.

Now although the general ideas and philosophy of Aristotle moulded human thought for thousands of years, and his complicated system of spheres was believed in until long after Dante used it as a description of the universe in the *Divina Commedia,* the chief mathematical description of the universe in the Middle Ages was what we know as the Ptolemaic system. Ptolemy who flourished about A.D. 135 did not try to discover a real picture of the universe; he did not say "this is what the stars are, that is where they are, this is the machinery which keeps them moving"; he said, "the stars have been observed to move from here to there and I will solve this puzzle in geometry, I will think out a moving geometrical drawing which will imitate their motions; I shall not say this puzzle is correct in the sense of being what the stars in fact do; I will merely say that given the known facts they are imitated by my geometrical figures." The spheres of Aristotle did not even do this once men began to observe the heavens with some care.

There were two ways in which a geometrician could solve the puzzle stated in this way: he could construct a series of circles which accounted for the moon's observed motions by supposing that it moved in a circle round the earth but with the earth not exactly in the centre. If the moon moved in a circle with the earth at the centre, her observed positions in the sky were inexplicable, and so to explain the moon's eccentricities her path was supposed to be ex-centric, that is, with the earth away from the centre;—for that is why to this day we describe a person who does not behave as we expect him to behave, as 'eccentric.' By choosing the right-sized circles, and the right amount of eccentricity the geometrical puzzle of all the planets and stars could be solved.

It could also be solved in another way. Suppose that instead of the moon itself going round the earth in a circle, it went round a circle, the centre of which went round the earth in a circle: with a sufficient number of circles of the right size you can again account for the observed positions of all the heavenly bodies. Ptolemy chose this second way of solving his problem and by complicating the systems of earlier astronomers produced a solution so exact that there was no way of showing it to be incorrect until the coming of telescopes. We must remember that he was bound by the "overbeliefs" of his age to assume as given facts that the earth was the centre of the universe and that everything moved round it in perfect circles; as observation proved that a single circle round the earth was impossible, he had to preserve the general fact of circular motion in the way we have indicated; and it was a brilliant mathematical achievement to do so. No better solution was found for more than fourteen hundred years.

Ptolemy's picture of the universe thus became of equal importance with that of Aristotle: these are his fundamental astronomical assumptions, according to Dreyer: "the heavens is a sphere, turning round a fixed axis, as may be proved by the circular motion of the circumpolar stars and by the fact that other stars always rise and set at the same points of the horizon. The earth is a sphere, situated in the centre of the heavens; if it were not, one side of the heavens would appear nearer to us than the other and the stars would be larger there; . . . the earth is but as a point in comparison to the heavens, because the stars appear of the same magnitude and at the same distances *inter se*, no matter where the observer goes on the earth. It has no motion of translation, first, because there must be some fixed point to which the motions of the others may be referred, secondly, because heavy bodies descend to the centre of the heavens which is the centre of the earth. And if there was a motion it would be proportionate to the great mass of the earth, and would leave behind animals and objects thrown into the air." Against this background of beliefs Ptolemy constructed, as we have seen, a system of movements by means of "epicycles" which accounted for the known motions of the planets amid the stars as they could be observed by a man on the earth on any starry night.

Thus the medieval picture of the universe satisfied two very different needs; it explained what could be observed with human eyes, that is, it was scientific; and it agreed in shape and motions with what men conceived to be the necessary attributes of God's handiwork, that is, it was theologically satisfactory. Religion and science embraced one another in Ptolemy's epicycles and they became orthodox for the believing world. In them man's idea of God and his idea of the universe were equated and nobody was to suspect the temporary nature of this alliance until new discoveries paved the way for a new scientific idea of the universe. But it required a struggle for even the Ptolemaic system to become orthodox, which it did over the destroyed remnants of quite another system.

§ 4

We must now turn away for a moment from Aristotle and Ptolemy and the mathematicians to study this other system and the train of thought which led to it. We have said that it was Aristotle and Ptolemy who dominated the medieval mind for close on two thousand years; but there was a long interval, a dark age, when the Christian barbarians, determined to overthrow all paganism and its philosophy, turned their backs on the huge gains which they represented and fought for what was virtually a savage way of looking at the universe.

As we have seen, the importance of Aristotle and his followers was that they sought for reality and its Creator by scientific probing into the unknown: they felt that by comprehending the nature of the universe they would come to a comprehension of God, who would reveal himself more and more through a fuller understanding of his works. Side by side with them there was a school which believed that everything about not only God but the universe also was to be found within the pages of the Bible: that God had revealed himself there once and for all and had moreover described with sufficient accuracy the nature of his handiwork. We are apt to regard the fundamentalist as a person who denies Darwin and evolution and sticks to a belief in the literal interpretation of Genesis. But there were fundamentalists long before Darwin, who opposed, not the animal origin of man, but whatever happened to be the new scientific discovery of the moment, on the ground that reading the Bible taught astronomy, geology and the other sciences far more accurately than using one's eyes: indeed evolution is simply the last ditch left to be defended by fundamentalists in the nineteenth century, all other positions having been lost in the course of centuries of warfare. In the early days of Christianity the battleground between science and fundamentalism was the question of the roundness of the earth.

Lactantius, a charming writer of about A.D. 300, rightly noted for his style, had ridiculed the philosophers, who

suggested that people might live on the other side of
the world, using all the arguments which would still
occur to a child of six: "How is it with those," he asks,
"who imagine that there are antipodes opposite to our
footsteps? Do they say anything to the purpose? Or is
there anyone so senseless as to believe that there are men
whose footsteps are higher than their heads? or that the
things that with us are in a recumbent position, with
them hang in an inverted direction? that the crops and
trees grow downwards? And does anyone wonder that
hanging gardens (of Babylon) are mentioned among the
seven wonders of the world, when philosophers make
hanging fields, and seas, and cities, and mountains? . . .
What course of argument, therefore, led them to the idea
of the antipodes? They saw the courses of the stars
travelling towards the west; they saw that the sun and
the moon always set towards the same quarter, and rise
from the same. But since they did not perceive what
contrivance regulated their courses, nor how they returned from the west to the east, but supposed that the
heaven itself sloped downwards in every direction, which
appearance it must present on account of its great breadth,
they thought that the universe is round like a ball, and
they fancied that the heaven revolves in accordance with
the motion of the heavenly bodies; and thus that the stars
and sun, when they have set, by the very rapidity of the
motion of the universe are borne back to the east. It followed therefore from this rotundity of the heaven, that
the earth was enclosed in the midst of its curved surface.
But if this were so, the earth also itself must be like a
globe; for that could not possibly be anything but round,
which was held enclosed by that which was round. But

if the earth also were round, it must necessarily happen that it should present the same appearance to all parts of the heaven; that is, that it should raise aloft mountains, extend plains, and have level seas. And if this were so, that last consequence also followed, that there would be no part of the earth uninhabited by men and the other animals. Thus the rotundity of the earth leads, in addition, to the invention of these suspended antipodes.

"But if you inquire from those who defend these marvellous fictions, why all things do not fall into that lower part of the heaven, they reply that such is the nature of things, that heavy bodies are borne to the middle . . . I am at a loss what to say respecting those who, when they have once erred, consistently persevere in their folly, and defend one vain thing by another: . . . but I should be able to prove by many arguments that it is impossible for the heaven to be lower than the earth, were it not that this book must now be concluded."

It is clear that Lactantius understood the ancient astronomers about as well as William Jennings Bryan understood Darwin; but his contempt for such as imagined the earth to be round has the excuse that he believed all such knowledge to be absolutely useless: "to investigate," he writes, "or wish to know the causes of natural things,—whether the sun is as great as it appears to be, or is many times greater than the whole of this earth; also whether the moon be spherical or concave; and whether the stars are fixed to the heaven, or are borne with free course through the air; of what magnitude the heaven itself is, of what material it is composed; whether it is at rest or immovable, or is turned round with incredible swiftness; how great is the thickness of the earth, or on what foundations it is poised and suspended, —to wish to comprehend these things, I say, by disputation and conjectures, is as though we should wish to discuss what we may suppose to be the character of a city in some very remote country, which we have never seen, and of which we have heard nothing more than the name. . . . How much more are they to be judged mad and senseless, who imagine that they know natural things, which cannot be known by men!"

Here we have the opposite point of view from that which we have been studying: a definite contempt for all natural knowledge and an assertion that knowledge of the universe cannot help us to know God because it is impossible to obtain. Lactantius left it at that; he had no time or space for his refutations but we can guess what they would have been from other Christian writers who, culminating in Cosmas Indicopleustes, the writer of *The Christian Topography*, offer us a different way of ascertaining the shape of the earth and the universe in general. In Isaiah God is spoken of as "he that sitteth upon the circle of the earth, . . . that stretcheth out the heavens as a curtain, and spreadeth them out as a tent to dwell in." In Genesis, we read, "And God said, Let there be a firmament in the midst of the waters, and let it divide the waters from the waters," and how at the time of the Flood "were all the fountains of the great deep broken-up, and the windows (or floodgates) of heaven were opened." In Exodus Moses and others went up unto the Lord "and they saw the God of Israel: and there was under his feet as it were a paved work of a sapphire stone, and as it were the body of heaven in his clearness." In Job we read, "the pillars of heaven tremble and are astonished at his reproof" and "hast thou with him spread out the sky, which is strong, and as a molten looking-glass?"; in the Psalms, "Praise him, ye heaven of heavens, and ye waters that be above the heavens." All these texts, assuming that the Bible is literally true, must be taken into account by anyone wishing to understand the shape, size, movements, velocities of the earth and universe. If the Bible is literally correct in deriving the first woman from Adam's rib, or in making the whole of creation take six days, there is no reason why it should not be correct about the shape of the heavens; if the Bible speaks of a water above the firmament, of pillars, of tents, then these were the elements of the universe. Moreover Moses expressly states that the Tabernacle set up in the wilderness was a model of the universe, and the writer of the Epistle to the Hebrews reaffirms this statement; so that instead of wasting time taking measurements and doing sums the fundamentalist learns his astronomy from reading the description of Moses' tabernacle.

Cosmas Indicopleustes did this work most thoroughly: "the division of the Tabernacle into two places, by means of the veil, typified the division of the universe into two worlds—an upper and a lower, by means of the firmament. The table of shew-bread, again, with its waved border, represented the earth surrounded by the ocean, while its other parts and the things upon it symbolized each some object or other in the natural world. Now, as the table was twice as long as it was broad, and was placed lengthwise from east to west, and breadth wise from north to south, from this we learn that the earth is a rectangular plane which extends in length from east to west, and in breadth from north to south, and is twice as long as it is broad. The ocean, he further gives us to know, is unnavigable, and, while encompassing this earth of ours, is itself encompassed by another earth, which had been the seat of Paradise and the abode of man until the Ark, floating on the billows of the Flood, wafted Noah and his family over into this earth.

"The heavens come downward to us in four walls, which, at their lower sides, are welded to the four sides of the earth beyond ocean, each to each. The upper side of the northern wall, at the summit of heaven, curved round and over, till it unites with the upper side of the southern wall, and thus forms, in the shape of an oblong vault, the canopy of heaven, which Cosmas likens to the vaulted roof of a bathroom. This vast rectangular hall is divided at the middle into two stories by the firmament, which thus serves as a ceiling for the lower story and a floor for the upper. The lower story is this world, where men and angels have their abode until the Resurrection, and the story above is heaven—the place of the future state.

"As to the position of the earth in the scheme of things, Scripture left Cosmas in no doubt. The Psalmist had declared that the Creator had founded the earth upon its own stability; Job, that he had hanged it on nothing; and Isaiah, that, while heaven was His throne the earth was His footstool. Clearly, therefore, the place of the earth was at the bottom of the universe—a position to which it must naturally have sunk at the very instant of its creation. What then can be more absurd than the Pagan doctrine that the earth is in the middle of the universe? Were it in the middle, there must be something below it as well as above it; but there is nothing below it, since we learn from Genesis that God made heaven and earth and nothing else beyond these." [I. W. McCrindle in *Introduction to Christian Topography of Cosmas an Egyptian Monk,* 1897, Hakluyt Society, London.]

§ 5

Are these three different ways of looking at the universe, that of Aristotle, of Ptolemy, of Cosmas Indicopleustes, just matters of ancient history? On the contrary they have the clearest lesson for the modern man in his search for God and religion, and it is in this light that we must consider them still further.

As we see them today they have one character in common, they are all "wrong"; that is, they do not "save the phenomena" as we now know them. Aristotle with his belief that fifty-five hollow transparent spheres one within the next and the earth at the centre was a true description of fact; Ptolemy with his series of circles neatly revolving to satisfy the arrangement of the night sky, not claiming to discover a true description of fact but only to solve a given mathematical problem; Cosmas refusing to look at anything but the Bible and roundly declaring that if the things seen by human eyes did not tally with the descriptions of Moses, or David, or St. Paul, so much the worse for the evidence of men's senses; they can all be dismissed as ignorant of a great deal that we now know. Of the three it is hardest to argue against Cosmas because he starts by denying the efficacy of human reason, observation, or logic, and unless we assume their efficiency, it is impossible to argue at all.

But even though the conclusions at which these three arrived were all wrong—for even fundamentalists do not today accept the cosmography of Cosmas, although to be consistent they should do so—it nevertheless remains a fact that there is no other method possible to man for discovering the universe than one of these three methods. Either knowledge must be found in inspired writings, where Cosmas learned that the universe was shaped like a bathroom; or by a mixture of observation and metaphysical reasoning such as made Aristotle ascribe rotundity to earth and sky, because a sphere is the "perfect" shape; or we must with Ptolemy modestly say that such and such geometrical constructions do fit observed facts although quite possibly reality may be something quite different.

Now in the Middle Ages and especially in the case of Copernicus, as we shall see later, it was only by adopting the third attitude that the type of thought which we call "scientific" managed to survive; the scientist could and did combat orthodox dogmatism by saying "of course my theory has nothing to do with reality; it is just a mathematical exercise which gives the right answer; if I multiply $a-b$ by $a+b$ I get a^2-b^2 but I have no idea what a or b may be, and in the same way I have no idea what the universe is, and as a good orthodox Christian I accept whatever happens to be dictated by popes and bishops and inquisitors for the time being." In this way scientific theory was able to develop.

On the other hand, Cosmas and the fundamentalists could not succeed in convincing the orthodox Christian world for long that the earth was not a sphere and by the eighth century this line of defence had been evacuated for ever by fundamentalism. However, much later, sects have sprung up preaching that the earth is flat, while Gervase of Tilbury tells in the thirteenth century of some churchgoers being surprised to see an anchor suspended above their heads and to hear sailors' voices somewhere in the sky; presently a sailor descended by the anchor chain and upon touching the ground died of drowning—something had gone wrong with a boat cruising on the waters above the firmament.

With the rediscovery of Aristotle the orthodox attitude was that the Bible on the one hand and Natural Philosophy on the other must both be used for the exploration of truth; and Augustine's wise words of centuries before finally became accepted as the best attitude by men like Thomas Aquinas: "it very often happens," he had said, "that there is some question as to the earth or the sky, or the other elements of this world respecting which one who is not a Christian has knowledge derived from most certain reasoning or observation; and it is very disgraceful and mischievous and of all things to be carefully avoided, that a Christian speaking of such matters, as being according to the Christian Scriptures, should be heard by an unbeliever talking such nonsense, that the unbeliever, perceiving him to be as wide from the mark as east from west, can hardly restrain from laughing."

Thomas Aquinas (A.D. 1250) wrote commentaries on Aristotle, showed where Ptolemy disagreed with him and considered their work as being just as important in astronomical matters as the Bible; and gradually we find variations of their cosmologies accepted by the whole Christian world, a perfect example of them being Dante's.

Nothing gives a clearer introduction to medieval thought than the realisation that to all the most learned men of the time the universe actually was very much as it is described in the *Divine Comedy*. In the centre was the earth, divided into a hemisphere of earth with Jerusalem in the middle and a hemisphere of water out of which rose purgatory and on top the earthly paradise. Beneath the earth's surface was hell; above it a realm of air; then a realm of fire; then in this order the separate spheres of the Moon, Mercury, Venus, the Sun, Mars, Jupiter, Saturn, and the Fixed Stars. Outside this, another sphere had been added, the Crystalline or that of the Primum Mobile, introduced because in course of time it had been noticed that even the sphere of the fixed stars had another motion besides the daily one, known to us as the precession of the equinoxes, so that there must be a ninth sphere outside to impart all the motions to the others. Beyond this came the tenth sphere, the Empyrean Paradise, where God dwelt.

Such a picture was believed in by most medieval thinkers not merely in the sense that Ptolemy believed in his system, but in the sense that Aristotle believed in his: that is, as a reality. Dante moreover followed Aristotle in giving to every sphere its thrones and dominations; just as Aristotle believed that God dwelt in the outside sphere, which was to him that of the fixed stars, the most perfect because the fastest moving, so he put minor deities, powers, angels in control of the other spheres; in the same way Dante says that the Seraphim guided the Primum Mobile, the Cherubim the Fixed Stars, the Thrones, Saturn, and so forth down to the Moon's sphere which was in charge of angels. It was out of this belief that there grew the superstition of Astrology, which, foolish in itself, can be forgiven for the value it has been as the handmaiden of Astronomy.

§ 6

It was not only in matters to do with the stars that Aristotle was regarded as absolutely infallible: everything that he said upon any subject was regarded as final and incontrovertible.

No better way of showing the continuity, or rather stagnation, of human knowledge about the universe from the time of Aristotle to the time of Shakespeare, could be found than a comparison between passages in Aristotle's *History of Animals* and the various books which were the authorities on natural history in Shakespeare's day. The following are a few examples:

1. The chameleon resembles the lizard in the general configuration of its body, but the ribs stretch downwards and meet together under the belly as is the case with fishes, and the spine sticks up as with the fish. Its face resembles that of the baboon. The change in its colour takes place when it is inflated with air; it is then black, not unlike the crocodile, or green like the lizard but black-spotted like the pard. [Aristotle, H. A., II, 11.]

Chameleon is a little beast and his sides be even long to the nether parts of his womb as it were a fish; his face is as it were a beast compounded of a swine and of an ape. And changeth his colour when his skin is blown, and his colour is somewhat black with black speckles therein. [Berthelet's trans. of *Bartholomew the Englishman* XVIII. 21, 1535.]

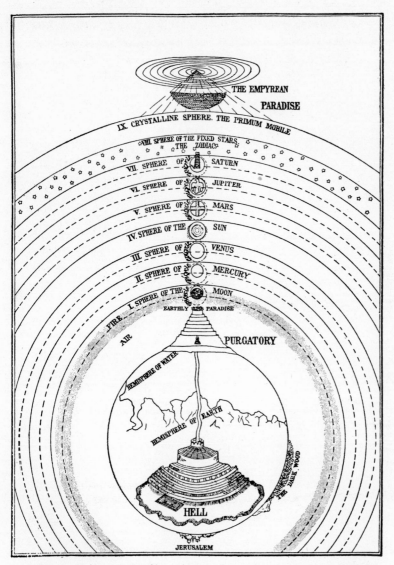

THE EMPYREAN

PARADISE

IX. CRYSTALLINE SPHERE. THE PRIMUM MOBILE

VIII. SPHERE OF THE FIXED STARS.
THE ZODIAC

VII. SPHERE OF SATURN

VI. SPHERE OF JUPITER

V. SPHERE OF MARS

IV. SPHERE OF THE SUN

III. SPHERE OF VENUS

II. SPHERE OF MERCURY

I. SPHERE OF THE MOON

EARTHLY PARADISE

FIRE

AIR

HEMISPHERE OF WATER

HEMISPHERE OF EARTH

PURGATORY

THE DARK WOOD

HELL

JERUSALEM

Dante's Universe. "Nothing gives a clearer introduction to medieval thought than the realization that to all the most learned men of the time the universe was very much as it is described in the Divine Comedy." *(See p. 73.)*

2. Of all animals the newly born cub of the she-bear is the smallest in proportion to the size of the mother: that is to say, it is larger than a mouse but smaller than a weasel. It is also smooth and blind and its legs and most of its organs are as yet inarticulate [i.e., shapeless]. [Aristotle, H. A., VI, 30.]

For the whelp is a piece of flesh little more than a mouse, having neither eyes nor hair, and so this lump she licketh, and shapeth a whelp with licking. [Berthelet, XVIII, 112.]

This is the origin of our phrase "licking into shape" and Aristotle says that foxes do the same with their cubs, while Pliny is responsible for the theory as far as bear cubs are concerned.

3. The weasel, when it fights with a snake, first eats wild rue, the smell of which is noxious to the snake. [Aristotle, H. A., IX, 6.]

The Weasel eateth rue, and balmeth herself with the juice thereof, and rages then on the cockatrice, and assaileth, and slayeth him without any dread bodily. [Berthelet, XVIII, 7.]

4. Now the Salamander is a clear case in point, to show us that animals do actually exist that fire cannot destroy; for this creature, so the story goes, not only walks through the fire but puts it out in doing so. [Aristotle, H. A., V, 19.]

The Salamander quencheth the fire that he toucheth as ice does, and water frozen. [Berthelet, XVIII, 92.]

5. The Syrian lion bears cubs five times: five cubs at the first litter, then four, then three, then two and lastly one; after this the lioness ceases to bear for the rest of her days . . . If a hunter hit him, without hurting him,

then if with a bound he gets hold of him, he will do him
no harm, not even with his claws, but after shaking him
and giving him a fright will let him go again. . . . The
cubs of the lioness when newly born are exceedingly
small, and can scarcely walk when two months old . . .
[Aristotle, H. A., *passim*.]

The lioness whelpeth first five whelps, and afterwards
four, and so each year less by one, and waxeth barren
when she whelpeth one at last. And she whelpeth whelps
evil shapen and small, in size of a weasel in the beginning. And whelps of two months may hardly move. If
a man shoot at him the Lion chaseth him and throweth
him down, and woundeth him not, nor hurteth him.
[Berthelet, XVIII, 65.]

6. The Halcyon breeds at the season of the winter
solstice. Accordingly, when this season is marked with
calm weather the name of "halcyon days" is given to the
seven days preceding, and to as many following, the
solstice; as Simonides the poet says;

> God lulls for fourteen days the winds to sleep
> In winter; and this temperate interlude
> Men call the Holy season, when the deep
> Cradles the mother Halcyon and her brood.

And these days are calm, when southerly winds prevail,
at the solstice, northerly ones having been the accompaniment of the Pleiads. [Aristotle, H. A., V, 8.]

She deposits her eggs in the sand, and that in mid-
winter, when the sea rises highest, and the waves beat
very strongly on the shore; but while she hatches out,
the sea grows suddenly quiet, and all windy storms cease.

And she sits on her eggs for seven days, and then brings out her young, whom she rears for other seven days. And therefore seamen watch for these XIV days, expecting calms. [Hortus Sanitatis, III, 8, 1490.]

These few passages illustrate more clearly than any other means the great fact that for all those hundreds of years from Aristotle's day until the sixteenth century nobody ever looked at the Universe to obtain their knowledge but at what Aristotle had to say about it. Trivial as they are, these stupid ideas about animals make one realise one of the main differences between the human imagination in those days and in our own: knowledge did not lie all about us, but in the past, bottled and preserved by Aristotle and Pliny for all time. And indeed if someone looked at a bear cub and found that it was not a shapeless hairless mass of jelly, while Aristotle or Pliny had definitely stated it was jelly, why then so much the worse for that man's powers of observation. The authority of the authorities could not be shaken thus.

We find a perfect example of what this attitude meant, in a controversy which took place over a human bone. What Aristotle was to general philosophy, Ptolemy to astronomy, Pliny to natural history, Galen was to medicine; and Vesalius, the father of modern anatomy, dared at times to dispute his absolute wisdom. On one such occasion "Vesalius (1514-64)," says Osborne, "had brought the charge against Galen (131-200) that his work could not have been founded upon the human body, because he had described an intermaxilliary bone. This bone, Vesalius observed, is found in the lower animals but not in man. Sylvius (1614-72) defended Galen warmly, and argues that the fact that man had no inter-maxilliary bone at present was no proof that he did not have it in Galen's time. 'It is luxury,' he said, 'it is sensuality, which has gradually deprived man of this bone.'" In short the word of Aristotle, Galen, or Pliny was the word of God and not to be altered as a result of mere human observation.

It is very important that we should understand this because it means that there was not just one sacred, inspired book, the Bible, which was all true and unalterable: *all* books, especially the more ancient, that could be fitted into a general Christian-Aristotelian view of the universe, were sacred and it was as impious to attack what Aristotle said about the spheres of the planets, or what Galen said about blood vessels and humours of the body, or what Pliny said about elephants, or what "Moses" said about the Garden of Eden, as to attack what Jesus said about human conduct, or St. Paul about the Resurrection of the Body. Knowledge absolute and complete lay in the past, and had been preserved in libraries, and nobody should dare to waste time in finding out anything more.

Thus for all this long time men believed in Aristotle's theory of the universe and, moreover, did not think it advisable or possible to check it or supplement it. Only where there was a conflict between his inspired writings and the even more inspired Bible was there any need for speculation and as time went on the crude, stupid barbarian outlook of the church writers from Lactantius to Cosmas Indicopleustes gave way to the more enlightened attitude early represented by Augustine and finally by Thomas Aquinas.

But in this universe, sphere within sphere, what was man? How was he related to the world? How were both related to God?

§ 7

That the universe as a whole had had a beginning and would have an end was clear from the Bible; it was a temporary dwelling place and for Christians a sigh . between two everlasting smiles. Either the temporary nature of the universe made the laws which governed it of no interest, and man's passage through it merely an unimportant episode, a waiting period; or the universe was, so to speak, a finely constructed timepiece built about man in order that he, by learning to tell the time, should arrive punctually for an appointment arranged before time began. This second view was the most important for the medieval mind.

It meant that the universe was in its parts and as a whole made for man; more even than that, the universe was a sort of symbol, an allegory which, when understood, explained man's being and his destiny. Except for its value as a symbol it had no reality whatever.

And so there grew up as a dominant belief the idea that God had created two universes; the great cosmos, or macrocosm, which was everything outside the human being, and the little cosmos, or microcosm, which was man's body and soul. These two creations, the microcosm and the macrocosm, corresponded part by part, and the macrocosm influenced the microcosm as a whole, and part by part. For example, we have seen that Aristotle and Dante alike set angels and powers and dominations over each of the spheres; these powers not only ruled over their own sphere, but they ruled a part of every human body; every limb, every organ came under the sway of some sphere, or star, or planet. "All the virtues," said Albertus Magnus, "which the soul comprehends in the body it draws from the supercelestial spheres and bodies."

We can see what this belief meant in practical affairs by turning to that curious treatise ascribed to Albertus Magnus and called "On the Secrets of Women." This tract was highly popular for hundreds of years and sums up the knowledge of sexual matters of the later middle ages; it outlived the Middle Ages, however, and was several times printed in the seventeenth century and as late as 1740: so that as it was written in the thirteenth century it remained a practical text-book for five hundred years. It was prohibited by the Catholic Church and put on the Index, partly because it was thought too indecent to be as popularly read as it was, and partly because it was not quite orthodox in many particulars. In most editions the text is accompanied by a running commentary or gloss which often contradicts it, but the general sense can be judged from the following summary.

First of all the writer describes from the physiological standpoint the formation of the embryo; the gloss says that it is doubtful which member is first formed but by a reference to Aristotle it shows that it must be the heart. Avicenna and Averroes, the two great Arabic commentators on Aristotle, are appealed to for facts which a course of practical obstetrics would have revealed more correctly and after some strange biological details we are told of the influence of the stars upon the unborn child.

Each sphere "rules over" a month of the pregnancy and each sphere gives certain qualities to the embryo. The fourth month is ruled over by the sun which makes the heart, wherefore Aristotle and the gloss are probably wrong after all about the heart being made first; moreover so important is the sun that in a sense every man is a child of the sun as well as of human parentage. The fifth month is ruled over by Venus and it is obvious what physical parts are formed under her influence; again the gloss considers whether these parts, or the heart or the head are the chief members and therefore first formed, but argues for the heart and the head as being more important, since their loss means loss of life. Next month Mercury produces voice, eyes, hair, nails; then Saturn dries up the embryo in the eighth month, so that many astronomers say that children born in this period are moribund; whereas if they are born at the end of nine months Jupiter can see to it that they are strong.

In short, the influence of the stars is the greatest influence upon the growth and life of mankind; it was, moreover, nothing mysterious, this influence, but rather the chief of the natural causes; the sun's influence on the four months' old embryo is just as natural as the congress of the two parents who gave it life: that Saturn emaciates the embryo born at eight months is a natural cause, just as our explanation that a child born before the end of the natural term is necessarily weak, because it is not fully developed, is a natural cause. And so Astrology was just as much a natural science as Astronomy: unfortunately, it was wrong in its assumptions and in its methods, because Aristotle and medieval philosophy were wrong in their teachings about what science may assume and how science must work. Albertus goes into astonishing details about the effect of stars and planets upon the embryo so that most of his book consists of astrological jargon—yet this was the Advice to Young Mothers for hundreds of years.

This idea of microcosm and macrocosm, of the influence of the stars upon human beings, seemed as reasonable and proven in the Middle Ages as germ-diseases, gravity and radio-activity seem today, only their upholders argued from the words of inspired authorities, while supporters of the modern theories argue from results and experiments. You could not have refuted Aristotle by showing experimentally that he was wrong, you could only refute him by showing that he probably meant something else.

If we turn to the remarkable dreams of Hildegarde of Bingen we get a beautiful picture of what this belief meant. "O man, look at man!" she cries. "For man has in himself heavens and earth and in him all things are latent."

"Presently," says Thorndike, "she compares the firmament to man's head, sun, moon, and stars to the eyes, air to the hearing, the winds to smelling, dew to taste, and 'the sides of the world' to the arms and sense of touch. The earth is like the heart, and other creatures in the world are like the belly. Between the divine image in human form which she sees in her visions and the wheel or sphere of the universe she notes such relationships as these. The sun spreads its rays from the brain to the heel, and the moon directs its rays from the eyebrows to the ankles. The eyebrows of man declare the journeyings of the moon, namely, the one route by which it approaches the sun in order to restore itself, and the other by which it recedes after it has been burnt by the sun! Again, from the top of the cerebral cavity to 'the last extremity of the forehead' there are seven distinct and equal spaces, by which are signified the seven planets which are equidistant from one another in the firmament. An even more surprising assumption as to astronomical distances is involved in the comparison that as the three intervals between the top of the human head and the end of the throat and the navel and the groin are all equal, so are the spaces intervening between the highest firmament and lowest clouds and the earth's surface and centre. Corresponding to these intervals Hildegarde notes three ages of man: infancy, adolescence, and old age." [1]

Such likenesses as these were not just amusing similarities, nor pretty metaphors, they were evidence that the thing in the macrocosm like to the thing in the microcosm acted on it and controlled it. Indeed if you could discover hidden similarities in natural objects those were the keys to unlock all sorts of valuable powers; if a plant had leaves like some organ of the human body that was proof that it cured diseases of that organ; all sorts of plants and animals had these "signatures" which explained their use to mankind.

In short, the medieval mind was convinced that everything in the world around him had a "meaning" to be discovered by consulting the old books, that the cosmos was at once the body of God, a symbol of the body of man, the machine made by God, and the controller of man's physical and mental life. This, added to Aristotelian theories of goodness lying in such things as

[1] *Magic and Experimental Science,* II, 154.

spherical shapes, circular motions, and rapid transit, accepted with a worship of authority which blinded the eyes of observation, made up the picture of the universe which was responsible for the medieval outlook on life as a whole. But before we collect together the various strands and examine their pattern, let us consider how they influenced the human imagination over one practical and altogether astonishing question of conduct, namely the existence and nature of witches and witchcraft; for by considering this episode in human history we will gain an excellent insight into the whole of our story.

§ 8

Suppose a modern scientific man is asked whether he believes that certain women can produce mysterious apparitions, describe beings they have never seen, move chairs and tables without touching them, rise off the ground into the air as a result of "levitation"; he will probably say that he believes these things cannot happen because all the evidence he has seen has been inconclusive and often fraudulent; but, he will add that he is perfectly willing to consider fresh evidence. If Miss X. subjects herself to rigorous examination under test conditions, he will make the experiment, just as he would make an experiment with the germs of disease or the crossing of various plants. He will insist that as much care be taken to eliminate fraud and deception as if it was any other scientific experiment. He will candidly admit that he is predisposed to expect the experiment to fail, as it does not fit in with the apparent scheme of things, but this will only make him surprised, and not annoyed, if the experiment gives favourable results.

Now consider a medieval man faced with the question: "Does witchcraft exist?" His arguments both for and against would never occur to anybody at all today. Here, to begin with, are the medieval arguments *against* witchcraft as they are put at the beginning of the first great text-book on witchcraft, Sprenger's *Malleus Maleficorum*, written expressly by the Pope's orders near the end of the fifteenth century.

"Whether the belief that there are such things as witches is so essential a part of the Catholic faith that obstinately to maintain the opposite opinion manifestly savours of heresy." Notice the form in which the question occurs to the medieval mind: it is not a simple matter of fact to be considered on its own merits, it is related to the whole fabric of philosophy and religion: to be wrong about it is to be a heretic, to be false to Christianity. Next come the arguments against this question: first of all, "that a firm belief in witches is not a Catholic doctrine, because, whoever believes that any creature can be changed for the better or the worse, or transformed into another kind or likeness, except by the Creator of all things, is worse than a pagan and a heretic. And so when they report such things are done by witches it is not Catholic, but plainly heretical, to maintain this opinion."

In the second place, "no operation of witchcraft has a permanent effect upon us. And this is the proof thereof: For if it were so, it would be effected by the operation of demons. But to maintain that the devil has power to change human bodies or to do them permanent harm does not seem in accordance with the teaching of the Church. For in this way they could destroy the whole world, and bring it to utter confusion."

In the third place, "every alteration that takes place in a human body—for example, a state of health or a state of sickness—can be brought down to a question of natural causes, as Aristotle has shown in his 7th book of Physics. And the greatest of these is the influence of the stars. But the devil cannot interfere with the movement of the stars. This is the opinion of Dionysus in his epistle of S. Polycarp. For this alone can God do. Therefore it is evident the demons cannot actually effect any permanent transformation in human bodies; that is to say, no real metamorphosis. And so we must refer the appearance of any such change to some dark and occult cause . . .

"As it is unlawful to hold that the devil's evil craft can apparently exceed the work of God, so it is unlawful to believe that the noblest works of creation, that is to say, man and beast, can be harmed and spoiled by the power of the devil.

"Moreover, that which is under the influence of a material object cannot have power over corporeal objects. But devils are subservient to certain influences of the stars, because magicians observe the course of certain stars in order to evoke the devil. Therefore they have not the power of effecting any change in a corporeal object, and it follows that witches have even less power then the demons possess."

To put it shortly, this boils down to a statement that witches cannot alter human bodies or cause damage by interfering with crops, herds, rain, or alter shapes, because such things are dependent on the stars and these cannot be altered by the devil, but by God alone. If there is evidence of these things having been done then it can only be by hallucination. Put thus it is remarkably like what a scientific person would say today only his words would be different: he would say, "I do not believe that mediums or witches can tamper with the natural laws of the universe, which are fixed and unalterable, and if these things appear to have been done then it is a matter of hypnotism or hallucination of some sort or another."

Now let us consider the refutation of this point of view as it is made by the authors of the book. They divide up the people who deny witchcraft into three classes: "Certain writers pretending to base their opinions upon the words of S. Thomas, when he treats of impediments brought about by magic charms, have tried to maintain that there is not such a thing as magic, that it only exists in the imagination of those men who ascribe natural effects, the causes whereof are not known, to witchcraft and spells. There are others who acknowledge indeed that witches exist, but they declare that the influence of magic and the effects of charms are purely imaginary and phantasmical. A third class of writers maintain that the effects said to be wrought by magic spells are altogether illusory and fanciful, although it may be that the devil does really lend his aid to some witch."

Why is it perfectly clear that all these three classes are quite wrong in their points of view? Because many orthodox writers, and especially St. Thomas Aquinas, say that such views are contrary to the authority of the saints and founded on infidelity. Moreover the Bible constantly states that witches exist—the witch of Endor; the sons of God who fell and misbehaved with the daughters of men; Deuteronomy commands the destruction of wizards; Leviticus says, "the soul which goeth to wizards and soothsayers to commit fornication with them, I will set my face against that soul"; and many other texts show that the Bible affirms the existence of witchcraft. Nor is it easy to see how any modern fundamentalist who refuses to believe in evolution because he believes in Genesis can consistently fail to believe in witches: probably he regards witchcraft as a thing conveniently obsolete like miracles, and therefore not susceptible to verification nowadays.

Now since sacred writings and church authorities all agree that there are witches, all that remains to be done is to investigate their nature. The modern scientist would take every case on its own merits, examine the evidence and after collecting as many facts as possible form a theory to account for them. If he found that certain women were said to have intercourse with devils, he would first of all want very definite evidence that these women did have some experience that needed explanation; then he would wish to eliminate all chance of hallucinations, hypnotism, madness, from those experiences. If there still remained irrefragible, objective evidence of the existence of devils and women having intercourse, seen, proven and attested, then and then only would he believe in devils at all. Having been forced by the evidence to this belief he would say that the facts showed not only that devils existed, but that the creative force or god responsible for the conduct of the universe did not prevent such corruption of innocent girls by evil powers, and that it either did not desire to do so, or could not. He would end in all probability by assuming that the universe either did not contain a god, or that god was an arch-fiend.

Not so the medievalist: with him facts came last and any evidence sufficed to verify them, because having begun by learnedly arguing for an idea of god and of devils which leads one to expect witchcraft, he was in no way disposed to doubt any stories of witches that might come to his ears, since in this way there were proofs that his ideas of god and devils were correct. A woman, crazy, superstitious and ignorant, is submitted to torture because some village gossip has spread third-hand scandal about her; she confesses that the devil had often approached her in various forms and had sexual intercourse with her. She describes his actions and her feelings and claims that her daughter is the offspring of their sinful delights. A neighbour says that when this daughter had been in the house an infant had immediately died and that the mother and daughter are known to go to some old barn at night time to meet the devil. What does the judge do? Sift the evidence? No. He could not if he would. Have both mad women detained in some place of refuge? Madness is itself akin to witchcraft and heresy. The facts matter very little especially as the accused confess to all of them. What does matter is the establishment of general theological principles which will square with anything that any crazy woman may claim to have done; and this has been carefully argued out for him by Sprenger in *Malleus Maleficorum*, the inquisitor's handbook to witchcraft, from which we have already quoted.

There he will read the exact arguments necessary on such questions as, "Whether the Permission of Almighty God is an Accompaniment of Witchcraft." Once the difficulties of this question have been resolved there is no reason at all why witches should be doubted, whatever foul absurdity they may claim to have done.

The modern man will get a very clear idea of the medieval picture of the universe and how it was attained, from a study of this detail about witchcraft, for the method of approaching the problem is typical of the way in which every problem was approached in those days. There are four matters to be considered, says Sprenger, in this matter of the Divine permission and witchcraft: first, whether such permission must accompany a work of witchcraft; second, why God allows a creature wicked by nature to perpetuate such foul crimes; third, how witchcraft is the worst of all crimes; and fourth, how to preach all this to the people. Next he puts quite clearly the point of view of those who feel that it is incompatible with the idea of a kind deity to suppose that he allows such horrible things to happen. It is Catholic, these opponents say, to refute such things as appear to be to the disparagement of the Creator, and therefore it is Catholic to deny that God allows the devil such power against innocent people, since to admit it would be to disparage God's kindness. If the works of witchcraft are permitted by God, they are not kept away by him: and if he does not keep them away then he is not a wise provider, and all things are not subject to his providence: which is absurd, therefore God does not permit witchcraft.

So far the argument is quite clear, but it is further

From the days of Aristotle and Pliny until after Shakespeare people never learned about animals by looking at them, but always by reading the descriptions written by Aristotle or Pliny. (See p. 74.)

elaborated with many subtle additions such as this: "that which happens of necessity has no need of provident permission or prudence. This is clearly shown in Aristotle's Ethics Book II: Prudence is a right reasoning concerning things which happen and are subject to counsel and choice. But several effects of witchcraft happen of necessity; as when for some reason, or owing to the influence of the stars, diseases come, or any other things which we judge to be witchcraft. Therefore they are not always subject to Divine permission."

To us the first statement of the argument seems pretty conclusive without the added subtleties, but no one can object to Sprenger's liberal embellishments of his opponent's position, which having been honestly stated he now proceeds to demolish.

"Among men," he says, "a wise provider does all that he can to keep away all defect and harm from those who are his care; why then does God not keep away evil from his children, in some way or other? Now we must remember that among men the provider is a particular provider, but God is a universal provider, which are two very different things. For the particular provider must of necessity keep away all the harm he can, since he is not able to extract good out of evil. But God is the universal provider and controller of the whole world, and can extract much good from particular evils; through the persecution of tyrants came the patience of martyrs and through the works of witches comes the purgation of the faith of the just. Therefore it is not God's purpose to prevent all evil, lest the universe should lack the cause of much good. Wherefore S. Augustine says: So merciful is Almighty God, that he would not allow any evil to be in his works unless he were so omnipotent and good that he can bring good even out of evil."

And we have an example of this in the actions of natural things. For although the corruptions and defects which occur in natural things are contrary to the purpose of that particular thing (as when a thief is hanged, or when animals are killed for human food), they are yet in accordance with the universal purpose of nature (as that man's life and property should be kept intact); and thus the universal good is preserved. For it is necessary for the conservation of the species that the death of one should be the preservation of another. For lions are kept alive by the slaughter of other animals.

Sprenger now proceeds to his second argument which is rather difficult to follow but seems to amount to this: God in his justice permits the prevalence of evil, both that of sin and that of pain, and especially now that the world is cooling and declining to its end; and this can be proved by proving two postulates; first, that God would not—or let us rather say, that it is impossible that any creature, man or Angel, can be of such a nature that it cannot sin and, second, that God justly permits man to sin; and therefore it is impossible that God does not permit witchcraft to be permitted with the help of devils.

The proof of the first postulate is given by St. Thomas Aquinas: It is impossible that any creature can be of such a nature that it cannot sin, for if this quality were communicable to any creature, God would have communicated it. Moreover, if it could have been and was not communicated, then the universe would not be perfect, since its perfection lies in the fact that all communicable good has been communicated. And again to say that God, being all-good, would make sinlessness a characteristic of his creations, is also wrong because in that case the inability to sin would arise, not from any exterior cause or from grace, but from its own nature: in which case it would be God, which is absurd. St. Thomas treats of this and says that whenever there happens to any creature something that can only be caused by a superior influence, the lower nature cannot of itself cause that effect without the co-operation of the higher nature. For example, a gas becomes ignited by fire; but it could not of its own nature light itself without fire.

All of this proves conclusively that witchcraft exists with God's permission, and this once proven, it takes no time at all for Sprenger and his contemporaries to believe heartily the sort of tale of which the following is typical, except that it is not as lewd and disgusting as most: A certain high-born Count in the ward of Wester-ich, in the diocese of Strasburg, married a noble girl of equal birth; but after he had celebrated the wedding, he was for three years unable to know her carnally, on account, as the event proved, of a certain charm which prevented him. In great anxiety, and not knowing what to do, he called loudly on the Saints of God. It happened that he went to the state of Metz to negotiate some business; and while he was walking about the streets and squares of the city, attended by his servants and domestics, he met a certain woman who had formerly been his mistress. Seeing her, and not at all thinking of the spell that was on him, he spontaneously addressed her kindly for the sake of their old friendship, asking her how she did, and whether she was well. And she, seeing the Count's gentleness, in her turn asked very particularly after his health and affairs; and when he answered that he was well, and that everything prospered with him, she was astonished and was silent for a time.

The Count, seeing her thus astonished, again spoke kindly to her, inviting her to converse with him.

So she inquired after his wife, and received a similar reply, that she was in all respects well. Then she asked if he had any children; and the Count said he had three sons, one born each year. At that she was more astonished, and was again silent for a while. And the Count asked her: Why, my dear, do you make such careful inquiries? I am sure that you congratulate me on my happiness. Then she answered: Certainly I congratulate you; but curse that old woman who said she would bewitch your body so that you could not have connection with your wife! And in proof of this, there is a pot in the well in the middle of your yard containing certain objects evilly bewitched, and this was placed there in order that, as long as its contents were preserved intact, for so long you would be unable to cohabit. But see! it is all in vain, and I am glad.

On his return home the Count did not delay to have the well drained; and, finding the pot, burned its contents and all, whereupon he immediately recovered his virility which he had lost. Wherefore the Countess again invited all the nobility to a fresh wedding celebration, saying that she was now the Lady of that castle and estate, after having for so long remained a virgin.

For the sake of the Count's reputation it is not expedient to name that castle and estate; but we have related this story in order that the truth of the matter may be known, to bring so great a crime into open detestation.[1]

Since the Bible attests the reality of witchcraft and since the question as to whether the permission of Almighty God is an accompaniment of witchcraft has been satisfactorily argued, there is nothing in the least surprising about this story; it fits in perfectly with the idea of the universe which was received at the time. So do the following habits of witches which Sprenger discusses at length arguing from first principles whether children can be generated by Incubi and Succubi; whether witches can sway the minds of men to love or hatred; whether witches can hebetate the powers of generation or obstruct the venereal act; whether witches may work some prestidigitatory illusion so that the male organ appears to be entirely removed and separate from the body; whether witches can by some glamour change men into beasts and whether witches, who are midwives, in various ways kill the child conceived in the womb, and procure an abortion; or if they do not do this, offer new-born children to devils.

§ 9

So much for some of the aspects of the medieval picture of the universe and of the outlook on life which corresponded with it. It was necessary to use the illustration of witchcraft beliefs at what may seem inordinate

---

[1] *Malleus Maleficorum,* 1487. The quotations about witchcraft in this section have been taken from the English translation published by John Rodker, London, 1928.

length for long-windedness is of the very essence of the medieval mind. For the modern man wondering about his own position in the universe the first necessity is to realise that there lies hidden within him more than a thousand years of this sort of thing. He cannot avoid having once lived in the Middle Ages any more than he can avoid having once lived up a tree: the fact that in both cases his mind was in the body of an ancestor makes very little difference, for he has not lost the memories of the past, whether they come to him with his tissues or float in on him from the air about him. For good as well as for ill a medieval mist hangs here and there about the shapes of reality.

One thing that must strike any observer about this picture is the way it hangs together; the composition is perfect, logical, reasonable: compared with it the muddled picture of most men today is painfully inferior. The shape of the universe, the cause of the wanderings of the planets, the methods of a witch, the existence of a flower, the machinery of a human body, everything rested upon the nature of God. The whole body of knowledge had been so fused together that you could not prick a single minute part without shattering the whole. If the power of a witch to transport herself on a broomstick was to be doubted you might as well doubt the power of God to save souls; if a planet did not move in a perfect circle then God was not the perfect creator that he must be.

Here and there we notice that God even in the Middle Ages was limited by reason and logic; he had to create the world in six days, he could not make man sinless by nature, he must pay attention to the laws of perfection.

And so even omnipotent God did not make the best of all imaginable universes, but the best of all possible universes: an idea which later was to bear important philosophic fruit as man's picture of the universe began to change.

There was only one way in which change could come to any part of this attitude towards life and that was by new light upon the nature of the universe. Since the same authority bound one to belief in witchcraft as bound one to belief in the spheres and epicycles of Ptolemy and Aristotle, no one could shatter the one without the other; but if somehow or other it could be shown that authority was wrong about the picture of the universe, then perhaps authority might begin to be doubted about the morality of witch persecution. In Spanish documents we sometimes find that the men eligible for some important council or junta are spoken of as men of *ciencia y conciencia*, of science and conscience; the phrase has much meaning for us in our study. For it is abundantly clear that science and conscience go together; science, knowledge of the world, is the mentor of conscience, knowledge of good. When science changes, conscience changes too. The central fact about the Middle Ages is that science and conscience for hundreds of years were so united and intermingled that they seemed to be but opposite faces of the same thing. Science was fixed and static beneath the thumb of authority, and conscience also. Then science began to alter, a fact or two here and there was thrown in the face of Aristotle, at some little distance behind followed conscience. Science shattered the system upon which belief in witches rested, long before conscience grew ashamed of delusions about witchcraft. It will be our task to watch how this change came about, how the tranquil unity of a thousand years between science and conscience set mankind moving towards a goal at which we have not as yet perhaps succeeded in arriving.

CHAPTER THREE

‹‹

The First Renaissance

§ 1

LET the Modern Man imagine for a moment that he is an intelligent, well-read European sitting at his table in the year 1543. Almost certainly he is a monk or a priest, for there were few laymen in those days who were either intelligent or well-read. Probably he is an Italian or a German, although there were of course a few intelligent Englishmen and quite a number of intelligent Frenchmen. He has a big library full of manuscripts and books, most of them in Latin; and on the table in front of him are two volumes recently printed and sent him, one from Nuremberg in Germany, the other from Venice; the first written by an aged Pole, who received a copy of his work as he lay semi-conscious on his deathbed, the second written by a young Belgian of twenty-eight, a professor of anatomy at the University of Padua. One is called *Concerning the Revolutions of the Heavenly Bodies* and is by Copernicus; the other is *Concerning the Fabric of the Human Body* by Andreas Vesalius.

You sat there that evening over the pages of those two books, feeling uncomfortable and uneasy; you had heard a good deal about them, one way and another; you knew that they treated the macrocosm and the microcosm in a very peculiar way; that they were exceedingly dis-

⌐99⌐

turbing to professors and learned men generally. Even Sylvius, who had taught Vesalius medicine, was horrified with his own pupil and had actually called him "an impious madman, who is poisoning the air of all Europe with his vapourings."

Now in 1929 you imagine that these two books containing *new* ideas and claiming to be *advances* in knowledge must have seemed to you in 1543 for that very reason attractive and desirable. You forget how much you have changed since 1543; you forget how much the fashions and crazes which influence you have changed. Of course in New York or in London in 1915 or 1921 you rushed to embrace Freud or Einstein; but in 1543 you were not looking for light from the future, but for light from the past; you had built the palace of your dreams on Aristotle, on Ptolemy, on Galen, on Pliny, rocks firm and reliable; you had as little fear as desire that the foundations could be disturbed. Imagine going one day into the garden and finding the rock beneath your mansion gaping; imagine somebody telling you that this thing which you called rock, was sand, seemingly hard-baked because of centuries of sun, but really sand, crumbling away and bringing down the house with it. Would you be pleased? Neither were you pleased in 1543 when these two books appeared on the table: long before you opened them you were prejudiced against them for the very sufficient reason that they contained something new. Not that they were not very carefully written, these books: you could not actually show them to be irreligious and atheistical. This young man, Vesalius, for example, was exceedingly careful about what he wrote and apparently quite anxious lest he should offend his brother professors; it seemed that he could not find certain pores through which, so Galen had said, the blood passed from the right side of the heart to the left; you were glad to find that he did not bluntly say that Galen was wrong, he had some respect for persons, and so "We are driven," he wrote, "to wonder at the handiwork of the Creator, by means of which the blood sweats from the right into the left ventricle through passages which escape the human vision." In short, Vesalius had tact; which was more than could be said for his colleague Servetus in Vienna, a thorough crank who flatly contradicted Galen and said that the blood passed "by unknown channels" through the lungs. But then Servetus was altogether dangerous and had said that Judea was not "a land flowing with milk and honey," but arid and desert, thus contradicting Moses and the Bible. John Calvin was to avenge the blasphemy in 1553 when he showed that such a statement "necessarily inculpated Moses, and grievously outraged the Holy Ghost." Servetus was burned at the stake, though Calvinists may be glad to hear that Calvin would have preferred him to be beheaded.

That was exactly where the trouble lay, you felt; once people began to question authority they soon gathered momentum down the slippery path. What Galen said about blood was mysteriously bound up with everything else in the universe; question Galen on blood and you would soon be questioning the authorities on the nature of God and the Trinity. That you were right in your fears about where this could lead Servetus was soon to prove, and for that matter, Vesalius himself was to follow the same path, for having "got away with" publishing his difficulty about Galen's invisible pores, he went further

in the second edition and altered the passage about them
to "Although sometimes these pits are conspicuous, yet
none, so far as the senses can perceive, passes from the
right to the left ventricle. I have not yet come across
even the most hidden channels by which the septum of
the ventricles is pierced. Yet such channels are described
by teachers of anatomy, who have absolutely decided that
the blood is taken from the right to the left ventricle.
I, however, am in great doubt as to the action of the
heart in this matter." A serious thing when professors
with pupils from all over the world begin to suggest that
men like Galen may be wrong! If you have forgotten by
this time how this displeased you in 1543 imagine your
feelings in 1930 if somebody were to come along and
say that the whole fabric of modern science was mistaken
in its methods, its discoveries, its idea of the universe;
you would get a faint replica of the emotion you got from
these agnostic sentences of Vesalius, faint because now
you do not so fully see that science and your idea of
God, your religion, are bound up with one another, a
fact which you fully realised in 1543. Then people who
preached new doctrines about your body and blood were
as good as preaching heresies about the Body and Blood
of Christ; the two were so interwoven in your medieval mind.

And so even the careful Vesalius, tactful, respectful,
filled you with a good deal of uneasiness. You had picked
up his book first because, perhaps, you had been attracted
to the pictures, drawn by a pupil of Titian; a frontispiece
showing the author demonstrating a human dissection
before a crowd of people, and other woodcuts of human
bodies and their parts, attractive all of them in execution

as well as subject matter. Now you turned to the other book.

A closely argued mathematical puzzle this, tactful also, as was necessary when the subject matter is considered. Copernicus, who died as the first copy of his book was put into his hands, was an irreproachable monk, but as was apparent from this work he liked to play with fire. The book was sound and Catholic enough at first sight, it was dedicated to the Pope in fact, and was merely the pastime of a mathematician; therefore it was just the book for a man like you, a lover of intellectual games, so long as there was no doubt about their orthodoxy; especially as it quite definitely denied any desire to say whether the solution of the mathematical problem bore any resemblance to reality.

How important this denial was, will be judged when we say that this solution was none other than the revolutionary, half-shocking, half-laughable idea that the earth instead of being the centre of the universe moves round the sun.

Obviously heretical as well as absurd, you felt, as you fingered the leaves and but for the preface "To the reader about the hypotheses of this book," you would not have dared to read it. But there you found carefully stated that the idea of the earth moving ought not to give anyone any offence, because it was only a conjecture used by a geometrician to enable him to compute and prophesy future positions of the heavenly bodies; and though the conjecture may not be true, may indeed be quite absurd, that does not matter if it enables this to be done. The conjecture has nothing to do with truth and therefore does not interfere with any orthodox teaching.

It is the sort of thing which any schoolboy does when in geometry he says, "suppose the line AB to be equal to the line CD, then such a thing follows," he does not say that AB and CD are really equal. So Copernicus says, "suppose the sun to be the centre of a circle round which the earth moves, then these are the motions of the planets, and to prove it these will be the positions of the planets on Wednesday next." He does not say that the sun *is* the centre. He could have worked out a solution with Mars at the centre and other motions which would have given the right positions for next Wednesday just as well.

This preface reassured you, for you could not know that in fact Copernicus had never written it at all; would never have written it, because he did actually believe in his own theory, not as a mathematical solution, but as a reality. A tactful friend named Osiander had inserted it to remove the prejudices of just such men as you; and he had succeeded, for you took him at his word and began to read the book.

At the beginning you wondered why anybody should take so much trouble to work out an abstruse theory in which apparently he did not believe. Why should Copernicus have wanted to prove that black was white, to assume that the moon was made of green cheese, to stand on his head intellectually in this learned way? In 1929 you would have thought such behaviour the tedious mannerism of a crank; but in 1543 you were steeped in logical conundrums and paradoxes and thought none the worse of people who indulged in them. But it was interesting to read that Copernicus had a special reason for this particular paradox, which he confided to the Pope in his dedicatory letter. He had been irritated by the poor reasons given for the movements of the heavenly bodies, he explained; Ptolemy's system was so clumsy, needing as it did eighty epicycles to explain the motions satisfactorily. A messy sort of picture of the universe this seemed, no economy of design about it, nothing to make the observer of the universe say as a modern observer of an aeroplane might say, "a *beautiful* machine that, neat and graceful"; nothing to please the *æsthetic* taste. "When, therefore," wrote Copernicus to Paul III, "I had long considered this uncertainty of traditional mathematics, it began to weary me that no more definite explanation of the movement of the world-machine established on our behalf by the best and most systematic builder of all, existed among the philosophers, who had studied so exactly, in other respects, the minutest details in regard to the sphere. Wherefore I took upon myself the task of re-reading the books of all the philosophers which I could obtain, to seek out whether anyone had ever conjectured that the motions of the sphere of the universe were other than they supposed, who taught mathematics in the schools. And I found first that according to Cicero, Nicetus had thought the earth was moved. Then later I discovered, according to Plutarch, that certain others had held the same opinion.

"When from this, therefore, I had conceived its possibility, I myself also began to meditate upon the mobility of the earth. And although the opinion seemed absurd, yet because I knew the liberty had been accorded to others before me of imagining whatsoever circles they pleased to explain the phenomena of the stars, I thought I also might readily be allowed to experiment whether, by supposing the earth to have some motion, stronger demonstrations than those of the others could be found as to the revolution of the celestial sphere.

"Thus supposing these motions which I attribute to the earth later in this book, I found at length by much and long observation, that if the motions of the other planets were added to the rotation of the earth and calculated as for the revolution of that planet, not only the phenomena of the others followed from this, but also it so bound together both the order and magnitude of all the planets and the spheres and the heaven itself, that in no single part could one thing be altered without confusion among the other parts and in all the universe. Hence for this reason in the course of this work I have followed this system."

Now here was a reason which appealed to you in 1543 in the strongest possible manner: you had been brought up under the spell of Aristotle; you believed in beauty, particularly in the beauty of simplicity; certainly it was a fine idea this which got rid of so many of Ptolemy's epicycles, leaving in fact only thirty-four epicycles to "save the phenomena." You could not fail to feel that a God who created a machine needing only thirty-four epicycles was a better craftsman than one who created a machine needing as many as eighty, and if this were so, clearly it would be blasphemous not to believe that Copernicus' system was more than a conjecture, in fact a reality. Did he after all mean this? True there was the preface "about the hypotheses of this book" but perhaps that was mere eyewash; otherwise why had he added in the letter to the Pope, "if perchance there should be foolish speakers who, together with those ignorant of mathematics, will take it upon themselves to decide concerning these things, and because of some place in the Scriptures wickedly distorted to their purpose, should dare to assail this my work, they are of no importance to me, to such an extent do I despise their judgment as rash"? A dangerous remark this, and surely unnecessary if it was only a geometrician's puzzle!

Of course, you felt, anyone really trying to upset the earth and put the sun in its place was clearly a dangerous heretic, but it was certainly disconcerting that by this means the universe-machine would become less clumsy, and God, the creator, therefore, a better mechanic. You began to read the book itself, in an uneasy frame of mind.

As you turned the pages your uneasiness increased, for passage after passage seemed to have no other meaning than that Copernicus actually believed and was prepared to prove that the sun was the centre of the universe. What, otherwise, for example would be the point of this passage in the tenth chapter of the first book: "Then in the middle of all stands the sun. For who, in our most beautiful temple, could set this light in another or better place, than that from which it can at once illuminate the whole? Not to speak of the fact that not unfittingly do some call it the light of the world, others the soul, still others the governor. Tresmigistus calls it the visible God; Sophocles' Electra, the All-seer. And in fact does the sun, seated on his royal throne, guide his family of planets as they circle round him."

This is practically the language of heresy! Your uneasiness becomes more and more unbearable and there is only one way to cure it; placing the disconcerting book to your left, paper in front of you, and a light above it, you settle down to refute the whole of this mad, dangerous doctrine.

§ 2

In describing to you the refutation which you wrote of Copernicus' *De Revolutionibus* in 1543 I cannot give you a full picture of your own intelligence at that date; for like a modern lawyer your intelligence in those days was to be measured largely by the width of your reading and your ingenuity in trumping up quotations, instances and authorities. In consequence your refutation was immensely long; and I can only give a brief epitome of it, out of which all the learnedness will have leaked. But I want to assure you that I am really assuming that in 1543 you were far above the general level of intelligence; a fact which is in no way to be doubted because you did not accept the theory that the earth moved.

You began by quoting from the Bible, the church fathers, the schoolmen, and from Aristotle and all the philosphers, and all these agreed that the sun went round the earth. Just as Cosmas Indicopleustes found texts to prove that the earth was not a sphere, so you found others which showed it to be a sphere fixed in the midst of the universe. Why suggest anything else? you asked, seeing that it has always hitherto been agreed that what seems true to the senses is in fact really true. You used the same argument as I found recently used by a learned Spanish historian, when he wanted to prove that St. James had been to Spain: "tradition," says Don Antonio Lopez Ferreiro in Volume I of his *History of the Church of Santiago de Compostella*, 1898, "is nothing

⌒108⌒

more than the firm persuasion about some deed or doctrine transmitted successively, and without interruption from fathers to sons, who always refer to the testimony of their ancestors. Three are the channels whereby traditions are handed down, by the living voice, by writing, or by certain acts or practices. But it must be said that the channel of writing, although very convenient and useful, is not essential for the tradition; thus the Council of Trent defined that the catholic doctrine is contained, not only in the scriptures, but also in unwritten traditions, *et sine scripta traditionibus*. Even if a tradition is perpetuated in only one family, it is not without some value. But our tradition is not of one family, but of a province; more than of a province, of a nation, of a continent, of the whole globe. This universal and simultaneous consent to the affirmation of an act or doctrine, was always reputed as the securest basis of credibility, since it is founded on what the logicians call *common sense*." Therefore although all the documents are forged, there can be no doubt that Santiago came to Spain. Everybody says so and so it is common sense that it is so.

And that was your first argument against Copernicus; that common sense added to the united testimony of all the authorities was against him. Next, lest anybody should think that Copernicus was backed up by every sense except common sense, you showed that sight and touch united in proclaiming the solid and immobile earth beneath your feet, and the far less solid moving heavens all around. What had eyes to offer as evidence that all this *terra firma* was being whirled at a mighty pace through the heavens? Men's stomachs which could not stand the tossing of a wave-covered sea proved that the earth at least was steady.

Then you came to an even more serious objection to these newfangled ideas; they were not to be judged on their own merits for they did not stand alone; if they were true, then a vast philosophy embracing all life and death and immortality would be affected and possibly destroyed. Upon this part of your argument I will quote the comments of a modern writer: "there had been built up," says Burtt in *The Metaphysical Foundations of Modern Physical Science*, "on the basis of this supposedly unshakeable testimony of the senses, a natural philosophy of the universe, which furnished a fairly complete and satisfactory background for man's thinking. The four elements of earth, water, air, fire in their ascending scale, not only as to actual spacial relations, but also in dignity and value, were the categories in which men's thinking about the inanimate realm had become accustomed to proceed. There was necessarily involved in this mode of thinking the assumption that the heavenly bodies were more noble in quality and more noble in fact than the earth, and when these prepossessions were added to the other fundamentals of the Aristotelian metaphysics, which brought this astronomical conception into general harmony with the totality of human experience to date, the suggestion of a widely different theory in astronomy would inevitably appear in the light of a contradiction of every important item of knowledge man had gained about his world."

In short, you pointed out that what Copernicus was doing was to muddle up all human conceptions about good and evil, about the dignity of God, about man's power to know truths and to know God—things which have become gradually so separated from astronomy that you have difficulty in seeing their connection in 1929.

But your refutation did not stop there; yours was far above the ordinary intelligence, as I have said, and so you added almost as a postscript certain objections which in 1543 you did not regard as anything like so important as these others, though in 1929 they would seem far more important. You pointed out that the only possible way of judging between Copernicus and Ptolemy on scientific grounds as distinct from these religious and philosophical grounds was by considering which of them accurately "saved the phenomena." Now it is actually a fact that all the habits of the stars which had been observed by 1543 could be just as well accounted for by supposing Ptolemy right and the earth in the centre of the universe, as by supposing Copernicus right and the sun in the centre. More than that, you could prophesy where the stars would be next week just as well by using the old system. Ptolemy had improved on his forerunners and made a better system than they; Copernicus had not even done this. There was therefore no scientific reason at all for departing from the traditional view; for not even astronomers gained anything by the change; while, as we have seen, everyone else, theologians and philosophers alike, would be nonplussed.

Finally there were two easy experiments which people who thought such things of any intellectual interest could try for themselves: first, let them throw a stone straight up in the air; if the earth were really moving it ought to fall down again to the west of where the thrower stood; since this did not happen, the earth cannot be moving. It is only because we have been told a story about a man watching an apple fall to the ground more than a hundred years after Copernicus was dead, that we think we can understand why this "proof" of the earth's stability, which seemed excellent in 1543, does not prove anything of the sort.

The second experiment was even more conclusive: fix your eyes on a near object shutting first one eye and then the other; it will change its position. Measure out a line a hundred yards long and look at a neighbouring hill through telescopes at both ends of the line; the telescopes will make different angles with the line at each point and from these you can calculate the distance of the hill. In the same way as in these two experiments the base line, in one case the distance between the eyes, in the other of a hundred measured yards, is the side of a triangle ending at the object in view, so, if the earth goes round the sun and the diameter of its orbit is used as a base line, each star should form the apex of a triangle and we should be able to measure the distance of a star from the earth. Yet when you in 1543 tried this experiment no shift of the star could be seen and the lines pointing to the stars did not form a triangle with the base line; therefore there could not be a base line and you were always looking at the stars from the same place. Today we know that this is because the stars are so far away that only the most delicate modern instruments can detect their parallax, as it is called. Indeed it was not until two hundred and ninety-five years after Copernicus was dead that a parallax was detected, thus adding one more proof to his theory. But in 1543 nobody dreamed of the stars being so far away and the absence of parallax was tanta-

mount to a proof that the earth had no vast orbit round
the sun to provide a base line for its observation.

And so by common sense and all the other senses,
by logic and by experiment, by theology and philosophy
you proved fairly conclusively that Copernicus was
wrong. You laid your pen down and gazed at the parch-
ment before you; you ought to have been pleased and
at ease and you would have been but for one thing.
That Copernicus was satisfactorily refuted was certain;
but why was it that the Great Geometrician, he who
measured out the heavens with a rod, had made a
machine which required eighty epicycles, when thirty-
four would have done just as well? Nothing could reconcile this fact to the whole body of medieval philosophy;
the very idea of the universe was based on ideas of perfection, of beauty, of simplicity and neatness. Even Copernicus never doubted for a moment that the planets moved
in perfect circles, he was not so impious as that. Why
had God, who chose the sphere because it was the perfect
figure, who ruled and lived in the outermost sphere because that had the fastest, that is, the most perfect, motion; why had he missed perfection in his general scheme?
If a man takes eighty to go round a nine-hole golf course
he is not as good a golfer as a man who takes thirty-
four. Why, why, why?

I have taken this "you" as the epitome of human
intelligence in 1543 and I have suggested that your mind,
tranquil and at rest before reading Copernicus' *De Revolutionibus Orbium Cœlestium*, became confused about the
very nature of God from that moment. And this is indeed
really what did happen to the human imagination; the
medieval intellect, the medieval outlook on the universe,

the medieval idea of God was for ever muddled in 1543 because Copernicus had discovered a neater, more mathematical, more æsthetic God than the God of Ptolemy and Aristotle, a God who could go round the universe, as it were, in thirty-four instead of eighty.

Let us above all not be deluded by loose talk about the conflict between science and religion into imagining that a controversy had been started between religious obscurantists and the rationalist Copernicus: Copernicus was not in opposition to God; he had discovered a better God than the orthodox, a better mathematician, a better mechanic, a more æsthetic and a more perfect God. His whole work was a search after the nature of God and not a cold-blooded search after astronomical formulæ and his tragedy, or rather the tragedy of those who came after him, for he himself suffered nothing, lies in this, that those who seek God most assiduously always outstrip the orthodox idea of God and are persecuted by priests in consequence.

It was not because Copernican astronomy fitted the facts better that it arrested the attention of man, but because it fitted better with the idea of God as the perfect, æsthetic artificer of the universe. That is why you as an intelligent man in 1543 were disturbed for ever out of the slumber which comes from living beneath the wings of a perfectly satisfactory, complete, unified view of the universe and of God.

§ 3

The medieval system was not, however, a Jericho to fall down at the blast of a trumpet and nothing very

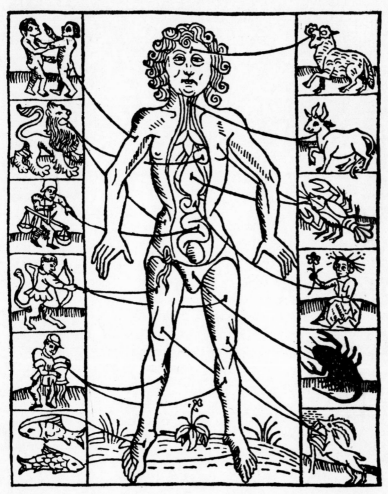

"... the universe was in its parts and as a whole made for man; more even than that, the universe was a sort of symbol, an allegory which, when understood, explained man's being and his destiny. Except for its value as a symbol it had no reality whatever." (See p. 79.)

much happened for many years after Copernicus was dead. His arguments and discoveries, his superior God, were rather like a minute splinter in a limb of the Middle Ages, irritating, increasingly so, but apt to be forgotten by the body as a whole. If you feel affronted because I have suggested that in 1543 you did not accept the Copernican theory, it can only be because you have not yet grasped the strength of the philosophy which wrapped you round like a child in swaddling bands. It is high praise that I should suggest that you gave the matter any attention and that on examination you were in the least perturbed. Just look for a minute at some of the books on your shelves in 1543; no matter what their subject, they all of them conform absolutely to this perfect, unified outlook on the universe; no walk of life but is covered by the formulæ learned from the Holy Fathers and the almost equally holy Aristotle. These formulæ cover every possible human activity and there is no end to the foolishness which merely being logical permits to the most learned of men. Take, for example, that folio over there printed twelve years ago, in 1531, and written by a great legal authority of Provence, Bartholomew Chassenée. If you can swallow that, and you can, what possible chance is there of your rejecting Ptolemy and Aristotle on the immobility of the ground beneath your feet. It will be very instructive to look at Chassenée once more in 1929 and to try and feel what you thought as you read him respectfully in 1543.

He won his reputation as a jurist by defending some rats against the charge of having feloniously stolen and eaten the barley crop of Autun. The case had come before the ecclesiastical court of the province and the bishop's vicar cited the accused rodents to appear on a certain day, and appointed Chassenée as their defending counsel.

The day arrived and the rats did not appear in court: Chassenée defended their absence: his clients were numerous and it could not be assumed that all of them or any one of them had heard or received the single summons. The court ruled in his favour and ordered that the summons be read again in every parish church throughout the districts inhabited by the rats.

This took some time and not until it was done did the court sit again. But even then the rats had not appeared to answer the summons; a very serious offence amounting to aggravated contempt of court which put Chassenée to a good many shifts for an adequate defence. He argued that if defendants in an action at law had an excessively long or dangerous journey before they could appear in person, they could legally disobey the writ and lodge an appeal; nor was it ever legal at common law to demand that defendants, innocent as they might well be, should be forced to appear in person to answer a charge at the risk of their lives. Now it was notorious that his clients were in grave danger, if they came to court, seeing that their hereditary enemies, the cats, were on the look-out for them at many points on the road.

This point was accepted by the court and the trial was proceeded with in the absence of the rats, to what end we are not told. Perhaps the arguments followed the same lines as those in a trial of certain insects who in 1587 were accused of destroying the vines which produce the wine known until this day as St. Julien. The counsel for these insects—we quote from E. P. Evans, *The Criminal Prosecution and Capital Punishment of Ani-*

mals—"affirms that his clients have kept within their rights and not rendered themselves liable to excommunication, since, as we read in the second book of Genesis, the lower animals were created before man, and God said to them: Let the earth bring forth living creatures after his kind, cattle and creeping thing, and beast of the earth after his kind: and he blessed them saying, Be fruitful and multiply and fill the waters of the seas, and let fowl multiply in the earth.

"Now the Creator would not have given this command, had he not intended that these creatures should have suitable and sufficient means of support, indeed he has expressly stated that to every thing that creepeth upon the earth every green herb has been given for meat. It is therefore evident that the accused, in taking up their abode in the vines of the plaintiffs, are only exercising a legitimate right conferred upon them at the time of their creation. Furthermore, it is absurd and unreasonable to invoke the power of civil and canonical law against brute beasts, which are subject only to natural law and the impulses of instinct."

In this way months of legal argument went by, both counsel for the defence and counsel for the prosecution enjoying themselves thoroughly while the noxious insects continued to consume the vines. Finally on the advice of the prosecuting counsel a meeting of citizens was held to discuss the setting aside of a plot of land outside the vineyards for the use and proper maintenance of these insects.

"A piece of ground in the vicinity was selected and set apart as a sort of insect enclosure, the inhabitants of St. Julien, however, reserving for themselves the right to pass through the said tract of land 'without prejudice to the pasture of the said animals,' and to make use of the springs of water contained therein, 'which are also to be at the service of the said animals'; they reserve furthermore the right of working the mines of ochre and other mineral colours found there, without doing detriment to the means of subsistence of the said animals; and finally the right of taking refuge in this spot in time of war."

The counsel for the insects refused on behalf of his clients to accept the proffered land as it was too sterile and a commission was appointed to examine it on the spot. After eight months the trial came to an end, but once more we do not know the result, for the last page of the records has been destroyed by insects! Possibly this fact suggests that the judgment went against the defendants.

We will return now to Chassenée whose large book on law reposed in your library in 1543. In the "Consilium primum" he treats of the "excommunication of insect beasts," dividing his subject beneath five headings: "First, lest I may seem to discourse to the populace, how are these our animals called in the Latin tongue; second, whether these our animals can be summoned; third, whether they can be summoned by procurators, and if they are cited to appear personally, whether they can appear by proxy; fourth, what judge, whether layman or ecclesiastic is competent to try them, and how is he to proceed against them and to pass and execute sentence upon them; fifth, what constitutes an anathema and how does it differ from excommunication." All these points he argues and elucidates in the true medieval manner combining the method "of a lawyer, who quotes precedents and examines witnesses, with that of a theologian, who balances authorities and serves us with texts instead of arguments."

He quotes the Bible, Virgil, Ovid, Pliny, Cicero, Aristotle, Seneca, Gregory the Great, Pico della Mirandola, the Institutes of Justinian. That anathemas against animals are suitable is proved by the serpent who goes on its belly ever since it was cursed in the Garden of Eden; by David cursing the mountains of Gilboa in his lament over Saul and Jonathan; by God's curse of Jericho; and especially by the blasting of the fig tree by Jesus. He turns to modern instances; a priest anathematized an orchard since it tempted the parish children to play truant from church; the Bishop of Lausanne cursed the eels of Lake Leman when they had become so numerous as to interfere with the boating.

He discusses whether animals are laymen or entitled to benefit of clergy. He distinguishes "between punitive and preventive purposes in the prosecution of animals, between inflicting penalties upon them for crimes committed and taking precautionary measures to keep them from doing damage." He instances Balaam and his ass and generally illustrates all the niceties of his subject in an erudite, logical and conscientious manner.

What he seems to forget is that you may summons a cow but it will not appear in court; you may prohibit a rat from entering a dwelling but it will not keep out for all that; you may banish a locust from your own to your neighbour's fields, but it will refuse to go; in short, that though every point is legally sound, logically argued, theologically excellent, it will not make a pennyworth of difference to man or beast; it has nothing to do with reality. And that is the medieval dream palace, beautifully constructed of air, through living in which for so long you, intelligent though you were in 1543, could not agree with Copernicus. Indeed your case is even worse than this, for in all probability in 1610, intelligent though you still will be, you will not agree with Galileo. Let us see.

§ 4

Before we can reach Galileo there is another figure that we have to examine: it is of a man whom many of us have known since schooldays as the discoverer of three "laws," namely, I. That planets move in ellipses, with the sun at one focus. II. That the line joining the sun and planet sweeps out equal areas in equal times. III. That the square of the time of revolution of each planet is proportional to the cube of its mean distance from the sun. That is Kepler to the writer of elementary text-books on astronomy; what is he to the modern man in search of a religion and a God?

Kepler has more than one point of interest to those of us who are trying in 1929 to understand exactly where we are in the world. Copernicus, as we have seen, started a new stage in the hunt for God by discovering a description of the universe which required only thirty-four epicycles instead of eighty. His impulse was entirely the artist's impulse to discover significant form; only, whereas the artist creates the significant form on a piece of canvas and glories in it as a piece of self-expression, a man like Copernicus searches for it in the world outside and glories in it as a revelation of God. Kepler helps us to understand this attitude more clearly.

And let us say at once that this God of Copernicus is no muscular Jehovah, no military general useful for defeating one's enemies, no tribal god exalted and mysteriously transformed into a universal father by the ramifications of human imagination; he is above all a mathematician. Indeed the modern scientific age is the period during which the human imagination has sought after the perfect scientist and called him God; at first this god was actually a man-like being, or at any rate a man-like intellect; later, as we shall see, this personality vanished into something more immense. What the line of thinkers who began with Copernicus were really doing was to change the God of muscle and bad temper still worshipped by army chaplains and fundamentalists into a God of intellectual subtlety and mathematical genius. As we shall see, the nineteenth century rationalists, children of their own age, were blinded by its limitations, and could never see this. That is why most "rationalists" even today are dated. But that belongs to a later chapter, and we must return to Kepler.

Kepler was a sickly child born in 1571 and sent by his poverty-stricken parents to a monastic school and then to the university of Tübingen. Chance gave him an appointment as lecturer in astronomy and quite early in his career he accepted the Copernican system. Was he in any way like the popular picture of the cool calculating scientist? Not in the least.

As far as we can see his chief reason for adopting the Copernican system was that he was in some way or other a sun-worshipper. Listen to this quotation from his own writings: "In the first place, lest perchance a blind man might deny it to you," says Kepler, "of all the bodies in the universe the most excellent is the sun, whose whole essence is nothing else than the purest light, than which there is no greater star; which singly and alone is the producer, conserver and warmer of all things; it is a fountain of light, rich in fruitful heat, most fair, limpid and pure to the sight, the source of vision, portrayer of all colours, though himself empty of colour, called king of the planets for his motion, heart of the world for his power, its eye for his beauty, and which alone we should judge worthy of the most high God, should he be pleased with a material domicile and choose a place in which to dwell with the blessed angels."

It is of course possible that modern astronomers feel like this towards the sun, but they do not publish their feelings aloud to the world, least of all in their scientific works.

Indeed we may quote for comparison with Kepler a passage in Eddington's *Stars and Atoms* in which he describes the inside of this "fountain of light"—"a hurly-burly of atoms, electrons and ether-waves. Dishevelled atoms tear along at 100 miles a second, their normal array of electrons being torn from them in the scrimmage. The lost electrons are speeding 100 times faster to find new resting places. Let us follow the progress of one of them. There is almost a collision as an electron approaches an atomic nucleus, but putting on speed it sweeps round in a sharp curve. Sometimes there is a side-slip at the curve, but the electron goes on with increased or reduced energy. After a thousand narrow shaves all happening within a thousand millionth of a second, the hectic career is ended by a worse side-slip than usual. The electron is fairly caught, and attached to an atom. But scarcely has it taken its place when an X-ray bursts into the atom. Sucking up the energy of the ray the electron darts off again on its next adventure. I am afraid the knockabout comedy of modern atomic physics is not very tender towards our aesthetic ideals. The stately drama of stellar evolution turns out to be more like the hair-breadth escapades on the films. The music of the spheres has almost a suggestion of jazz. And what is the result of all this bustle? Very little. The atoms and electrons for all their hurry never get anywhere; they only change places."

But to Kepler the idea of God and the idea of the sun were bound up together; he was a mystic and, strange though it may seem, he was an astronomer not in spite of, but because of his mysticism. The motives which impelled him in his extraordinarily arduous studies and calculations were two: first, to increase his feeling of nearness to God by learning more and more about the universe, and second, to satisfy a mental itch by setting himself mathematical puzzles and then solving them. It was the first motive, the purely religious one, which enabled him to accept Copernicus from the start: for let us remember that there was really no astronomical or scientific reason at all for accepting him, since his system could explain ascertained facts no better than Ptolemy's, and therefore there had to be a religious or philosophic reason to make anyone choose him rather than stick to tradition and to Ptolemy.

Most of the world stuck to Ptolemy for religious reasons, but Kepler adopted Copernicus, and equally for religious reasons: "since," he wrote, "it does not benefit

the first mover(i.e., God) to be diffused throughout an
orbit, but rather to proceed from one certain principle,
and as it were, point, no part of the world, and no star
accounts itself worthy of such a great honour; hence by
the highest right we return to the sun, who alone appears
by virtue of his dignity and power, suited for this motive
duty and worthy to become the home of God himself,
not to say the first mover." And if the sun was the home
of God, Kepler felt that it was clearly the centre of the
universe and, starting with this religious assumption, he
settled down to prove it by conjuring with figures and
calculations.

By a lucky coincidence this born calculator, this fanati-
cal sun-worshipper became associated with a very different
type of person; a man who made few calculations, but
enormous numbers of excellent observations; a man who
would have nothing to do with Copernicus' system because he felt it was opposed to his religious beliefs, Tycho
Brahe. The modern man, when he is ignorant, tends to
agree with the medieval man that people like Tycho
Brahe who sit in an observatory or in a laboratory recording minute facts are dull and unimaginative. Tycho
Brahe spent most of his life recording the exact position
in the sky of the planets and the stars, hour by hour,
night after night; indeed he did very little else; and yet
Tycho was one of the men who are directly responsible
though he had no idea of it himself, for building up
the modern man's idea of God. These interminable observations, needing nothing but trained and careful tech-
nique, were precisely what were needed to bring about
the crash of medieval ideas about the universe. In the
hands of Kepler they explained at last what the planets

were actually doing as they moved across the night sky; they shattered for ever the Aristotelian outlook and proved that true knowledge lay in the future and not in the past; they advanced one step further the conception of God which the new spirit of the age required.

As the air to the bird or the sea to the fish, so were numbers to Kepler; his mind breathed them and transformed them into light and heat. Faced with a mass of calculations he tried every conceivable theory which might fit them: he was convinced that numbers all had a "meaning." It was the same idea that orthodox astronomers used for contraverting the system of Copernicus; Francesco Sizzi, for example, argued that there must be seven planets, i. e., the moon, the sun, Mercury, Venus, Mars, Jupiter, Saturn, because "there are seven windows in the head, two nostrils, two eyes, two ears and a mouth; so in the heavens there are two favourable stars, two unpropitious, two luminaries and Mercury alone undecided and indifferent. From which and many other similar phenomena of nature, such as the seven metals, etc., which it were tedious to enumerate, we gather that the number of planets is necessarily seven." Now the modern man reading this smiles and says that there is no particular virtue in the number seven and that it is merely mystical superstition to suppose that because there are seven openings to the head there *must* be seven planets. Kepler did not take this line at all; nobody believed more than he in the magic virtues of numbers, and if "seven" had to be scrapped it could only be because it was in this instance the wrong magic number.

According to the Copernican idea the seven old "planets" were replaced by six bodies going round the sun, real planets this time, namely, Saturn, Jupiter, Mars, Earth, Venus, Mercury; Kepler asked himself: why *six*? After a great deal of calculation he discovered that their distances from the sun were such that round each orbit you could build one of the five regular solids. A regular solid is a solid having all its faces, edges, angles, etc., absolutely alike, and they are called the cube, the tetrahedron, dodecahedron, icosahedron, and octahedron, and there are only five of them; Euclid has a simple proof in his geometry, that there can be only five such volumes. Here then was the reason why God made six and only six planets, because there would have been no regular solid to go round a seventh! Kepler was transported with joy, "the intense pleasure I have received from this discovery," he said, "can never be told in words. I regretted no more the time wasted; I tired of no labour; I shunned no toil of reckoning, days and nights spent in calculation, until I could see whether my hypothesis would agree with the orbits of Copernicus or whether my joy was to vanish into thin air." Of course, the "discovery" was ridiculous; the orbits of Copernicus were wrong; the solids fitted very badly; Uranus and Neptune, two further planets, were twinkling out of sight, ready to upset by their discovery the proof that God could only invent six planets. Yet what a flood of light the whole incident throws upon human motive; this insatiable desire to give form and pattern and therefore significance to the universe.

It is indeed a strange idea to us, this God of Kepler's who was so good at jig-saw puzzles that he had fitted the planets to the regular solids, yet so bound by convention that he could not invent another planet once the regular solids were used up. Yet, strange as this idea of God may be, it is essential that we grasp it: substitute true laws of this eternal binding nature and eliminate the idea of a personal God between them and things created, and we find an attitude towards God and the universe familiar to all of us, the attitude towards which Kepler and all the early astronomers were groping. It is because of this that to us explorers hunting for the modern man's Bible, as to Kepler himself, his fantastic discovery is almost more important than his three genuine contributions to science. For it throws a light on the wanderings of the human imagination, which we shall need as our search continues.

However, the three "laws" of Kepler are of course vital to the history of science and therefore they too are important to us. The first of them was startling enough: planets move not in circles at all but in ellipses. To the modern man it would not matter in what curve they moved provided the earth always continued to get warmth and light from the sun; of course it would not be pleasant if the earth, like a stone thrown into the air, moved round the sun in a parabola, for then we should first pass near enough to the sun to be fried to cinders and after that one excessive summer would move for ever and ever towards a constantly increasing winter of despair; but as between an ellipse and a circle or even any irregular sort of curve we have really no personal preference. Not so the intelligent man in Kepler's time, for he was direct heir to generations, which for two thousand years had assumed that all the motions of the heavenly bodies must be circular, because circular motion is the most perfect motion, and to imagine his creations moving in a less perfect way would be an aspersion against God himself.

Probably Kepler hated his first law; it must have jarred his emotions; but his second made up for it. One of the most unpleasant features of the Copernican system had been that in order to fit in with observations the planets must be moving now faster, now slower. Such an idea was unbearable for human beings in those days; it made them shudder like a violin played out of tune; for it meant that *God varied*. God was the direct source of motion and if he could not keep a uniform motion—it was impossible to believe that such a possibility could exist. It would be as if God was the inefficient governor of a machine, and, if that were so, God, the Governor of the universe in two senses, had been found wanting. Kepler in his second "law" showed that although the planets certainly did move with uneven velocity along their paths nevertheless a line drawn from the sun to the planet swept out an equal area in an equal time. The divine plan was vindicated; God was good.

§ 5

And now, having glanced at Copernicus, Tycho Brahe and Kepler, we come at last to Galileo.

In the fourth book of Aristotle's work *On the Heavens* and in the first section it is written: "That body is heavier than another which, in an equal bulk, moves downward quicker"; or, in other words, if two bodies, one heavier than the other, are dropped from a height together, the heavier body will hit the ground first. That must have been written in about 350 B.C.: for one thou sand nine hundred and forty years nobody seems to have disputed it; during all that long time men either did not think of the matter at all or they knew without possible loophole for doubt that a heavy body fell faster than a light one, because Aristotle had said so.

But in about 1590, a young mathematical professor, Galileo Galilei, earning seven pence halfpenny a day at the University of Pisa, climbed the Leaning Tower, carrying a one-pound and a ten-pound weight, and then, in the presence of the university faculty and students assembled, dropped them at the same moment over the railing. A second or so later they reached the ground together.

The University Authorities returned to their library, took down Aristotle's *On the Heavens*, read the passage, which we have quoted above, over again carefully and declared that a ten-pound weight would reach the ground more rapidly than a one-pound weight; and that Galileo was simply wasting time climbing up towers and making ridiculous experiments.

In 1604 a New Star suddenly blazed forth: Galileo studied it and then lectured on it to a large crowd, who had been much excited by the unusual novelty. He proved to them that it could not be a meteor near the earth, or any sublunary phenomenon; but that whatever it was it came from the sphere of the fixed stars.

Now, as we have seen, Aristotle and everybody else believed that the sublunary world was imperfect and full of change, but that the starry spheres were changeless and immortal, as befitted the realm of God and the angels. Galileo took the opportunity to point out to the general public that Aristotle was clearly wrong.

Remember that all medieval thought hung together as a whole, so that if one part trembled all trembled; remember that hitherto people had spoken softly and in learned books about their doubts, whereas Galileo broadcast the news in a university town under the nose of the professors, and you will see what a serious matter this new star had become. Galileo was once more suggesting that Aristotle could be proved wrong by use of eye and brain.

Five years later Galileo visited Venice and there heard of a curious instrument, made by a Dutchman named Lippershey, which magnified distant objects. He set to work and constructed another like it, but better. It was a great success and the Venetian senators "though of advanced age, mounted to the top of one of the highest towers to watch the ships, which were visible through my glass two hours before they were seen entering the harbour, for it makes a thing fifty miles off as near and clear as if it were only five." The senate was pleased and doubled his salary and gave him a life professorship. But then Galileo turned his telescope from ships at sea to the skies; and that was to cost him everything except the bare bones of life.

First he turned to the moon and announced that it was pockmarked with mountains and valleys like the earth; and the Aristotelians, who taught that all the heavenly bodies were crystalline and perfect, gnashed their teeth. He said that the "old moon in the new moon's arms" was earth-light reflected back to the moon and that this was evidence that the earth was a shining sphere like the other planets. This deprived the anti-Copernicans of another of their arguments, that the earth did not shine. Galileo's enemies increased daily.

Then he looked at Jupiter through the telescope. This was on January 7, 1610. He noticed two bright little stars near the planet to the right and one to the left. Next day "led by I know not what fate," he again turned the telescope towards Jupiter and found that all the three stars were on one side and closer together. Further observation convinced him that there were circling round Jupiter four moons similar in nature to our own. The news spread through Europe with great rapidity and Kepler among others wrote to him and told him how it reached him: "I was sitting idle at home thinking of you, most excellent Galileo, and your letters, when the news was brought me of the discovery of four planets by the help of the double eyeglass. Wachenfels stopped his carriage at my door to tell me, when such a fit of wonder seized me at a report, which seemed so very absurd that, confounded as we were at such a novelty, we were hardly capable, he of speaking or I of listening. —On our separating, I immediately fell to thinking how there could be any addition to the number of planets without overturning my Mysterium Cosmographicon, published thirteen years ago, according to which Euclid's five regular solids do not allow more than six planets round the sun. But I am so far from disbelieving the existence of the four circumjovial planets that I long for a telescope to anticipate you if possible in discovering two round Mars (as the proportion seems to me to require) six or eight round Saturn, and one each round Mercury and Venus."

On the other hand, Francesco Sizzi, whom we have

already read on the necessity of there being seven and only seven planets, was not so pleased: he attacked the new-found Jupiter's moons, or circumjovial planets as Kepler called them, with this argument: "the satellites are invisible to the naked eye, and therefore can have no influence on the earth, and therefore would be useless, and therefore do not exist. Besides the Jews and other ancient nations as well as modern Europeans have adopted the division of the week into seven days, and have named them from the seven planets: now if we increase the number of the planets this whole system falls to the ground." But in spite of Francesco Sizzi and his like the satellites went on circling circumjovially for all who would look through a telescope to see.

But some people would not look through Galileo's telescope for love or money; especially did the Aristotelians avoid it. They said it was a distorting mirror. "Oh my dear Kepler," wrote Galileo to his friend, "how I wish that we could have one hearty laugh together! Here, at Padua, is the principal professor of philosophy, whom I have repeatedly and urgently requested to look at the moon and planets through my glass, which he pertinaciously refuses to do. Why are you not here? What shouts of laughter we should have at this glorious folly! And to hear the professor of philosophy at Pisa labouring before the Grand Duke with logical arguments, as if with magical incantations to charm the new planets out of the sky."

Meanwhile Father Caccini began to preach sermons to the text, "Ye men of Galilee, why stand ye gazing up into heaven?" The storm was gathering and soon the

Sizzis and Silviuses and Caccinis would be taking arms against these men, who, here and there throughout Europe, looked about them and used their eyes.

Galileo did not stop for all the sermons Caccini could preach; having discovered moons to Jupiter, spots on the moon, new stars in the unchanging spheres, he proceeded to insult the sun. In 1612 he wrote to Marcus Velserius Linceus a series of letters announcing that on carefully examining the sun through his telescope he had seen a series of dark spots which as day followed day moved across the face of the globe. Next year these letters were published with excellent engravings of the spots. Once more the fat was in the fire: Galileo, like the impious heretic that he was, had now gone so far as to impugn the perfect beauty of the sun itself. The Aristotelians could stand it no longer and in 1616 Galileo was forbidden to express his opinions any more either in books or lectures; moreover the irritation was so strong that Copernicus' book, seventy-three years old, in spite of its soothing preface was at last suppressed.

§ 6

What had Galileo done that makes him important to the modern man in his search for a sane outlook on life? He had destroyed one state of the human imagination and he had shown the way to a far richer future for that imagination, than the past had ever been.

In the first place, he had, of course, provided the concrete evidence which proved the Copernican system more in accordance with reality than the system of Ptolemy. In the second place, he altered man's way of looking at the universe and thereby the way by which men in future would seek to understand life and to find God.

Until Galileo had turned his little telescope to the sky there were no good scientific reasons for embracing the Copernican system. There were only mystical reasons such as that God was shown to be more efficient and the sun given a place more worthy of its excellence. Galileo discovered several excellent arguments of a strictly scientific nature.

The fact that satellites went round Jupiter as the moon went round the earth, and that the earthshine on the face of the moon suggested that the earth also shone like a planet, made Jupiter and the earth seem very much alike in their nature: indeed it was hard to resist after such evidence the conviction that they were alike. Then the fact that Venus showed phases like the moon made it probable that she too was shining with the reflected light of the sun and only upon the side turned toward it. Sunspots, tides, new stars, all of them contributed to destroy the Aristotelian universe and to put in its place that of Copernicus.

But it was the general effect upon thought and philosophy which such discoveries produced, that makes Galileo really of immeasurable importance to us. He represents a new stage in humanity's progress, a stage which was being indicated by other workers beside him elsewhere. Thus the Englishman Gilbert of Colchester, in his study of magnetism published in 1600, heralded the dawn of a new age: "Why should I submit," he wrote, "this noble philosophy to the judgement of *men who have taken oath to follow the opinions of others* . . . to be heaped with contumely. To you alone, true philosophers, ingenious minds, who *not only in books but in things themselves look for knowledge*, have I dedicated these foundations." Here was a new attitude, a new spirit of the age, a new stage in man's imaginative adventure.

Galileo himself expresses the same spirit when he defends himself against the first attacks of the Inquisition in some letters to the Grand Duchess Cristina: "Methinks that in the discussion of natural problems we ought not to begin with the authority of passages from Scripture, but with sensible experiments and necessary demonstrations . . . Nature being inexorable, acting only through immutable laws which she never transgresses, and caring nothing whether her reasons and methods of operating be or be not understandable by men, I hold that our conception of her works, which either sensible experience sets before our eyes, or necessary demonstrations prove, ought not to be called in question—much less condemned upon the testimony of Scriptural texts, which may conceal under their words senses or meanings seemingly opposite. To command professors of astronomy that they see to confuting their own observations and demonstrations is to ask the impossible. . . . As to opinions which are not directly articles of faith, certainly, no man doubts that his Holiness hath always an absolute power of admitting or condemning them, but it is not in the power of any creature to make them to be true or false otherwise than as they are."

To us such sentiments may not seem extreme, but in 1615 they amounted to a claim to upset not merely the foundations of science but of conscience as well. Pope Urban VIII, an enlightened man for his period, would have liked to find a way of safeguarding conscience and at the same time of allowing science to go as far as was expedient. When in 1630 Galileo sought to publish his chef-d'œuvre, *The Dialogue on the Two Chief Systems of the World, the Ptolemaic, and the Copernican,* permission was granted upon two main conditions: first, the possibility of the Copernican system was to be treated as a hypothesis, not as a reality; that is, as a mathematical puzzle, not as a picture of the universe; and, second, the book must conclude with this argument about the nature of the tides: "God is all-powerful; all things are therefore possible to Him; therefore the tides cannot be adduced as a necessary proof of the double motion of the earth without limiting God's omnipotence." This is the same as saying that you may not say that the angles of a triangle are necessarily equal to two right angles, because God could, being omnipotent, make a triangle with angles equal to three right angles.

Galileo kept even the first of these conditions fairly well; and made one of his characters suggest that God lets us think about the nature of the universe, so as to keep our intellects from getting dull, though he prevented us from ever really knowing its true nature. But this same character also says that "to make the universe revolve in order to maintain the immobility of the earth is as little reasonable as to require in order to see Venice from the top of the Campanile, that the whole panorama should move round the spectator instead of his simply moving his head."

It is not surprising that so brilliant an attack on orthodoxy was not allowed to go unpunished, and as everybody knows, Galileo was forced by the Inquisition to abjure the astronomical system of Copernicus. The popular story is that directly he had performed the necessary ceremony and denied that the earth moved, he muttered "e pur si muove"—"nevertheless it does move": the story is certainly not true, and we should not be misled into believing that the whole trial was due to the Inquisition disliking the idea that the sun did not go round the earth. That of course was the immediate cause of all the trouble, but the point at issue was far deeper, as the accusation of the Inquisitors shows: "you have rendered yourself," it ran, "vehemently suspected by this Holy Office of heresy, in that (1) you have believed and held the doctrine (which is false and contrary to the Holy and Divine Scriptures) that the sun is the centre of the world and that it does not move from east to west, and that the earth does move and is not the centre of the world; and (2) that an opinion can be held and defended as probable after it has been decreed contrary to the Holy Scriptures, and, consequently, that you have incurred all the censures and penalties enjoined in the sacred canons and other general and particular codes against delinquents of this description."

Now there can be no doubt whatever that what Galileo taught was contrary to the Scriptures: no fundamentalist can possibly believe that the sun does not move round the earth in the face of the obvious meaning of various texts in the Bible. Moreover, as we have seen, the medieval scheme of life made every part of philosophy, moral as well as natural, so dependent upon the rest that nothing was safe if Galileo could have his way.

To the modern man therefore the whole story is important because it shows more clearly than ever the truth of what we have so frequently repeated, that a man's outlook on life as a whole, that is his religion, is ultimately dependent upon the picture of the universe which he possesses. Galileo's doctrine was immoral in the strictest sense, for his new science must sooner or later demand a new conscience; and a new conscience is always immoral to the old.

§ 7

The Modern Man was asked at the beginning of this chapter to imagine that he was an intelligent man sitting at his table in the year 1543; a hundred years have now gone by and it is 1643; you are sitting once more at your table and your pen is in your hand. You are middle aged and, urged on by increasing grey hairs, you feel the need of thinking carefully where you stand with regard to the universe around you.

Five years have passed since Galileo died; he who had seen so much more than other men had ended life unable to see as much as a new-born babe, blind, old, dishonoured. But on your library shelves are those books of his which have escaped the Inquisition, and in them is preserved the meaning and importance of all he saw. Moreover there is something on your table which you did not possess one hundred years ago, a small tube with lenses, a telescope with which you have read things as strange as are to be found in any of your books. Through it you have looked on clear nights at Jupiter's moons and the crescent shape of Venus, and by day you have produced with it an image of the sun upon your room wall, and marked how a sunspot moved slowly across the brilliant circle, disappearing at last on the farther edge.

One thing is very clear to you as you sharpen your quill; the world no longer contains one single point of view about life in general; two great warring creeds exist side by side and it is certain that one or other must sooner or later conquer the other. Of course outwardly there is still but one great orthodoxy, challenged it is true over large parts of Europe by the "Lutheran heresy"; but an intelligent man like yourself, communing with his own soul, can see that really there are two rival ways of seeking God, two rival gods almost, and that the differences between Pope and Luther are as nothing compared with the difference between both of them and this other way. In order to clear your mind you write down the following notes. "God, the universe and my soul" you call them.

Galileo dropped weights at Pisa and they fell to the ground at one and the same moment. Aristotle thought otherwise and his professors were faithful to him. Shall I follow Aristotle or Galileo? If Galileo, it follows that truth must be sought not in authorities but in experiment. Then truth is something to be found in the future; it will grow we can become wiser; it is not crystallised in the books of past days. And if this is true of simple facts such as how weights fall to the ground, then it is true of more serious matters.

It almost seems that Aristotle's view of life and the universe is not a firm creation but a dream palace, a coloured bubble; prick it, and life and the universe fall back into chaos. We will then have to build it up again. Is it not safer to stand fast in the faith of this dream palace? Is not the Inquisition right? At least it is best to keep quiet and if the mind aches for speculation there is no need to shout aloud about it. I believe that doubt is no sin and perhaps through doubting I may find God. Perhaps that philosopher Descartes was right when in the book he published six years ago he laid down that to doubt all was the only sure beginning of knowledge. Doubt or faith? Faith led the professors into doubting their own senses when they saw the weights fall; would not faith in senses lead to doubting faith?

At least there can be no harm in experimenting about harmless things and at any rate authority is sometimes wrong. And perhaps after all we are getting to a fuller knowledge of God as we learn how he reveals himself in his works.

Then again if Copernicus and Galileo are right, as the telescope certainly seems to have shown, in denying that the earth is the centre of the universe; and if Kepler is right in denying that the heavenly bodies move in circles and stating that they move in inferior curves called ellipses; whither will all this lead us? Must we give up our ideas about perfection and all our sense of values? We have always been taught that God had to make the universe in a special way because that way was the perfect way, spheres, circles, seven planets, unvarying speeds: now it looks as if this was all wrong. The perfect spheres do not exist, the perfect seven planets do not exist, their speeds vary from day to day, the perfect circles are miserable ellipses. What if all these ideas about perfection are meaningless, man-made? Then we cannot find God through them.

Perhaps all the Aristotelian idea of God, fitted so nicely into the revealed religion of Christianity, as the highest good, "the last for which the first was made," is meaningless.

Perhaps we cannot say that our globe is composed of earth, water, air, fire, each above the other, each better than the last, with the even better and higher spheres next, and last of all the highest good, the great perfection, God himself. All this talk of good and better, of imperfection and perfection, may lead nowhere. It is not of the nature of fire to be better than water, as we have all thought for two thousand years; fire is fire and water water, and the differences between them are *things we can measure*, and *not ethical differences*.

It was at this point that you began to see the significance of the title you had chosen for your notes: "God, the universe and my soul"; for all these changes brought in by men like Galileo, discoveries of Jupiter's moons, of sunspots, of elliptical paths about the sun, were not mere dry astronomical facts, they were the fire which had melted in the crucible of your mind the whole outlook of the Middle Ages about these three into the vague beginnings of a new outlook.

To you in 1543 the relationship between God, the universe and your soul had been this: the universe existed to serve man; its meaning was to be found in its use to him —remember the objection to Jupiter's satellites that as they could not be seen by the naked eye they could not be of any use, and therefore did not exist—and man existed to aspire to God; man was the "why" of the universe, God the "why" of man. But now you saw a quite different point of view: the universe seemed to go on like a wound-up watch, taking no notice of God or man. Man was certainly not the "why" of the universe;

instead, the universe seemed to be something made by God and then left to itself; and man was something else made by God, though whether man also was left to himself you did not discuss as yet: that was to come later.

Moreover this universe, made by God and left complete to work according to rules, was not a moral thing, but a mathematical thing, a clock ticking away, neither good nor bad, but purely mechanical.

If you think in 1930 of how this change must have affected you in 1643, you will see how stupid it is to think that the Inquisition condemned Galileo simply because he said the earth moved: what Galileo was doing was to challenge an idea of God and the universe upon which every human thought and emotion, noble as well as base, had rested for two thousand years: it would have been madness for the Inquisition to have done other than it did, for if Galileo was right, the sooner men ceased to try to understand God by the old methods, the better for them; mathematics not theology was the true basis for an honest outlook on life. Hidden in the future lay the laws which God decreed for the working of the universe, laws which explained his nature far more clearly than the Hebrew Ten Commandments, laws not man-made like these, but made before mankind began its course.

In 1643 as you sat at your table trying to elucidate your attitude towards life, there lay in his cradle an infant who was to reveal these laws and complete the work begun by Galileo, an infant of whom Alexander Pope was to write:

> Nature and Nature's laws lay hid in night;
> God said, let Newton be!—and all was light.

CHAPTER FOUR

→→→→→→→→→→→→→→→→→→→→→→→→→→→⇥⇤←←←←←←←←←←←←←←←←←←←←←←←←

Newton

§ 1

"I do not know what I may appear to the world, but to myself I seem to have been only a boy playing on the seashore, and diverting myself in now and then finding a smoother pebble or a prettier shell than ordinary, whilst the great ocean of truth lay all undiscovered before me." So wrote Newton in his later years: and although the world rightly knows him as the greatest genius in the pathway of modern intellectual evolution, the picture of him as a boy picking up pebbles is peculiarly felicitous. His mental supremacy is founded on youthful curiosity infinitely developed, and the same emotions, which make the schoolboy naturalist, revealed the secrets of unalterable law to Newton.

Not that he was a mere collector of facts like Tycho Brahe; he was far less interested in this sort of pastime than in observing things and then finding out how they worked. He devised beautifully simple experiments and solved all sorts of little problems that never so much as occurred to most people. As a boy he was supposed to busy himself in farming; but instead of going to market to sell his produce, he would sit under the hedge and read books on mathematics. On the night Oliver Cromwell died there was a great gale and Newton, aged sixteen, amused himself by jumping first with the wind and then against it so as to calculate its velocity. He made water clocks and sundials, and models of engines and instruments; like Galileo he was fascinated by telescopes and, from observing their defects, he discovered laws of optics. He saw halos round the moon and proved that some must be made by particles of water, others by particles of ice. He invented new ways of attacking mathematical problems, revolutionising the whole science of mathematics by his discovery of differential calculus. He made experiments in alchemy. From early childhood he never ceased to observe, to think and to invent.

What did all this activity contribute to the Modern Man's problem of his attitude to the universe? Can we understand our life or imagine God without knowing what Newton gave the human imagination? It is absolutely impossible to have a useful opinion about God, or life, or the universe without first getting a glimpse of this gift.

And yet all most of us know or care about it is that Newton "saw an apple fall and discovered gravitation," a fact, if fact it is, which means very little and certainly does not help us to know ourselves or God.

I wish to give a brief and simple description of Newton's main achievement, admitting only so much of mathematics as is essential to perceive its significance: and to do this we must glance at his method and the steps by which he passed to the greatest discovery of all time; the discovery which lies beneath all sound thought about the universe and the life which is passed in it. We will first trace the discovery of this thing gravitation, and then consider its significance to the Modern Man.

"If I have seen farther," wrote Newton, "it is by standing on the shoulders of giants": we have been considering some of these giants in preceding chapters. It is perfectly true that Newton's greatest achievement was to collect all the discovery and reasoning of the past and to weld it into a complete and perfect whole, complete and perfect in the same sense as the Aristotelian picture of the universe was perfect. We have already seen how the human imagination busies itself with the recreating of the universe, and how out of each successive recreation a new religion is formed: first there was the savage picture of the universe and the savage picture of God; then the Aristotelian or medieval picture, disintegrated by all the spirit which lies behind Copernicus, Kepler, Tycho Brahe, Galileo. This picture was not supplanted by another until Newton came to paint it. Galileo did not paint it, he merely squeezed the colours on to a palette for Newton to use. We must glance at the way he used it.

So far we have seen a continually increasing chaos in human thought: the net result of the revolutions in knowledge has been that the old answers to how the universe behaves, and why it behaves as it does, have been found to be wrong; a new answer to the how has been given, nobody has as yet tackled the why. The intelligent man of the Middle Ages reasoned like this, "how does the universe move? in circles, in spheres, by uniform speeds. How do I know this? because such things are perfect and needed to manifest God." In short, the why, God's nature, is taken as known, and the how is deduced from it. "God is perfect; therefore his creation is perfect and moves according to the standards of perfection; and that is how I know that the heavenly spheres

move in circles round the earth." Then came the appalling discovery that the "how" was entirely wrong and
that therefore the "why" was also wrong. The people who
made this discovery said, "I will tell you how the universe behaves, but apart from my answer showing that
the old answer to the why must be wrong, I shall have
to leave the why entirely alone." It was thus far that the
giants, on whose shoulders Newton stood, had gone:
Newton answered the why. Let us see how he set about
this task.

Kepler showed that the earth went round the sun in
an ellipse with the sun in one focus and also that in its
journey a line from it to the sun swept over an equal
area in an equal time. He was quite unable to give any
reason as to why this should be so. For one thing he had
a wrong idea as to the very nature of motion and of the
forces which produce it. The Middle Ages imagined
that the heavenly bodies were pushed round the sky by
angels or other supernatural beings rather as a swimmer
might push a football before him on the surface of the
sea. If these angels were to stop, the planet also would
stop and remain where it was until the pushing began
all over again. Probably Kepler had very much this idea
for he was pleased that the perfection of God, as it were,
jeopardized by the fact that the planets sometimes moved
faster and sometimes slower, had been saved by the discovery of this law of equal areas; for, although he had
demonstrated, thanks to Tycho Brahe's observations, that
the "how" was not a matter of perfect circles, the "why"
remained the same, namely God's necessary perfection.

Now Galileo as an old man saw that this idea of how
the planets were propelled was wrong. Instead of a con-

stant force, like a man swimming or an angel flying, being necessary to maintain the speed of the body, one push at the beginning of things was all that was required. Instead of a planet or any other body coming to rest directly the pushing ceased, it would go on and on for ever in a straight line until some other push stopped it or altered its direction. This makes all the difference to the problem of the way in which the universe moves and behaves, for instead of requiring to discover a pushing force, an angel or a God, the real thing which is wanted is some force which pushes the earth out of the straight line in which it would naturally move and sends it round the sun in an ellipse.

It was the realisation of this that made it possible for Newton to go much farther than his predecessors. If what was wanted was a force which prevented the earth from going on and on in a straight line for ever, what could be found to help in the quest for it? Well, among other things it must be such a force that, as Kepler showed, in consequence of its action a line from the sun to the earth swept out an equal area in an equal time: wherever the earth was in its course round the sun, whether nearer or farther from it, if you drew a line to the sun from its position at Sunday midday and another from its position Monday midday, the area so formed would be exactly equal to that formed by the lines on Tuesday and Wednesday or any other interval of an equal number of hours. This had been found from observation, it had been measured, not reasoned out, and there could be no doubt about it.

Newton was able to show that as this was undoubtedly true some important things followed from it. Above all,

Kepler's discovery about the equal areas proves beyond all possible doubt that the force responsible for the earth's motion comes from the sun and from nowhere else. A few diagrams can make this clear to anyone:[1]

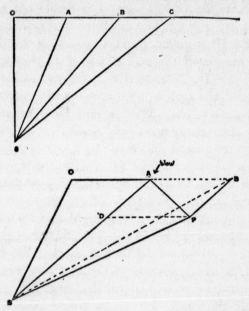

Let O A B C be points on a straight line an equal distance from one another and let S be the sun. Suppose the earth is at O and moving in the direction of C with a uniform speed and that no kind of force comes from the sun: then by Newton's or Galileo's first law of motion A B C are places which will be occupied by the earth moving in a straight line from O after equal successive intervals of time.

[1] These diagrams and their explanation are after Sir Oliver Lodge's *Pioneers of Science.*

If O A B C are joined up to S a series of triangles will be formed which will be of equal area because they have equal bases and the same height and such triangles are, as Euclid proves, equal in area.

Now let us suppose that this steadily moving body the earth which is moving towards C in accordance with this first law of motion reaches A and there receives a push or blow in the direction of S of such strength that it would on its own push the earth to a point D in exactly the same time as the earth, if left undisturbed, would have taken to get to B, then in accordance with simple mathematics the earth, moved by two forces at once, one in the direction of B, the other in the direction of D will move to neither B nor D but to a point P at the other corner of a parallelogram formed by AD and AB. In consequence, instead of sweeping out the area SAB it will sweep out the area SAP. Once more a little simple mathematics shows that these two areas SAB and SAP are equal because they are on the same base AS and between the same parallels AS and BP.

In this way we see that if a blow or push is received when the earth is at A, provided that blow is actually in the direction of the sun S, then equal areas will be made; just as they would be if no force at all came from S and the earth continued on its way in a straight line towards B. A little more mathematics will show that if the blow were in any other direction at all equal areas would not be produced; from which it follows that since equal areas *are* produced in nature, the force acting on the earth and pushing it out of its natural straight line is *a pull in the direction of the sun.* Of course in order to get a true picture of what happens we must imagine the distances O, A, P, etc., as very small indeed until the points at which a push comes are not separated by more than an infinitely small distance and then the pushes become continuous. This continuous push or pull from the sun is the cause of the planets' paths.

It was when Newton had proceeded thus far that he took the step which makes him a genius and explains his importance to the Modern Man. He could have rested content with stating that the earth was ruled by a force which the sun exerted on it, he could have given it a name, solar attraction or something, and some people would have believed that a new discovery had been made. If a doctor tells a patient that he has a running nose the smallest fee he can ask will seem exorbitant, but if he says that the patient has rhinitis he will be willingly paid: and so with the scientist, he runs a constant moral danger from the world being pleased with names. Galileo saw this when he made one of the speakers in his *Dialogues on the Two Great Systems of the World* say that if any man explains why Mars or Jupiter moves, he will explain why a stone falls to the ground; the other replies that everyone knows this to be due to gravity: "you should say that everyone knows that it is *called* gravity," the other replies, "but I do not question you about the name, but about the essence." And so Newton was not interested in giving a name to this force which he saw must exist in the sun; he wanted to do more than be a scientific priest christening a new baby; he wanted to account for the fact that the new baby existed.

He was about twenty at the time and at his home in Lincolnshire; it is quite possible that he sat in his garden wondering what force this could be which the sun exerted on the earth and that while he was sitting there an apple fell. It is quite possible that this apple suggested to him the thought: "what if the same force which makes the apple fall keeps the earth circling about the sun and the moon about the earth?" At any rate, writing about this time he says, "I began to think of gravity extending to the orb of the moon and thereby compared the force requisite to keep the moon in her orb with the force of gravity at the surface of the earth, and found them answer pretty nearly."

Here indeed was a speculation of the grandest proportions; for it would lead to a proof that all the motions of bodies, whether suns or planets or stones or the minutest particles of matter are due to one and the same binding law.

But a long time was to elapse before the proof was reached. Possibly because he used wrong measurements of the earth's size, possibly because he could not find certain necessary subsidiary proofs, Newton failed to establish that the force which kept the moon in place and made the apple fall was one and the same. Instead of getting the figure 16, as he had expected, in the answer to his sum, he got the figure 13.9 and supposing there was nothing in it he put his calculations away in a drawer for thirteen years. He had been put off the scent either by wrongly believing that a degree of the earth's surface was 60 miles instead of 69.5, or because he could not see how to prove certain things about the mass of a sphere.

Meanwhile his busy curious mind took up a hundred different problems, great and small, and he made a series of discoveries in optics and mathematics which would be sufficient alone to make him famous for ever in the history of science. How observant he was, how thirsty for every sort of information can be seen from a letter he wrote to a young friend who was about to travel abroad. Here are the things he advises him to observe: "1 The policies, wealth, and state of affairs of nations, as far as a solitary traveller may conveniently doe. 2 Their impositions upon all sorts of people, trades and commodities, that are remarkable. 3 Their laws and customs, how far they differ from ours. 4 Their trades and arts, wherein they excell or come short of us in England. 5 Such fortifications as you shall meet with, their fashion, strength, and advantages for defence, and other such military affairs are as considerable. 6 The powers and respect belonging to their degrees of nobility or magistracy. 7 It will not be time misspent to make a catalogue of the names and excellencys of those men that are most wise, learned or esteemed in any nation. 8 Observe the mechanisms and manner of guiding ships. 9 Observe the products of nature in several places, especially in mines, with the circumstances of mining and of extracting metals or minerals out of their oare and of refining them; and if you meet with any transmutations out of their own species into another as out of iron into copper, out of any metall into quicksilver; out of one salt into another, or into any insipid body etc. those, above all, will be worth your noting, being the most luciferous, and many times luciferous experiments in philosophy. 10 The prices of diet and other things—and the staple commodity of places. . . .

"As for particulars, those that follow are all that I can now think of; viz; Whether at Schemnitium, in Hungary

they change iron into copper by dissolving it into a vitri-
olate water, which they find in cavitys of rocks in the
mines, and then melting the slimy solution in a strong
fire, which in the cooling proves copper. 2 Whether in
Hungary, Sclavonia, Bohemia etc., there be rivers whose
waters are impregnated with gold, perhaps, the gold
being dissolved by some corrosive waters like aqua regis,
and the solution carried along with the streame, that
runs through the mines. And whether the practise of
laying mercury in the rivers, till it be tinged with gold,
and then straining the mercury through leather, that the
gold may stay behind, be a secret yet, or openly practised. 3 There is newly contrived in Holland, a mill to
grind glasses plane withall, and I think polishing them
too; perhaps it will be worth while to see it. 4 There
is in Holland one Borry, who some years since was imprisoned by the Pope, to have extorted from him secrets
(as I am told) of great worth, both as to medecine and
profit, but he escaped into Holland, where they have
granted him a guard. I think he usually goes cloathed in
green. Pray enquire what you can of him, and whether
his ingenuity be of any profit to the Dutch. You may
inform yourself whether the Dutch have any tricks to
keep their ships from being all worm eaten in their
voyages to the Indies. Whether pendulum clocks do any
service in finding out the longitude etc."

This curious catalogue helps us to understand Newton's mind and also the intellectual temper of the age.
We see reflected in it an eagerness for routing out odd
scraps of information, which is very foreign to the scientific habit of our own time. In the seventeenth century
there was so much to be found out, so much to be col-

lected, that it was the golden age of the field naturalist. The man of science could afford to be interested in everything; today he must specialize; then, any scrap of knowledge might come in useful, unexpected treasure might lurk anywhere; nowadays all the crops seem garnered and the traveller cannot hope to find anything which is not far more accessible in a local library. The spirit of the age was one of collecting unconsidered trifles, of salvaging important truths from neglected dross and a man like Newton could easily forget one calculation that went wrong in a multiplicity of other interests.

The crying need was for co-ordination of knowledge, for means of communication between one scientist and another, and this need was beginning to be satisfied in England by the newly founded Royal Society. It is instructive to read the sort of thing which was discussed at early meetings of this body, and we find there just the same generalised spirit of inquiry, which we have noted in Newton's letter to his friend.

Thus, in June, 1661, Sir Kenelm Digby—whose cookery book, the *Closet of Sir Kenelm Digby*, contains some fascinating recipes—"related that the calcined powder of toades reverberated, being applyed in baggs upon the stomach of a pestiferous body, cures it by severall applications."

The meeting on September 10, 1662, contained a varied programme:

"Mersennus, his account of the tenacity of cylindricall bodies was read by Mr Croone, to whom the prosecution of that matter by consulting Galileo was referred. . . .

"Dr Goddard made an experiment concerning the force that presseth the air into less dimensions; and it

ABOMINATION DES SORCIERS

"Nor is it easy to see how any modern fundamentalist who refuses to believe in evolution because he believes in Genesis can consistently fail to believe in witches." (See p. 88.)

was found that twelve ounces did contract 1/24th part of Air. The quantity of air is wanting. . . .

"Dr Wren was put in mind to prosecute Mr Rook's observations concerning the motions of the satellites of Jupiter.

"Dr Charleton read an essay of his concerning the velocity of sounds. . . .

"Dr Goddard made the Experiment to show how much air a man's lungs may hold, by sucking up water into a separate glass after the lungs have been well emptied of air. Several persons of the Society trying it, some sucked up in one suction about three pints of water, one six, another eight pints and three quarters etc. . . .

"It was discoursed whether there be any such thing as sexes in trees and other plants; some instances were brought forth of palm trees, plum trees, hollies, ash trees, quinces, peonies etc. wherein a difference was said to be found, either in their bearing of fruit, or in their hardness or softness, or in their medical operations. . . .

"Mr Bole showed a puppy in a certain liquor, wherein it had been preserved during all the hot months of the summer, though in a broken and unsealed glass. . . ."

How different all this is from any meeting of the Royal Society today! Nowadays nobody can understand the subject matter of any other branch of science but their own and nobody who is not a scientist can tell from the title of a paper whether the subject is a plant, a star or a disease. It is difficult to imagine present-day fellows sucking up water in solemn assembly, and nobody would be interested in Sir Kenelm Digby's "calcined powder of toades reverberated."

In those days there was a good deal of opposition to

the Royal Society, partly on religious grounds; and its early historian Sprat, writing in 1667, tells us that "some over-zealous divines do much reprobate Natural Philosophy as a carnal knowledge, and a too much minding worldly things." Even its royal founder Charles II, who often came to their meetings, did not think much of some of their experiments; and Pepys tells us that the king, "mightily laughed at them, for spending time only in weighing air, and doing nothing else since they sat."

Everybody knows the greatest attack on them in all literature, for it was of the Royal Society that Swift was thinking when he wrote in *Gulliver's Travels* the bitter satire about the wise men of the Grand Academy of Lagado. One of these had been eight years upon a project for extracting sunbeams out of cucumbers, which were to be put into vials hermetically sealed, and let out to warm the air in raw inclement summers. Another was at work to calcine ice into gunpowder and had written a treatise concerning the malleability of fire. An architect had perfected a way of building houses, by beginning at the roof, and working downwards to the foundations, which he justified by the practice of bees and spiders. A blind man was instructing blind apprentices in the choosing of colours by touch and smell. An astronomer had undertaken to place a sundial upon the great weathercock on the town house, by adjusting the annual and diurnal motions of the earth and sun, so as to answer and coincide with all accidental turnings by the wind.

It was easy to laugh at the Royal Society and to satirise the odd enthusiasms of its early members, but out of all this scientific enthusiasm and ferment was to grow the fruition of the work begun by Copernicus, Kepler and Galileo. Newton was typical of the very form of mental activity that men like Swift could only satirise. What is more, it was this mental activity which was binding up the new religion, which even intellects like Swift could never understand.

Newton became a fellow of the Royal Society in 1672 at the age of thirty: he had invented differential calculus, laid the foundations of optics, constructed a reflecting telescope and proved himself in every way a mathematical genius; but still his reflections upon the moon and falling apples had led him nowhere. In the same year as he became a fellow, a Frenchman Picard communicated to the Royal Society his method of measuring a degree of the earth's surface and the accurate result which he obtained. Apparently as far as Newton was concerned, these lay buried among piles of observations such as those of Sir Kenelm Digby on "powder of toades reverberated" for twelve long years.

Then in 1684 he thought once again of his old researches into the moon's motions; he substituted the new figures into the calculations and immediately obtained the result required. Before him lay the proof that one and the same force kept the earth moving about the sun, the moon about the earth, and made every movable body fall towards the earth's centre. Not only had he been able to show, as we have seen, that a force from the sun was responsible for the shape and size of the earth's orbit, but, far more important than this, that this was a universal force responsible for the motion of everything great and small.

§ 2

In order to appreciate the importance for the human imagination of Newton's work we must consider its effect on human ideas about the universe and then its effect upon human ideas about God. We have come to a crisis in our story; all that has gone before culminates in this, all that comes after is only intelligible if we realise its importance. The reader who has from time to time been impatient because he has not seen what light is being thrown on his own personal problems by descriptions of the history of science, of Galileo, of Kepler, of Copernicus must now be forced to see how vital to him such a study is.

First of all, what did Newton's work on gravitation do in the field of science itself? Instead of adding a new isolated discovery to all the jumble of things already known, it took that jumble, laid many of its constituent parts side by side and tied them up into a neat bundle. All sorts of facts about the universe which had seemed to have nothing at all to do with one another now could be shown to be due to one and the same cause.

Newton had begun by wondering if by any chance the same cause which made the apple fall to the ground could possibly keep the moon in its orbit about the earth: and by brilliant calculation he showed that it could. He was able to work out a formula and to prove that this formula described a law or necessity of matter which made it not merely possible but necessary for things to be as they are. Because the apple fell to the ground at a certain speed and because the moon was, like the apple, a body of matter, the moon had to move round the earth in precisely the way it did.

Now in doing this Newton was providing a "why" which explained the "how" of all sorts of things in the universe. Things happened because gravity was universal. This was one step further in the relations between man and the universe: first a medieval "how" deduced from an assumed "why," a universe working in circles and spheres, because the nature of God was to make things according to the idea of perfection; next the medieval "how" found by observation and experiment to be completely untrue, so that the medieval "why" broke down as completely. In consequence of this we have seen a fight between those who felt that the "why" was so essential, that if human senses disproved the "how" on which it rested, then so much the worse for the human senses—that is the attitude of the opponents of Galileo—and those who felt that somehow or other the "how" revealed to the human senses must be the gateway to the true "why." Finally, in so far as anything is final in this epic, we reach Newton who is able to reconcile the "how" by finding a "why" which explains it. Of course by so doing he had to limit the "why" and say that a "why" was only useful, possible or true in so far as the "how" illustrated it; that beyond this point it was of no use looking for or discussing a "why" at all. We shall see to what this leads later; but first we must tie ourselves down to the effect of Newton on the concrete universe itself.

It took fifty years for the discovery of universal gravitation to sink into the human mind and during this time practically no great use was made of it. Just as the Copernican ideas had to struggle against those of Ptolemy, so Newton's ideas had to struggle against the ideas taught in the schools and universities of his day. It is interesting that universities are always the places which hold back new knowledge even though that new knowledge often, though by no means always, arises in them. Galileo had to fight all the Aristotelian professors; long after the *Principia* had won its place as the true fountain of knowledge, Oxford and other universities even in Great Britain taught a theory of vortices which Descartes had invented and which Newtonian physics showed to be quite fantastic. Indeed Newtonian physics gained their first foothold by the author of an orthodox text-book after Descartes adding in note form and without committing himself to any opinion, the objections to Cartesian physics which resulted from Newton's discoveries. Probably he hoped that here and there a student's eyes would wander from the text to the notes and thereby the truth might be disseminated.

To us, of course, it seems to be quite extraordinary that the greatest mathematicians of his time took years to accept Newton: we accepted him in the nursery when we heard the apple story and have not bothered about him since. Fortunately we are helped to realise the difficulty by the fact that in our own time Freud and Einstein have both met with opposition, the first with abuse, the second with lack of understanding, so that we still see the curricula of many schools and colleges continuing as if neither of these men had been born; while in the case of Einstein at least, the true significance of all that he has discovered has probably not been grasped by a hundred mathematicians today. Yet the children of tomorrow will be taught some little story about Einstein which will probably be pure fiction, and will take him for granted as Newton is taken for granted by their fathers.

When this preliminary period had passed and Newton's universal gravitation had succeeded in saturating the scientific imagination of man, all sorts of marvels were seen to come from the one simple statement that "every particle of matter attracts every other particle with a force directly proportional to the mass of each and to the inverse square of their mutual distance." Let us first look at some of the observed facts about the universe which can be explained by this one statement and which were so explained by Newton himself in the *Principia*.

First of all let us consider the moon in its path round the earth: in ancient times, as we have seen, Ptolemy saw that it was no use assuming that the moon simply went in circles round the earth. If you catalogue observations of the moon's position in the skies they will not fit into any such path; and so Ptolemy supposed that the moon went round in a circle the centre of which went round in another circle round the earth but eccentric to it, that is, with the earth not actually at its centre. As a matter of fact, Ptolemy's solution of the moon's motion is far more complicated than this, but all that concerns us is that as more and more accurate observations showed that the moon's motion was less and less that of a body going round in a circle, more and more complicated explanations were required. If Ptolemy had been able to know the facts of the moon's movement as they are known today, he would have gone mad, for there are about thirty separate variations or irregularities, and no possible assemblage of circles could have been conceived by Ptolemy or anyone else to account for them all.

To Newton, on the other hand, thanks to the fact of universal gravitation and the mathematical formulæ in which it can be described, not only were such irregularities powerless to complicate the truth, but they were actually necessary in order to preserve the simplicity of the truth. Indeed, from the simple truth Newton was able to prophesy the discovery of new irregularities which the limitations of the observing instruments of his day had been as yet unable to trace. Consider for a moment the difference between these two; for earlier astronomers every increased degree of accuracy in observation meant that things were harder and more complicated to explain; for Newton every increased degree of accuracy bringing to light fresh irregularities of motion only vindicated once more the truth of the simple law underlying them.

To Ptolemy the moon's behaviour was difficult enough and he would have despaired had he known what Tycho Brahe discovered, that the time taken to change from a waning half-moon to a new moon was less than might have been expected from a body moving uniformly round the earth, and that the moon took longer to wax to half-moon again than it should. These irregularities of waxing and waning are due to slowing down and speeding up at different points of its orbit. To Ptolemy this behaviour would be horrible and only to be saved from stark sacrilege by assuming all sorts of new epicycles and eccentrics. To Newton it was only to be expected since the moon in its motion round the earth is half the time on the side of the sun and half the time on the opposite side, so that for two weeks it is being pulled harder by the gravitation exercised by the sun, and for two weeks less hard than the average. In short, the law of universal gravitation explains this irregularity without the invention of anything new.

Again Tycho Brahe showed that at different times of the year the moon behaves in a slightly different way: its movements in spring and summer are not exactly the same. To Ptolemy this would have meant, had he been unfortunate enough to know of it, the need of one more complication, possibly beyond his powers to conceive. To Newton nothing could be more natural, for in spring and summer the distance between sun and earth is different owing to the eccentricity of the earth's orbit; and so the sun's attraction on the moon is different and plunges the moon into fresh eccentricities.

And so with all the other irregularities; they are every one the natural outcome of the simple truth. Every body in the solar system is interfering in accordance with a known law expressed by a known formula with every other body.

In exactly the same way all the motions of the planets can be calculated and although ever increasing accuracy of observation will reveal fresh irregularities, instead of these complicating the picture of the universe they will only testify to the simplicity of the fundamental law which guides it. When Mars is near the earth, the earth is pulling it out of its path, and Mars is pulling the earth out of its path, to a far greater degree than when the two planets are separated by the breadth of their orbit: to Ptolemy this would have meant new epicycles, to Aristotle another hollow, transparent sphere, to Newton nothing but a vindication of the one simple law.

Or take the history of a comet; even today an awe-inspiring visitor from unknown space. The ancient astronomers did not attempt to account for its advent, it was supernatural, a miracle, telling sad stories of the death of kings. To Democritus comets were due to the close approach to one another of two planets; to Aristotle they were a dry and hot exhalation from the earth carried into the upper heaven and there ignited and carried along by the general movement of the heavens; to Kepler a condensation of "ethereal air" in which the planets move, swimming like a whale in a straight line until the sunlight dispels it. So haphazard and lawless were the appearances of comets that they seemed to augur changes and catastrophes: every comet, wrote a thirteenth century scholar, Robert Grosseteste, is sublimated fire parted from earthly nature and joined to the stars; each one is attracted by one particular star like a magnet and this star is associated with a planet. The comet reduces the spiritual matter in terrestrial creatures by withdrawing to the skies and hence presages the coming of corruption and calamity to those who are under the astrological influences of the planet with which it is associated. In short, it is an upsetting and dangerous stranger to the normal course of heavenly bodies.

Newton showed that comets behaved as they did because, universal gravitation being what it is, they could not do otherwise. Their paths and appearances, it is true, are different from those of a planet, but throughout their history they obey the same law as governs the earth's and Jupiter's ellipses. Sometimes this law curves out for them an ellipse with foci infinitely far away and then the solar system knows them no more; sometimes Jupiter or some other planet traps them as they pass and forces them to become permanent members of the solar system moving for ever round the sun. Thanks to the formulæ of gravitation it can be prophesied that long lost comets will return; and Halley actually did predict from Newton's law the return of one such comet after seventy-five years; so that even these miraculous portents were shown to follow tamely the fiats of unalterable law.

Nor was it only the objects in the skies and their problems which were reduced to order by this one discovery: by it Newton was able to calculate that the earth must have a diameter through the equator twenty-eight miles greater than that through the poles, for otherwise it could be shown from the law of universal gravity that the waters of the oceans would be piled up fourteen miles high at the equator, leaving dry land at either pole, and since this was not so the earth must have adjusted itself to the necessities of a spinning globe by contracting or squashing itself down at the poles and bulging out at the equator.

So too these laws of gravity forcing a revolving sphere to become flattened at the poles can be used to tell how long Jupiter, for example, takes to revolve on its axis. Since Jupiter is flattened to such an extent that its diameters are as 16 to 17 it must be rotating very fast and calculations give to this enormous globe a day and night of only ten hours.

Again, why is it that, although on a pair of scales no difference in the weight of objects is ever seen between one place and another, with a spring balance an object will vary in weight according to its latitude? It is because objects on the earth's surface are farther from the earth's centre at the equator than at the poles and therefore the force of gravitation is less there, or in short they weigh less there. Naturally the pound weight on a scale is subject to the same variation as the object weighed against it, so that it is only on a spring balance that objects can be actually seen to vary in weight. All this was made clear by the Newtonian formulæ, which made it possible to show that 195 pounds at the equator is the same as 194 pounds at the pole.

Again, the one law explained something which had puzzled Hipparchus and every mathematician after him. "Here," says Oliver Lodge, "we come to a truly awful piece of reasoning. A sphere attracts as if its mass were concentrated at its centre, but a spheroid does not. The earth is a spheroid, and hence it pulls and is pulled by the moon with a slightly uncentric attraction. In other words, the line of pull does not pass through its precise centre. Now when we have a spinning body, say a top, overloaded on one side so that gravity acts on it unsymmetrically, what happens? The axis of rotation begins to rotate cone-wise, at a pace which depends on the rate of spin, and on the shape and mass of the top, as well as on the amount and leverage of the overloading.

"Newton calculated out the rapidity of this conical motion of the axis of the earth, produced by the slightly unsymmetrical pull of the moon, and found that it would complete a revolution in 26,000 years—exactly what was wanted to explain the precession of the equinoxes. In fact he had discovered the physical cause of that precession."

The precession of the equinoxes means, as a matter of observation, that the sun does not move in front of precisely the same background of stars at the time of equal daylight and darkness year after year, but moves its position from place to place throughout a cycle of 26,000 years after which it begins the same cycle over again. To Ptolemy this had been due to a slow rotation of the sphere of fixed stars from west to east involving therefore a special explanation of its own, a new motion of the entire heavens; for Newton it followed directly from the formulæ of universal gravitation.

We will mention no other of Newton's discoveries than that of the tides. Kepler had guessed that they had something to do with the moon by observing that they varied with the moon's motions, but of course he had no idea of how or why this should be. As for Galileo, "amongst all the famous men who have philosophated upon this admirable effect of nature," he wrote, "I more wonder at Kepler than any of the rest, who being of a free and piercing wit, and, having the motion ascribed to the earth before him, hath for all that given his ear and assent to the Moon's predominancy over the water, and to occult properties, and such like trifles."

Newton was able to show how the moon's gravitational pull being better able to move the movable waters than the solid earth created the tides and how spring tide and neap tide are due to the sun pulling with or against the moon according to whether both bodies are on the same side of the earth or on different sides. Tides too were a necessary consequence of the universal formula.

Since Newton's day problem after problem has been solved by the application of the same formulæ until scarcely even a minor phenomenon remained to be accounted for. One or two almost negligible matters, it is true, remained to be cleared up, and they will be important in a later part of our story.

What then had Newton done to man's picture of the universe? He had substituted for the chaos of many unrelated things, an order based upon law. Ever since the collapse of the medieval picture there had been no real order; now order came back again. But what a different kind of order from that of the Middle Ages. Then order existed, but upon the basis of moral law; now there was no moral law involved in the picture, but physical law only. Goodness and perfection fell from man's picture of the universe leaving only such things as mass, motion and measurable quantities; could any revolution be greater than this?

§ 3

And what had Newton done to God? Let us remember that the adventure of the human imagination which had so far culminated in him was from the first an attempt to learn about God from the nature of the universe. As the universe was to Aristotle, to Copernicus, to Kepler, to Galileo so was God to them: moreover it was a thirst after God which led them to want to know more about the universe. They thought of the universe as a creation of an artist, and when they found beauty, form, symmetry in the universe they realised to a greater degree the perfection of the artist. Ordinary men do not like artists; they prefer soldiers or politicians or men of action, hence the nature of all the popular gods from Jehovah onwards.

Then came the philosophic theologians of the Middle Ages: they seem to have admired the subtle lawyer type of mind, and in consequence their god was a lawyer, an argumentative person with a memory for precedents and legal minutiæ; indeed one sometimes feels that to the schoolmen the great object was so to argue their case at law that their subtleties would prevent God from being even more subtle and catching them out. To them the universe was almost nothing but a pretty piece of dialectic.

Next we have a revolt from reason; for that is what the scientific spirit really meant in its beginnings: reason had led mankind to fatuity of outlook, for reasoning had been carried on without any glance at reality, without any distinction being made between dreams and waking life. You fill your mind with hypotheses, with guesses accepted on faith, and from them you can argue to anything. We have seen where this could lead a man like Chassenée in his legal discussions about animals. It was this that made Newton say he would have nothing at all to do with any hypothesis, but would only infer general laws from observed things.

Now the revolt from reason, unsupported by observed facts or experiments, to a frame of mind which almost feared to generalise at all, brought about one very important change in the attitude towards God. The medievalist started from God and completed his picture from everything that was to be found in the universe; Newton, as far as his scientific side is concerned, never got beyond a one-sided view of God, never tried to conceive him as anything at all except the God which was necessary as a result of the picture of the universe which could be gained from mathematics. To the medievalist the universe was composed of such attributes as beauty, perfection, imperfection, ugliness, goodness, badness: fire was better than water, a circle more perfect than an ellipse, seven more beautiful than eight; and so the medieval God had beauty, perfection, goodness as attributes. To Newton the universe was a question of space, time, mass, movement, things that could be measured; and so Newton's God was nothing at all except a good mathematician. The search which in the early days with Kepler had accepted the sun as the centre of the universe because it fitted so well the idea of God as a morning bright Apollo, a laughing sun-God, culminated with Newton seeing him as a super-professor of mechanics, almost worse still, as we shall see, a superannuated mechanic.

In the medieval idea there was always implicit the thought that the universe was part of God, his body, controlled by his will, and kept eternally living by his perfect nature. This thought was mixed with the other simpler Biblical one of the universe as something made by him. The scientific movement had shown that this thing was a machine, constructed and wound up by God and kept going thanks to his administration. God or his angels were still there pushing the spheres round on their paths about the sun. But consider the effect upon a devout astronomer when Galileo hinted and Newton clearly stated the first law of motion: all this pushing was unnecessary, all that was wanted was an initial push and then the planets could go on for ever without any help from God at all. Once this was understood, like an old servant past his work his services were retained merely out of sympathy and other emotions.

The great chemist Robert Boyle, who was so devout that he never mentioned the Deity without pausing for a moment in silence, regarded mathematical and me-

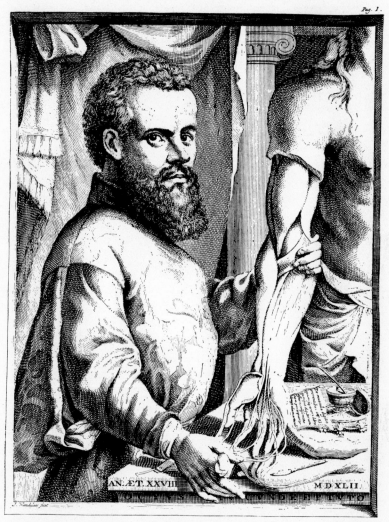

AN. ÆT. XXVII   MDXLII.

*Vesalius, "an impious madman, who is poisoning the air of all Europe
with his vapourings." He is demonstrating a dissection which contradicts a
text of Galen. By destroying respect for authority he helped to bring in a
new age.* (See p. 100.)

chanical principles as the "alphabet in which God wrote the world." He is an excellent example of the dilemma to which the human spirit had been led by the scientific search after God. He believed absolutely in Scriptural revelation yet he was forced by his scientific knowledge to see great difficulties about God's part in the universe. Somewhat faintheartedly he falls back on the probability of unknown proofs of God's presence; "I make great doubt," he says, "whether there be not some phenomena in nature, which the atomists cannot satisfactorily explain by any figuration, motion or connection of material particles whatsoever." Then he uses the most famous argument of all time, "that the consideration of the vastness, beauty, and regular motions of the heavenly bodies; the excellent structure of animals and plants; besides a multitude of other phenomena of nature, and the subserving of most of these to man, may justly induce him as a rational creature to conclude that this vast, beautiful, orderly and (in a word) many ways admirable system of things, that we call the world, was framed by an Author supremely powerful, wise and good, can scarce be denied by an intelligent and unprejudiced considerer."

But these two arguments are but the simple faith of any man and they have no part in the scientific mood which we are studying: Boyle, a great scientist, can however offer us more. How did he keep God in the universe as an active participant in spite of the increasing importance that every scientist must give to mechanical law? If God did not steer Venus round the sun, what did he do? He saw that the blind irrational planets which could not possibly understand laws, and therefore could not obey them of themselves, did what was legal. "I look upon a law as being indeed a notional thing," he writes, "according to which an intelligent and free agent is bound to regulate his actions. But inanimate bodies are utterly incapable of understanding what a law is and therefore the actions of inanimate bodies, which cannot incite or moderate their own actions, are produced by real power, not by laws." In short, the universe is a flock of sheep which must go through a gate into a field, but needs God to shepherd them. If God so willed he could at any time "by withholding his concourse, or changing the laws of motion, that depend entirely upon his will, invalidate most, if not all, the axioms of natural philosophy." The shepherd might decide not to help the sheep through the gate and the sheep would in consequence remain in the road outside.

Robert Boyle shows us the way in which things are going and with Newton we reach the end of the search. A very fortunate event has given us an exact exposition of what Newton deduced about the nature of God from his knowledge of the universe. In 1691 Robert Boyle died and left fifty pounds annually to establish a series of lectures to be given in a London church for the purpose of refuting the "principles of infidelity" and illustrating the evidences of Christianity. Dr. Bentley was the first lecturer and in his last two discourses he decided to demonstrate the existence of God from the principles of the physical universe established by Newton. In order to be quite certain that his words were scientifically correct he wrote to Newton and asked him to be good enough to help. Newton with his usual care replied in four letters in which he said that when he was writing the third book of the *Principia* he "had an eye upon such principles as might work with considering men, for the belief in a deity." According to Sir David Brewster, these are the reasons given for such a belief:

1. If matter were evenly diffused through a finite space, and endowed with innate gravity, it would fall down into the middle of space and form one great spherical mass; but if it were diffused through an infinite space, some of it would collect into one mass, and some into another, so as to form an infinite number of great masses. In this manner the sun and stars might be formed if the matter were of a lucid nature. But he thinks it inexplicable by natural causes and to be ascribed to the counsel and contrivance of a voluntary agent, that the matter should divide itself into two sorts, part of it composing a shining body like the sun, and part opaque bodies like the planets. Had a natural and blind cause, without contrivance and design, placed the earth in the centre of the moon's orbit, and Jupiter in the centre of his system of satellites, and the sun in the centre of the planetary system, the sun would have been a body like Jupiter and the earth, that is, without light and heat: and consequently, he knows no reason why there is only one body qualified to give light and heat to all the rest, but because the Author of the system thought it convenient, and because one was sufficient to warm and enlighten all the rest.

2. The motions which the planets now have could not spring from any natural cause alone, but were impressed by an intelligent agent. To make such a system with all its motions, required a cause which understood, and compared together the quantities of matter in the several bodies of the sun and planets, and the gravitating powers

resulting from thence; the several distances of the primary planets from the sun, and of the secondary ones
from Saturn, Jupiter and the earth, and the velocities with
which these planets could revolve about those quantities
of matter in the central bodies, and to compare and adjust
all these things together in so great a variety of bodies,
argues that cause to be not blind and fortuitous, but
very well skilled in mechanics and geometry.

3. He admits that gravity might put the planets in
motion, but he maintains that, without the Divine power,
it could never give them such a circulating motion as
they have about the sun, because a proper quantity of
transverse motion is necessary for this purpose; and he
concludes that he is compelled to ascribe the frame of
this system to an intelligent agent.

4. The hypothesis that matter is at first evenly diffused
through the universe, is in his opinion inconsistent with
the hypothesis of innate gravity without a supernatural
power to reconcile them, and therefore it infers a Deity.
For if there be innate gravity, it is impossible now for
the matter of the earth and all the planets and stars to
fly up from them, and become evenly spread throughout
all the heavens without a supernatural power; and certainly that which can never be hereafter without a supernatural power, could never be heretofore without the
same power.

Here then was the end of an imaginative adventure
which had begun full of faith that through an exact
knowledge of the universe must come a greater experience of the beauty of God. The poem was simply a machine; the poet a mechanic; and although that part of
the human spirit which liked machinery might still find

satisfaction, that which preferred poetry was left unsatisfied.

We must not forget that the scientific adventure had been taken by the human imagination because it gave promise of emotional enjoyment; only in so far as it gave emotional enjoyment was it likely to be acceptable; directly it failed we can expect revolt. That it had failed was very probable, since few human beings could desire to see their appreciation of God as a creator of a universe that was perfectly beautiful changed to an appreciation of him as an assembler of the various parts of the universe into a working whole. It was good enough for Newton for such a God was merely Newton's shadow seen immense against the mist of infinity; but for men who were not Newton, to whom measurement was not poetry, such an idea of God was bound to prove insufficient.

Moreover, it was not only that Newton's God was coldly mechanical, he was also very far away; one could have no more interest in him than in the watchmaker from whom one had once bought a watch. Newton tried valiantly to bring him a little bit nearer by pointing out that supposing the watch needs regulating you become interested enough in the watchmaker again to go and seek him out to repair it. And this was precisely what God did in the universe today; he regulated it and saw that it did not run down. Newton believed that certain irregularities such as the interference with the orbits of the planets by comets must inevitably upset the order of the universe in course of time and, since a watchmaker who had made so excellent a watch would naturally want to preserve and protect it for ever, he assumed that from time to time God corrected the irregularities before they could have a serious cumulative effect: "Sir Isaac Newton," wrote Leibnitz to the Princess of Wales, of all people, "and his followers have also a very odd opinion concerning the Work of God. According to their doctrine, God Almighty wants to wind up his watch from time to time, otherwise it would cease to move. He had not, it seems, sufficient foresight to make it a perpetual motion. Nay, the machine of God's making is so imperfect according to these gentlemen, that he is obliged to clean it now and then by an extraordinary concourse, and even to mend it as a clockmaker mends his work; who must consequently be so much the more unskilful a workman, as he is oftener obliged to mend his work, and to set it right."

Of course Leibnitz had his own axe to grind, but his words are very nearly true. Newton practically limited God's present existence in the universe to this need of adjusting those irregularities which would in time accumulate and destroy the order of things. Burtt excellently describes what this ultimately did to God: "It proved a vertiable boomerang to his cherished philosophy of religion, that as the result of all his pious ransackings the main providential function he could attribute to the Deity was this cosmic plumbery, this meticulous defence of his arbitrarily imposed mechanical laws against the threatening encroachments of irregularity. Really, the notion of the divine eye as constantly roaming the universe on the search for leaks to mend, or gears to replace in the mighty machinery would have been quite laughable, did not its pitifulness become earlier evident. For to stake the present existence and activity of God on imperfections in the cosmic machine was to court rapid disaster for theology. Not immediately, of course, indeed for many contemporary minds the purging of the world from all secondary qualities and the stress laid on the marvellous regularity of its whirrings only brought into fuller rational belief its divine Creator and govern-ing Will."

It suited the eighteenth century admirably to think of God as a practical engineer, for just as the Hebrew tribesmen admired a chieftain who could smite the neighbouring nations, and so created Jehovah; and just as the Middle Ages admired a hair-splitting dialectical recluse and invented a super-schoolman to worship; and just as Mr. Bruce Barton saw that what Rotary clubs wanted for their God was a super Rotarian; and just as lonely and unsuccessful people have always adored the Man of Sorrows; so the eighteenth century, a period of rationalisation in politics and expanding trade, wanted and got a first-class organiser with an efficient practical mind for their God. Fortunately or unfortunately the human imagination is infinite in its needs and pleasures: though the fact that all these globes and bodies moved about in accordance with a pull varying inversely with the square of its distance could please some people nearly all the time, and nearly all people for a small part of the time, there were others who sighed for a picture of the universe wherein the morning stars sang together and all the sons of God shouted for joy.

And what of Newton himself? Was he absolutely satisfied with the God which his picture of the universe forced upon him? In so far as that God was uncommonly like its creator in temperament and habits, he was; but in as much as the law of universal gravitation gave no promise of a life beyond death, no sense of some protecting guide to whom he might pray, no arbiter of human conduct or rewarder of the good, Newton's imagination supplemented his scientific view of God, with a perfectly orthodox hypothesis of a thoroughly Christian God: while one part of his mind showed him a God who prevented comets from wrecking the solar system, a task undertaken so as to preserve a piece of machinery of which its inventor was rightly proud, another part showed him a Deity to whom he could pray, of whom he might be afraid, with whom he might live after death. And here we have a clear example of what the scientific adventure did to humanity; it split the human mind into separate compartments—more or less watertight or idea-tight, and thereby made the picture of God, the attitude to life, the idea of the universe inconsistent and muddled. The medievalist could give his whole and undivided mind to a realisation of his God: no modern man can ever do this, however hard he may try. Some people have tried to pretend that if you throw out of the universe everything except space, time, mass and other measurable quantities, you can get a single and satisfying view of life and of God: these are of course the materialists or the curiously named rationalists. They are undoubtedly right as to the singleness of the view, but there never was much satisfaction to be got from the equation $o = o$. Others have been bold enough to throw out the measurable things themselves, though few have had the courage to go all the way. Most of us are content to admit the incompatibility of the scientific view with other views and to see that in this particular we are poorer than the

Middle Ages; for whereas the medievalist had achieved a perfect unity and harmony in his outlook on life without leaving out anything, we can only achieve such a harmony by looking at life in fragments. To go back to the harmony of medievalism is cowardly obscurantism, but to look forward to a new harmony, a new synthesis between the measurable and the unmeasurable in the far future is only common sense.

When the modern man has grasped this much, he has achieved the first part of his purpose: he will see that the so-called conflict between science and religion as generally understood by fundamentalists and village atheists is a mere street brawl. He will see that science is not entirely built out of pure reason but has its "metaphysics" just as much as any other use of the human imagination. He will see that science has all along only been worth while for purely unscientific reasons, that behind all the measurement has been hidden a search for greater knowledge of God and that therefore nobody has a right to bully him or his emotions by throwing at him the stones of science. He will remember, however, that although science is not the sole arbiter of ultimate things, it is supreme in its own sphere and that therefore it is of no use his insisting, for example, that the planets move in circles because that suits his private idea of God, for science can measure his circles and find them badly drawn.

Finally he can in one particular be more sensible than Newton; he will fight shy of "natural religion," of proving God from the need of a plumber to do celestial repairs; because, sooner or later, further scientific discoveries are sure to prove that these repairs are not really necessary at all. Thus Laplace in his nebular hypothesis explained by purely mechanical means nearly all the things which Newton thought must need an intelligent being to produce or to repair.

And if this effort is too great for him there is one other thing that he can do: he can blandly and openly say: "I find that if I throw out everything from my picture of the universe except measurable things, that I throw away the baby with the bath water, and so as I really do not like the measurable things, I will reverse the process and throw away what Newton kept and keep what he threw away." Let us see where this can lead a man.

§ 4

Newton died in 1727; thirty years later there was born a man who was in every way Newton's opposite, and the opposite of the age which found Newton's attitude to the universe almost wholly satisfactory. This was William Blake, in his own way as remarkable a man as the discoverer of universal gravitation. Blake drew a portrait of Sir Isaac Newton which would have surprised the original very much indeed: it is the figure of a handsome youth, quite naked, drawing something in the sand. It would have been in vain that you told Blake that his picture was not at all like Sir Peter Lely's portrait of Newton; that was simply so much the worse for Sir Peter Lely; Blake's picture, you would have been told, was far more exactly a portrait of the subject because it represented his true nature; that of a man diligently writing in the unstable sand signs which the next tide

would completely erase; a man, in fact, who wasted his
time with utterly worthless activities.

> Mock on, mock on, Voltaire, Rousseau:
> Mock on, mock on; 'tis all in vain!
> You throw the sand against the wind,
> And the wind blows it back again.

> The Atoms of Democritus
> And Newton's particles of light
> Are sands upon the Red-sea shore,
> Where Israel's tents do shine so bright.

In short, the principles of mathematical philosophy,
the discoveries of science, the scientific spirit, the rational
political theories based on them are all worthless, childish, empty. Nothing that can be measured is worth studying and the world of the five senses is merely a dream.

> May god us keep
> From single vision and Newton's sleep.

Blake was not an ignorant and weak-minded babbler;
he understood perfectly the claims and objects of science:
he grasped Newton's significance to the adventures of the
human imagination so thoroughly that Newton became
a character in his mythology; because he knew the attitude which is personified by Newton, he poured abuse
upon his head. Newton measured the stars and regretted
his inability to measure a flower or to state the human
will in terms of mathematical forces. This was sheer
idiocy to Blake, who asked:

How do you know but every Bird that cuts the airy way,
Is an immense world of delight, clos'd by your senses five?

who explained his view of his own mission thus:

I come in self-annihilation and the grandeur of inspiration,
To cast off rational demonstration by faith in the saviour,
To cast off the rotten rags of memory by inspiration,
To cast off Bacon, Locke, and Newton from Albion's cover-
    ing,
To take off his filthy garments and clothe him with imagi-
    nation.

Blake knew perfectly well what enemy he was anxious
to conquer, it was the rational power in man, it was
Newton himself, and at the same time the devil tempting
Jesus in the wilderness:

The spectre like a hoar-frost and a mildew rose over Albion,
Saying I am God, O sons of Men! I am your rational power!
Am I not Bacon, and Newton and Locke who teach humility
    to man?
Who teach doubt and experiment: and my two wings Vol-
    taire, Rousseau.
Where is that friend of sinners? that rebel against my laws?
Who teaches belief to the nations and an unknown eternal
    life.
Come hither into the desert and turn these stones to bread.
Vain foolish man! wilt thou believe without experiment?

And once more:

A mighty spirit leaped from the land of Albion,
Nam'd Newton: he seized the trump and blow'd the enor-
    mous blast!
Yellow as leaves of autumn, the myriads of Angelic hosts
Fell through the wintry skies seeking their graves,
Rattling their hollow bones in howling and lamentation.

All this would have much astonished Newton had he been able to look down from another world through the cogs and gears of his orderly gravitational universe. A madman using his name as a symbol of intellectual blindness! Stranger still, a madman accusing him of irreligion and materialism; him, Newton, who had written long paraphrases of Biblical passages, and elucidated the prophecies of Daniel and the Book of Revelations! Yes, Blake would have replied,

> Both read the Bible day and night,
> But thou readst black where I read white.

Bacon, who said: "All depends on keeping the eye steadily fixed upon the facts of nature, and so receiving their images simply as they are; for God forbid that we should give out a dream of our own imagination for a pattern of the world; rather may he graciously grant to us to write an apocalypse or true vision of the footsteps of the creator imprinted on his creatures"; and Descartes, whose clue to right thinking was doubt of everything that was not self-evident, were the founders or at least the mouthpieces of the adventure of the human imagination which led to such astounding successes in Newton and his compeers. Blake replied to their philosophy that doubt was the devil:

> If the sun and moon should doubt
> They'd immediately go out,

and that as far as science was concerned you can "study science till you are blind."

We can sum up the history of the human imagination between 1400 and 1800 by saying that the unified spirit of humanity represented by the medieval philosopher had been split in two by the lightning of science and become Newton and Blake, two irreconcilable opposites. No longer did research into the unknown lead to the painting of a comprehensive panorama of the universe as a whole. The clearer the picture that Newton painted, the less it showed about the things which interested Blake most. Now we can use Blake's dramatic method of expressing things and say that "Newton" and "Blake" are both states of every human mind; within each one of us is a Newtonian part and a Blakian part; so that we can sum up the result of science on our imagination by saying that it put conflict and contradiction in it, where before had been harmony and peace.

To get to know accurately about life it has become necessary to strip life of all those things that we most like about life. Medievalism offered us an explanation of all in one: God, the sparrow and the stone illuminated and explained one another; but henceforth the more we know of stones and sparrows the less do we know about God, the less does God seem knowable, the less does God seem worth knowing.

There is a passage in Eddington's *Nature of the Physical World* which explains very clearly what happens in the modern picture of the universe. He is describing one of those mathematical problems which are tricked out to sound interesting to the young candidate: " 'An elephant slides down the grassy hillside ——' The experienced candidate knows that he need not pay much attention to this: it is only put in to give an impression of realism. He reads on: 'The mass of the elephant is two tons.' Now we are getting down to business; the elephant fades out of the problem and a mass of two tons takes his place. What exactly is this two tons, the real subject matter of the problem? It refers to some property or condition which we vaguely describe as 'ponderosity' occurring in a particular region of the external world. But we shall not get much further that way; the nature of the external world is inscrutable, and we shall only plunge into a quagmire of indescribables. Never mind what two tons *refers* to; what is it? How has it actually entered in so definite a way into our experience? Two tons *is* the reading of the pointer when the elephant was placed on a weighing machine. Let us pass on. 'The slope of the hill is 60°. Now the hillside fades out of the problem and an angle of 60° takes its place. What is 60°? There is no need to struggle with mystical conceptions of direction; 60° *is* the reading of a plumb line against the divisions of a protractor. Similarly for the other data of the problem. The softly yielding turf on which the elephant slid is replaced by a coefficient of friction —— And so we see that the poetry fades out of the problem, and by the time the serious application of exact science begins we are left with only pointer readings."

Here we have the problem in a nutshell: the modern man differs from the medieval man because his science assures him that two tons of elephant falling down a slope and two tons of roses falling, are the same; or at least that only in so far as they are the same can they be scientifically discussed. Of course other sciences come along and add details to the picture; biology may explain why a rose is not an elephant; psychology will have much to say on why a man feels different when faced with a rose rather than with an elephant. But all the time there is a suspicion that science can see a difference between them only when they have been reduced to different quantities of the same thing: physics says that two tons of roses are the same as two tons of elephant; biology that both are cells made of much the same material but differently arranged; and so with all the other sciences. Man, however, feels that it is the synthesis elephantine or rose that counts.

And so we can be Blake one day and laugh at the fact of the two tons, and Newton another day and ignore the elephant, but we can never reconcile ourselves to the implication that the same thing can be two tons and an elephant at once. Or in general our picture of the universe in terms of measurable things and our picture of the universe in terms of immeasurable qualities never combine into one stereoscopic whole.

The modern man is in a more difficult position than Newton, because Newton came too early to realise what science must finally do to his God. He could worship a *deus ex machina*, he could interpret the prophets and argue about the Trinity, he could even find a place and evidence for God in his own mechanical picture of the universe. But as time went on the cleavage became greater and greater, for science made the medieval idea of God look ridiculous, but the idea of God which it could substitute seemed even more absurd. The next two chapters will show us how this process worked out to its inevitable end.

CHAPTER FIVE

>>>>>>>>>>>>>>>>>>>>>>>><<<<<<<<<<<<<<<<<<<<<<<

Dalton's Dust

§ 1

So FAR we have watched how science has been an adventure of the human spirit in its search for God; that is for a meaning to the universe, which, if possible, can be loved; for that after all is what this eternal search after God really amounts to—the search for a meaning to the universe, which however infinite on its far side, on its near side is capable of arousing and accepting human emotions. We shall leave this major search, this supreme adventure of man's imagination, at a point where it has led to the discovery of a meaning which can be loved as easily as the unknown designer of a super-aeroplane, about whom we know nothing else than that he is an aeroplane designer: if, for example, you can love the person who made the machine which won the Schneider cup race, simply from seeing the race run, then you will be able, probably, to love the Newtonian Meaning of the universe, that is the Newtonian God. We shall turn now for a time to a minor adventure which aimed at accomplishing a less important, but nevertheless very persistent human desire.

Besides wanting God, man has always wanted to know the future, to live for ever in perpetual health and to be fabulously rich. His desire to know the future certainly helped him to learn the true nature of the universe; because the careful watching of night skies by ardent astrologers paved the way for Kepler, Galileo and Newton. Moreover, although astrology failed to tell men how to know what will happen next Wednesday, its natural offspring, astronomy, allows us to know tolerably well what will happen a million years hence.

Yes, the reader will say, but what the astrologer wanted to know when he consulted the stars was what would happen to *him*, while the astronomer has only found out what will happen to the stars. Now this would have seemed an excellent objection to the medieval astrologer, but the modern astronomer would probably reply that we must remember that we and the stars together are but dust, and that what happens to one heap of dust will eventually happen to the other; for we are bound up with the stars as closely as any medievalist ever imagined, but in a totally different way from any he would expect, namely by the material of which our bodies are made being exactly the same as the material to be found blazing in the sun and the distant stars. And so the modern man in his adventure of fixing his own personal place in the universe must consider what the human imagination has discovered about matter, about the stuff out of which he and the stars alike are made. Changing views of matter have meant changing views of God, changing overbeliefs about life as a whole.

Matter to Aristotle was of four kinds, earth, water, air and fire; these were the elements of which the world was made. There were moreover four qualities of matter which between them made up all the differences we see around us between one thing and another: these were hotness, coldness, wetness and dryness. Earth was dry and cold; water cold and wet; air, wet and hot; fire, hot and dry.

In the same way Hippocrates taught that the human body was made up of four kinds of "humour" or moisture: blood, phlegm, black bile and yellow bile. These humours were connected with the elements and qualities, so that blood like fire was hot and dry; phlegm like water was wet and cold; black bile like earth was dry and cold; and yellow bile like air was hot and wet. In each person one or other of these four moistures, elements and pairs of qualities predominated so that some people had a "temperament" in which blood, fire, hot and dry predominated and these were called *sanguine* people; others were *phlegmatic* people; those who had a great deal of black bile were called *melancholy*, from the Greek words for black and bile; and those with a superfluity of yellow bile were *choleric*. To this very day the four words remain to indicate certain types of character, so that though long ago everything that Aristotle taught or Hippocrates taught about elements, qualities, humours, and temperaments has been shown to be false, yet we still bear testimony in our vocabulary to their long reign in our minds. When you say that a person has a sanguine or a jaundiced view of life you show that you were once an Aristotelian. It was not until well into the seventeenth century that these ideas ceased to be acceptable to the human intellect.

Out of these ideas there grew a huge system of knowledge which aimed at healing the human body, conquering death and capturing infinite wealth. Today the human body still needs to be healed, death is still victor and poverty is even more apparent than wealth; yet out of the search have come modern medicine and modern chemistry, capable, the one of reducing pain and sickness to a comparatively low level, the other of doing everything except what was originally desired, namely to turn base metal into gold.

To the medieval mind the four elements, earth, water, air and fire, were not merely the four different sorts of matter out of which the universe and man had been formed; they had been endowed with varying degrees of perfection. Thus earth was not just a thing with the qualities of dryness and coldness, it was also the most ignoble of the elements; and in the same way fire was the noblest. Fire stretched upwards until it met the fifth or super-element of which the heavenly spheres were made. It was more virtuous, more beautiful, more perfect than the other three, in exactly the same way as the circle was more perfect than any other curve and the sphere more perfect than any other solid figure. In short, what the followers of Aristotle took for their guide in their search for the philosopher's stone and the elixir of life was the idea that all forms of matter had "virtues," moral qualities, good or bad, and that, by discovering these, man could achieve perfect youth in a millionaire's paradise. Naturally enough, too, they believed that all these secrets were known in the past and that the key to their rediscovery lay in the books written by the ancient authorities. The older and the more obscure these books were, the better opportunity they gave for learned and voluminous commentaries. Thus, for example, we have the following recipe or prescription for making gold:

"Take of moisture an ounce and a half: of meridional redness, that is the soul of the sun, a fourth part, that is half an ounce; of yellow seyr, likewise half an ounce; and of auripigmentum, a half ounce, making in all three ounces; know that the vine of wise men is extracted in threes, and its wine at last is completed in thirty." Since all this is infinitely vague and some of it, at least, without meaning, book after book was written to explain it by men who would occupy the best part of a life pouring liquids from crucible to crucible; melting one substance; boiling another; driving a third off into vapour; in order to accomplish what this paragraph may or may not have meant; all the time certain in their hearts that sooner or later gold would reward their efforts.

Nor were men like Isaac Newton free from this belief in the possibility of transmuting baser metals into gold, while M. Gros, "a clergyman of Geneva, of the most unexceptionable character, and at the same time a skilful physician and expert chemist," is responsible for the following story, which is typical of thousands of others:[1]

About the year 1650 an unknown Italian came to Geneva and took lodgings at the sign of the Green Cross. After remaining there a day or two, he requested De Luc, the landlord, to procure him a man acquainted with Italian, to accompany him through the town and point out those things which deserved to be examined. De Luc was acquainted with a M. Gros, at that time about twenty years of age, and a student in Geneva, and knowing his proficiency in the Italian language requested him to accompany the stranger. To this proposition he willingly acceded and attended the Italian

[1] I quote from Thomson's *History of Chemistry.*

everywhere for the space of a fortnight. The stranger now began to complain of want of money, which alarmed M. Gros not a little for at that time he was very poor, and he became apprehensive, from the tenour of the stranger's conversation, that he intended to ask a loan of money from him. But instead of this, the Italian asked him if he was acquainted with any goldsmith, whose bellows and other utensils they might be permitted to use, and who would not refuse to supply them with the different articles requisite for a particular process which he wanted to perform. M. Gros named a M. Bureau, to whom the Italian immediately repaired. He readily furnished crucibles, pure tin, quicksilver, and the other things required by the Italian. The goldsmith left his workshop, that the Italian might be under less restraint, leaving M. Gros with one of his own workmen, as an attendant. The Italian put a quantity of tin into one crucible, and a quantity of quicksilver into another. The tin was melted in the fire and the mercury heated. It was then poured into the melted tin, and at the same time a red powder enclosed in wax was projected into the amalgam. An agitation took place, and a great deal of smoke was exhaled from the crucible; but this speedily subsided, and the whole being poured out, formed six heavy ingots, having the colour of gold. The goldsmith was called in by the Italian, and requested to make a rigid examination of the smallest of these ingots. The goldsmith, not content with the touchstone and the application of aqua fortis, exposed the metal on the cupel with lead, and fused it with antimony, but it sustained no loss. He found it possessed of the ductility and the specific gravity of gold; and full of admiration, he exclaimed that he had never worked before upon gold so perfectly pure.

The Italian made him a present of the smallest ingot as a recompense, and then, accompanied by M. Gros he repaired to the mint, where he received from M. Bacuet, the

mint master, a quantity of Spanish gold coin, equal in weight
to the ingots which he had brought. To M. Gros he made a
present of twenty pieces, on account of the attention that
he had paid to him: and, after paying his bill at the inn, he
added fifteen pieces more, to serve to entertain M. Gros and
M. Bureau for some days, and in the mean time he ordered
a supper, that he might, on his return, have the pleasure of
supping with these two gentlemen. He went out, but never
returned, leaving behind him the greatest regret and
admiration.

Such stories abound throughout medieval literature
and far later and they describe clearly the chief incentive
to the study of "matter" in all its forms. Untold wealth
might at any time reward the whole-hearted experi-
menter, who could so avail himself of the natural virtues
of substances as to induce them to yield up gold. Moreover this was but the chief of many prizes, for there lay
hidden in everything gifts to be had for their discovery.
Substances such as precious stones or metals were sought
after not for their rarity, nor for their beauty, but for
their very special virtues whereby they benefited their
possessors. Thus an emerald "if put in drink is suitable
for deadly venoms, and for venomous bites, and punc-
tures of stings. If it be worn it increases substance, causes
persuasiveness in all business; makes men chaste and
cheerful of body and of speech; and helps in tempests.
Also it makes the memory good." Jet "is a boisterous
stone, and nevertheless it is precious. It giveth monition
of them that have fiends within them; and is holden
contrary to fiends; and giveth knowledge of maiden-
head. Also the power thereof is good to feeble teeth and
wagging." And so for all the precious stones and most

other substances to be found on the surface of the earth; all of them are capable of incredible good deeds if treated aright.

Out of this fairyland of magic the human imagination had to produce chemistry and it took a very long time to do. Not until the seventeenth century were the first steps taken, so that for two thousand years after Aristotle matter was as mysterious as any ghost to those who studied her. One picturesque figure facing both ways in this history is worthy to detain us: it is the figure of Philippus Aureolus Theophrastus Paracelsus Bombast ab Hohenheim.

§ 2

In the year 1526 Paracelsus became professor of medicine at the University of Basle in Switzerland. He seems to have had an excellent knowledge of how to gain the attention of his pupils, for he began his lecture course by entering the classroom with a bundle of volumes by Galen and Avicenna and lighting a bonfire with them. The orthodoxy of the Middle Ages went up in smoke and the burning was accompanied by much human thunder: "Me, me you shall follow, you Avicenna, you Galen, you Rhazes, you Montaguana, you Mesue. I shall not follow you, but you shall follow me. Nor shall anyone lurk in the darkest and most remote corner whom the dogs shall not piss upon. I shall be the monarch, the monarchy shall be mine. If I administer, and I bind up your loins, is he with whom you are at present delighted a Cacophrastus?

"What will your opinion be when you see your Cacophrastus constituted the chief of the monarchy? What will you think when you see the sect of Theophrastus leading on a solemn triumph, if I make you pass under the yoke of my philosophy? your Pliny will you call Cacopliny, and your Aristotle Cacoaristotle? If I use their writings and your Porphyry, Albertus and the rest as toilet paper?"

It did not mean very much, and what meaning it had was in very poor taste, but the students loved it and soon the lectures were attended by hundreds fascinated by the medical Billy Sunday of the sixteenth century. He taught them things he had learned in a life of wandering in Spain, Portugal, England, Prussia, Lithuania, Poland, Pannonia, Wallachia, Transylvania, Croatia, Illyricum, not merely from medical men but from surgeons, barbers, old women, magicians and chemists. He preferred to be drunk rather than sober, always used the wrong word if it would make his sense more mysterious, and referred to God as his instructor and inspirer upon all occasions. Indeed according to him God and the Cabala were the sole sources of medical knowledge.

Paracelsus scouted Galen and even denied what had scarcely been denied before, the four elements of Empedocles which, as we have seen, were the basis of all medieval learning. This destructive criticism is sufficient to establish his importance in spite of the oddness of what he put in the place of the orthodox knowledge of his time. He taught that there were five causes of disease; the first was the influence of the stars, some of which sulphurised the atmosphere, while others made it arsenical, saline or mercurial. The arsenic gave people diseases of the blood, the mercury pains in the head, while bitter

stars caused fevers. The second cause was digestive poisoning; in the stomach of every man lived a demon called
Archæus, responsible for correct digestion and the chief
cause of health and disease. To be a good doctor was
little more than to be on good terms with this demon.
When Archæus did his work badly the chemicals which
ought to escape from the body, as mercury through the
skin, white sulphur through the nose, arsenic through
the ears, etc., remained congealed within. The other
causes were natural, spiritual and Christian and were as
obscure as the first two.

To Paracelsus chemistry and medicine were still what
we should call today magic; that is, the actions and
reactions of substances upon one another, which he expected, in no way followed the natural laws which we
have since discovered to lie at the basis of true knowledge.
"The Cabala," says Thomson in his *History of Chemistry*,
"constantly directs Paracelsus in his therapeutics and
materia medica. As all terrestrial things have their image
in the region of the stars, and as diseases depend also on
the influence of the stars, we have nothing more to do,
in order to obtain a certain cure for these diseases than
to discover, by means of the Cabala, the harmony of the
constellations.

"Gold is a specific against all diseases of the heart, because, in the mystic sense, it is in harmony with that
viscus. The liquor of the moon and crystal cure the
diseases of the brain. The liquor alkahest and cheiri are
efficacious against those of the liver. When we employ
vegetable substances, we must consider their harmony
with the constellations, and their magical harmony with
the parts of the body and the diseases, each star drawing,

by a sort of magical virtue, the plant for which it has an affinity. So that plants are a kind of sublunary stars.

"To discover the virtues of plants we must study their anatomy and cheiromancy; for the leaves are their hands, and the lines observable on them enable us to appreciate the virtues which they possess. Thus the anatomy of the chelidonium shows us that it is a remedy for jaundice. These are the celebrated signatures by means of which we deduce the virtues of vegetables, and the medicines of analogy which they present in relation to their form. Medicines, like women, are known by the forms they affect. He who calls in question this principle, accuses the Divinity of falsehood, the infinite wisdom of whom has contrived these external characters to bring the study of them more upon a level with the weakness of the human understanding. On the corolla of the euphrasia there is a black dot; from this we may conclude that it furnishes an excellent remedy against all diseases of the eye. The lizard has the colour of malignant ulcers, and of the carbuncle; this points out the efficacy which that animal possesses as a remedy."

Such was the typical attitude of a man of science in the sixteenth century to the matter of which all things are made. Paracelsus was more advanced than his predecessors for he denied that the proper aim of chemistry was to transmute the elements into gold, and taught that it was in the production of medicines that the chemist must find his true labour. For centuries horrible concoctions were poured down the throats of countless invalids; some few cured, some killed, the majority merely acted as emetics, or did nothing at all; the invalids died and were no more seen; but out of the infinite experiments real facts began to be collected. Slowly it became evident that the old underlying ideas—stellar influence, signatures and so forth—were quite unreal and new ideas came to take their place. Paracelsus the bombastic, the charlatan, the drunkard, symbolised in his life the earlier stages of chemistry; but the later stages needed a very different life to symbolise them: a staid, Quakerly, colour-blind life like that of John Dalton, to whom the search illustrated by Paracelsus eventually leads us.

§ 3

Though characters like Paracelsus are undoubtedly attractive, human progress required that chemists and their ideas about matter should sober down somewhat, before a reasonable body of truth could be accumulated from the chaos of medieval laboratories. The life of Dalton beautifully symbolises the coming of this sobriety.

A Quaker, living in the greyness of Cumberland, his temperament was peculiarly fitted to do the necessary work. An early incident in his life concerns a pair of stockings. They were displayed in a window at Kendal and labelled "silk and newest fashion." He bought them as a birthday present for his mother, who received them with a surprise which was perplexing to her son. "Thou has bought me," she said, "a pair of grand hose, John, but what made thee fancy such a bright colour? Why I can never show myself at Meeting in them." To John these stockings seemed to be dark bluish drab in colour and so they did to his brother, but reference to a neighbour bore out his mother's assertion that they were "as red as a cherry."

In this way Dalton discovered that he was colour-blind and it led to his contributing his first paper to the Literary and Philosophical Society of Manchester in 1794 on "Extraordinary facts relating to the Vision of Colours: with Observations by Mr. John Dalton." Incidentally this was the first occasion upon which the quite common condition of colour-blindness received scientific consideration.

We need not follow Dalton along this line of his researches however; suffice it to say that the period of chemistry during which his figure was one of the greatest can be called in comparison with what went before and what was to come after, the colour-blind period of man's adventures with the nature of matter. It was a peculiarly virtuous period; from the libertine Paracelsus through the puritan Dalton to the spiritual passion of today, that is the progress of chemistry. First chemistry sowed its wild oats, then it learned some lessons, took some hard knocks, sobered down and finally embarked upon the imaginative adventure which is still going on at this moment.

Just as Paracelsus was exactly the right character to look for extraordinary medicines and to stir cauldrons as weird as any Macbeth saw, so Dalton was just the character to contribute the discipline which the human mind needed at a certain period of its evolution. Miss Johns of Manchester, lifelong friend of the great man, gives us the perfect description:

The doctor's habits for life [she says] were so uniform and unvaried as to be soon related. On Sundays he always dressed himself with the most scrupulous attention to neatness, attended public worship twice—except when indisposed, or on very particular occasions, which however, the writer does not remember to have occurred a dozen times in all during his life—dined with his friend Mr. Thomas Hoyle, printer of Mayfield, and, returning home to tea, spent the evening in his philosophical pursuits. His dress was that usually worn by the Quakers, avoiding, however, the extreme of formality, and always of the finest texture; hat, gloves, gaiters, and even a handsome cane to correspond. In his general intercourse, also, he never adopted their peculiar phraseology. With respect to his religious principles, I should be disposed to think that he had never made theology properly so called, a study. He certainly never mentioned having done so; but his reverence for the great Author of all things was deep and sincere, as also for the Scriptures, in which His revealed will is expressed. When the occasion called for it, I have heard him express his sense of the duty and propriety of the religious observance of Sunday, and also his serious disapprobation of its violation. Although frequently solicited, he refused all invitations to dine out on that day, except a very few times at Dr. Henry's, and once or twice elsewhere, when, as he observed to me, he was asked to meet a very distinguished professor whom he should otherwise have missed the opportunity of seeing. But when the same friend, presuming upon his former compliance, again invited him on that day he received a refusal which prevented any further application. His week-days—every day, and all day long— were spent in his laboratory, with the exception of Thursday afternoons, when he accompanied a party of friends about three miles into the country to bowl, and entered into the amusement with a zest infinitely amusing to all who were present. He also spent a few minutes, generally between light and dark, at the Portico, in reading the daily papers. He rose about eight in the morning, always lighted his laboratory fire before breakfast, after which meal

he finished his toilet and repaired to his laboratory, which
he seldom left until dinner. He dined at one, but always
came in in much haste when dinner was partly over—I
suppose to save time. He ate moderately, and drank only
water. He was obliged to eat very slowly on account of the
conformation of his throat, which was very narrow. After
dinner he always spent about a quarter, rarely half an hour,
in chatting with the different members of the family, or any
visitor, or in looking over any chance publication lying on
the table. After spending the afternoon in his laboratory, he
drank tea at five, rarely coming in until the family had finished. He was very methodical in the quantity he took at
meals. After tea, to his laboratory again, where he staid until
nine, (supper time), when he regularly shut up for the night,
ate a light supper, generally of meat and potatoes, until about
his sixtieth year, when he changed this for meal porridge,
with milk or treacle, or occasionally a couple of eggs. After
supper we all sat together, and generally had a nice chat,
for which the labours of the day had excellently prepared
us all; and I will venture to say that few firesides have ever
presented a scene of more innocent and pleasant recreation
than did ours during these the busy years of our life. The
doctor took little part in the conversation, though he showed
that he listened by frequently smiling, and now and then
uttering some dry, laconic witticism in reference to what was
passing. He and my father smoked their pipes unremittingly.
Not unfrequently we were joined by two or three political
friends, who talked over the news of the times, etc. The
doctor enjoyed their society, but took little part in the conversation, in politics none whatever, nor for years had we any
idea what his views on the subject were (Conservative).
Occasionally he took the chief part in the conversation; but
this only when we were quite alone, or when Mr. Ewart
stepped in, as he sometimes did. He and the doctor had a

great esteem for each other, which lasted through life. When, however, this gentleman was our visitor, the evening seldom ended without my father and he getting deep into meta-physics—a favourite study with both. The doctor generally listened intently, but, from an occasional ironical smile, I used to suspect that he thought it mostly 'vain wisdom all and false philosophy.' My sister Catherine's wit and animated nonsense were, I fancy, more to his taste. When we had no company we always withdrew before eleven, when the doctor pursued his meditations for nearly an hour longer, and then, having perambulated the lower part of the house to see that all fires were out, he himself went to bed, and by midnight all were at rest."

If we add to this description, a portion of one of Dalton's own letters, we shall have a sufficient picture of his peculiarly simple nature.

Methinks, [he wrote one day] there may be a question started from some side of the fire when this is read "I wonder whether John is going to marry yet or not?" I may answer that my head is too full of triangles, chymical processes, and electrical experiments etc., to think much of marriage. I must not, however, omit to mention that I was completely Sir Roger de Coverleyed a few weeks ago.

The occasion was this: Being desired to call upon a widow—a Friend, who thought of entering her son at the academy—I went, and was struck by the sight of the most perfect figure that ever human eyes beheld, in a plain but neat dress; her person, her features, were engaging beyond all description. Upon enquiry after, I found she was univer-sally allowed to be the handsomest woman in Manchester. Being invited by her to tea a few days after, along with a worthy man here, a public Friend, I should in any other circumstances have been highly pleased with an elegant tea

"*Tycho Brahe spent most of his life recording the exact position in the sky of the planets and the stars, hour by hour, night after night; indeed he did very little else; and yet Tycho was one of the men who are directly responsible, though he had no idea of it himself, for building up the modern man's idea of God.*" (See p. 124.)

equipage, American apples of the most delicious flavour, and choice wines; but in the present, these were only *secondary* objects. Deeming myself, however, fully proof against *mere beauty*, and knowing that its concomitants are often ignorance and vanity, I was not under much apprehension. But she began to descant upon the excellence of an exact acquaintance with English grammar and the art of letter writing; to compare the merits of Johnson's and Sheridan's dictionaries; to converse upon the use of dephlogisticated marine acid in bleaching; upon the effects of opium upon the animal system, etc., etc. I was no longer able to hold out, but surrendered at discretion. During my *captivity* which lasted about a week, I lost my appetite, and had other symptoms of *bondage* about me, as incoherent discourse etc., but now have happily regained my freedom. Having now wrote till I have tired my hand, and probably thine eyes in reading, I shall conclude with my love to Cousin Ruth and thyself and to all enquiring friends.

Dalton is of interest to us not merely as an important figure in the history of our general subject, but as a type of scientist. Probably it is because of the Daltons that the idea of the dry-as-dust scientist has become so popular; and certainly his life was largely uneventful and his adventures entirely those of the mind. But if we could enter into the feelings of such a man we should find them just as colourful, just as exciting as those of any artist in the Latin Quarter. The varieties of religious, æsthetic, emotional experience are legion, and the calm andantino of a Dalton is not only as exciting to its owner as anyone else's scherzo, but it is as valuable to the whole progress of the human imaginative adventure. If we do not envy the possessor of such a life, it is probably because we do not know the delights it really contained.

§ 4

It was Boyle who began the new period of our picture of matter by destroying for ever the old idea of the four elements. In his book *The Sceptical Chymist*, published in 1661, he made an entirely new definition of an element, as that substance which cannot be decomposed into anything else. Hitherto besides the four elements with which we are already familiar, most orthodox opinion held that everything was made of Salt, Sulphur and Mercury; Boyle attacked this and called the experiments which were used to prove it worthless and meaningless. He saw that there must be many more elements than were so far supposed; and imagined that these were made up of different kinds of particles or atoms, although nobody could show them by experiment.

Stated like this it is hard to see that in Boyle's new principles there lies an important revolution of ideas; that the new picture of the universe inherent in them was of a nature to produce new overbeliefs, founded by the emotions on a new intellectual conception of matter.

Indeed there was not enough in Boyle's work, true and far-reaching as it was, to capture the human imagination at once. It was forgotten, therefore, and for nearly a hundred years hardly influenced the world of science even, let alone the larger world which uses scientific discoveries for its own emotional purposes. Instead, an attractive theory of matter, containing in it something of the magical attitude of the Middle Ages dominated men's minds. It owed its popularity to the fact that of all the properties of matter none is so spectacular, so capable of moving the emotions and stimulating the imagination as the property of burning.

To the Middle Ages fire seemed the most perfect element; and, for long after, it remained the most fascinating. A flash of light, a brilliant flame, the transformation of a substance to dust and ashes: what an astounding event is this! Is it surprising that the dull theory of Boyle, "untroubled by a spark" in more senses than one, was forgotten in the face of a theory which saw in every substance an imprisoned soul, as it were, ready to break out and mount to heaven as a flame? The phlogiston theory was that every particle of matter consisted of water, acid or earth combined with "phlogiston," the spirit of combustion, which was liberated by the act of burning.

George Ernest Stahl is the chief name associated with the phlogiston theory, and it is interesting to note that, at the same time, he held a medical theory of disease of a very special kind: "he resolved," says Thomson, "all diseases into the actions of the *soul*, which was not merely the former of the body, but its ruler and regulator. When any of the functions are deranged, the soul exerts itself to restore them again to their healthy state; and she accomplishes this by what in common language is called disease. The business of a medical man, then, is not to prevent diseases, or to stop them short when they appear; because they are the efforts of the soul, the *vis medicatrix naturae,* to restore the deranged state of the functions." Now if we found beliefs such as this expressed among primitive people by medicine men or magicians we should call them examples of "lower animism" and, emotionally at least, we can say that until well on in the eighteenth century chemistry and medicine were both in the animistic stage; for in the mind of a man like Stahl a "soul" controlled the functions of the body, and another kind of soul called phlogiston controlled the functions of inanimate things. It was by the destruction of the theory of phlogiston that the "materialist" point of view really began, as we shall see.

Stahl was met with a considerable difficulty in his advocacy of phlogiston by the fact that when, for example, tin was heated sufficiently, the residue, instead of weighing less as might have been expected, actually proved to weigh more. Boyle thought that this meant that to the tin had been added another substance, *heat*, which therefore, he said, was shown to have weight; now if this was so how could one say that the tin after being heated had *lost phlogiston*, in which case it ought certainly to weigh less and not more? Ah, said Stahl, the tin has really lost phlogiston, for just as other substances have weight, phlogiston has levity and any substance deprived of it will in consequence weigh more! Such an idea, although accepted by the phlogistic school, was so absurd that it could hardly have persisted had it not been that chemical balances were very rarely used in experiments in those days, so that the fact that substances increase in weight after burning did not force itself upon human attention.

A hundred years later, at the time of the French Revolution, Antoine Laurent Lavoisier wrote of Stahl and his school that "chemists have turned phlogiston into a vague principle, which consequently adapts itself to all the explanations for which it may be required. Sometimes this principle has weight and sometimes it has not: sometimes it is free fire and sometimes it is fire combined with the earthy element; sometimes it passes through the pores of vessels, sometimes these are impervious to it; it explains both causticity and non-causticity, transparency and opacity, colours and their absence; it is a veritable Proteus changing in form at each instant." It was Lavoisier who destroyed for ever the mystical phlogistic theory and supplied a principle, lacking to Boyle's philosophy, capable of reacting on the human imagination to alter overbeliefs and modify religious feeling.

Lavoisier influenced the modern man's outlook on life as a whole and helped to prevent him ever again being a medievalist; and this is how he did it. He took phosphorus and burned it in air standing over mercury in such a way that he could measure the amount of phosphorus burned and the amount of air in which it was burned. He discovered that the phosphorus would burn for a time and then go out; if the air was confined in a bell-jar so that no other air could get in only a certain amount of phosphorus burned and no more. If he measured the air at the moment that the burning ceased he found that one-fifth of the air had disappeared. In the place of the burnt phosphorus there was some white solid matter which weighed almost exactly as much as the original phophorus plus the air which had disappeared. It is an experiment with which today every well-educated child is familiar; nevertheless it alters the whole picture of the universe and marks a stage in the progress of man's imaginative adventure with life. For from it there follows the great law of the conservation of mass.

Matter, whatever it is, can neither be created nor destroyed by man or nature: there is as much matter today as there was a million years ago and as there will be a million years hence. Nothing that man can do can alter this; he can rearrange but that is all. If we could collect together all the air which has entered a man's lungs and all the food which has entered his stomach and add their weight to his weight at birth and take away from the result all the weight of the CO_2 he has breathed out and the waste and other products he has excreted and secreted, we have the exact weight of the man today. Furthermore we could label each atom in his body with its original habitat in field and sky before it became a part of him. A man is merely a rearrangement of the atoms which happen to have passed into his mouth. Sooner or later the human imagination was bound to translate such a fact about matter into terms such as this: "there are in the universe a certain exact number of atoms which theoretically can be counted: there are N atoms, and there never can be $N + 1$ or $N - 1$. These atoms are constantly rearranging themselves and one of their rearrangements has produced me and all other human beings. Sooner or later they will rearrange themselves again to such an extent that I and my fellow men will have ceased to exist, in any recognisable form." Faced with such a picture of the universe as this, how could humanity have the same outlook on life, the same religion, after as before? I do not suggest that the effect upon men's overbelief is logically necessary, nor that every chemist since Lavoisier has been a materialist in the Victorian sense; but when this piece of man's picture of the universe was fitted into other pieces of a like complexion, the result was inevitably a definite type of outlook on life different from the medieval or even the Newtonian. The reign of the measurable was enlarged and the immeasurable almost ceased to exist. And now what was this "matter," indestructible and finite in quantity, of which both man and the universe were but arrangements? That is where Dalton comes in. The idea of atoms or particles of matter so small that they could be no smaller had long been familiar to scientific men. Newton fitted it in perfectly to his science and his theology. "It seems probable to me," he said, "that God in the beginning formed matter in solid, massy, hard, impenetrable, moveable particles, of such sizes and figures, and with such other properties, and in such proportion, as most conduced to the end for which He formed them; and that these primitive particles, being solids, are incomparably harder than any porous bodies composed of them; even so very hard as never to wear or break in pieces, no ordinary power being able to divide what God himself made one in the first creation. While particles continue entire they may compose bodies of one and the same nature and texture in all ages; but should they wear away, or break in pieces, the nature of things depending on them would be changed. Water and earth composed of old worn particles and fragments would not be of the same nature and texture with water and earth composed of entire particles in the beginning. And therefore, that nature may be lasting, the changes of corporeal things are to be placed only in the various situations, and new associations and motions of these permanent particles, compound bodies being apt to break, not in the midst of solid particles, but where those particles are laid together and only touch at a few points. . . . God is able to create particles of matter of several sizes and figures, and in several proportions to the space they occupy, and perhaps of different densities and forces. . . . At least I see nothing of contradiction in all this. . . . Now, by the help of these principles, all material things seem to have been composed of the hard and solid particles above mentioned—variously associated, in the first creation, by the counsel of an intelligent agent."

This theory as expressed by Newton can be called a *theological* atomic theory: that is, it is deduced from certain principles which Newton believed to be true about God as a workman. If we read it carefully we see that Newton thought he knew more about God than he did about the nature of matter. He argued from the known to the unknown, and in this case, this means from God to matter. In short, Newton was a medievalist in this sentence and might almost have been called a pupil of Aristotle. If we had nothing of Newton except this fragment, we would find it hard to say within five hundred years when he had lived.

Dalton by putting precisely the same theory in a different form, by testing it practically and making successful prophecies about it, and without ever mentioning in any step of his argument the nature of God or the method of his creating, took the step from theology to chemistry. It was the same gift to the sum total of human intellectual experience as Galileo's, when by dropping weights from the Tower of Pisa, he made such things as the effect of gravity upon mass no longer part of theology, but of mechanics instead.

Dalton knew that for generations people had believed that all matter was composed of invisible particles. Were all these particles exactly alike? People had suggested that it was so, and certainly the idea was attractive:

one would almost expect God to use only one basic material for his creation. "I believe in one God and one matter," is a very natural sort of creed. Some people, including Newton, did not believe this; they felt that God had used several ingredients and mixed them all up together. "I should apprehend," said Dalton, "that there are a considerable number of what may properly be called elementary principles, which never can be metamorphosed into one another by any power we can control." How were these elements different from one another? It was by answering this question that Dalton laid the foundation of modern chemistry. Their *weights* were different. He did not of course say how much the infinitely minute atom of oxygen, let us say, actually weighed; but he did say that it weighed a certain number of times as much as hydrogen. And so with the other elements; if experiment showed that a substance was a compound containing oxygen and one other element, then the relative weight of the unknown element could be added to the table which began with hydrogen and oxygen; and so on, until a table of atomic weights had been constructed. This table is of vast practical value, for it tells the chemist the quantity of various elements required to make various substances, and also it gives him an exact knowledge of the exact number of different things of which the universe is made. The answer is that the universe is made of ninety-two materials of which two are at present, in 1930, still unknown. When we consider Lavoisier's indestructibility of matter and Dalton's proof that this indestructible matter consists of ninety-two different kinds of dust; a picture very different from the earlier pictures of the universe seems to result.

Of course if human beings were reasonable and altogether deprived of emotional interferences with reason, all that would have happened would have been a realisation that humanity was a few steps further towards knowing everything; but that is not how mankind behaves. Chemistry was discovering not merely new things, but depressing new things.

Suppose we had been born into a world where there were no flowers, but only toadstools and fungi: we should have got along very well, not only practically but æsthetically. But suppose that next spring instead of bluebells and primroses and green things generally, nothing but brown and grey fungi came out of the earth: we should die of various diseases due to dietary deficiencies, but before we became ill we should be willing to die, because of the drab unbeautiful earth in which we had suddenly been doomed to live. So with Dalton's dust: coming as it did to take the place of charming and attractive visions of the nature of matter, it cast a gloom upon humanity. It is of no use saying that this gloom was unscientific, that it had nothing to do with chemistry: it had everything to do with chemistry and science in general, because it was an emotional overbelief based upon a scientific picture of the universe. By the Victorian epoch, thanks largely to chemistry, "materialism" had become a word as charged with unpleasant feelings, as "hell" had ever been; it could be used, this one word "materialism," to upset people, to raise opposition to scientific research, to force men back against the barbaric doctrines of the Middle Ages. Try to think of what the word "materialist" means today *emotionally* when instead of ninety-two different kinds of dusty dust matter is thought of in terms too subtle for thought; and compare the result with the emotion which must come if instead of this you remember that you are but dust, in Dalton's sense—but that belongs to a later chapter. It is amusing to think how surprised the Quaker, John Dalton, would have been if he could know the uses for his atomic weights which were to be found later by the village atheists of the 1880's.

CHAPTER SIX

>>>>>>>>>>>>>>>>>>>>>><<<<<<<<<<<<<<<<<<<<

Darwin and Evolution

§ 1

WE COME now to the climax of our story. Science the measurer and leveller is to lay its hand not on the sun, nor on the dust beneath our feet, but upon man. The whole trend of thought for centuries has been to reduce the universe and all it contains to machines, to slaves beneath unalterable laws. Little by little everything has fallen before the new way of approaching the universe; the great adventure of the human imagination which consisted in trying to measure everything, to find a mathematical formula for the atom and the star, has been marvellously successful and only one thing seems to stand out against the inexorable process, man himself, lord of creation. Surely no science can measure man! Human prejudice revolts against the idea!

We must remember that there was a time when every breath of wind, every setting of a star, every hatching of an egg seemed to be the result of the direct use of God's guiding hand: "are not two sparrows sold for a farthing? and," said Jesus, "one of them shall not fall to the ground without your father. But the very hairs of your head are numbered." It had been very comfortable to feel this in spite of the fact that the guiding hand as often as not seemed to prefer to let people stumble; and now science had slowly built up a picture of the universe wherein God had done absolutely nothing since he first made the vast machine. But there was a limit to what could be machinery: man at any rate was not a cog-wheel, or a grease spot on a cog-wheel; he was something different and all but atheists knew how to prove it; in the Bible one text seemed a sufficient bulwark, the wall of a city of refuge, from which it would be sacrilege to try and abduct the human form divine: "and the Lord God formed man of the dust of the ground, and breathed into his nostrils the breath of life; and man became a living soul." In short, man was a special creation and in him supernatural forces daily worked their influence, even though all the rest of nature must be handed over to the blindness of natural law. This text could be taken to mean that however mechanical the universe, man was an exception: whereas all else must move and behave blindly in accordance with fixed laws, he could think for himself, and even when he had to obey laws it was only after giving them the consent and approval of a free will. Whereas a planet must move in an ellipse and only in an ellipse, man could choose between alternatives. Moreover it was unthinkable that this thing called man could possibly be made of anything so indescribably dusty as Dalton's dust. The difference between clay and a clay pot is that the latter has significant form; some celestial potter had evidently given even Dalton's dust a form, which made it something very different from a mere part of Newton's machine.

The machine, men felt, had been made first of all; and then God made man, a living soul, to use and enjoy

215

it. Man and his universe were even more different from
one another than were a monkey and its cage at the Zoo.

The great quarrel which arose in the nineteenth century and which seems not to have died down even now
in the less civilised parts of the world was focused upon
the question of biological evolution; but at bottom it
amounted to a dispute as to whether there were any
limits as to what scientists might study. Must they content
themselves with everything but man, and even then pay
attention to the fragmentary ideas about the universe
preserved in certain ancient Hebrew writings? Must they
leave man, his origin and his destiny, to the theologians?
Huxley has stated the matter once and for all when he
says: "I had set out on a journey with no other purpose
than that of exploring a certain province of natural
knowledge; I strayed no hair's breadth from the course
which it was my right and my duty to pursue; and yet I
found that whatever route I took, before long, I came
to a tall and formidable looking fence. Confident as I
might be in the existence of an ancient and indefeasible
right of way, before me stood the thorny barrier with its
comminatory notice board—'No Thoroughfare—By Order
—Moses.' There seemed no way over; nor did the pros-
pect of creeping around, as I saw some do, attract me.
True there was no longer any cause to fear the spring
guns and man traps set by former lords of the manor;
but one is apt to get very dirty going on all fours."
Everybody knows where this quarrel led: however, it will
not concern us very deeply here, since its details are
common property.

Nor will it be necessary to describe in detail what the
theory of evolution is: the modern man cannot begin

to understand his own position until he knows a good deal about it, but fortunately innumerable simple books exist for his full enlightenment. Hitherto the obscurity which hangs about so much of our subject matter, the ignorance which most people permit themselves about Newton or Galileo, or cosmogony in general, has forced us to dwell on the content of scientific discovery; since Darwin's contributions are better known we may concentrate upon another side of the drama, namely, the way in which scientific discovery is made. Not only is evolution vital to the modern man's search for religion, but much elucidation will be found by following the steps by which the idea found entry into the human imagination. Fortunately we know a great deal about this.

The man around whom the tempest was to rage was twenty-two at the time when we must first observe him; he was on a walking tour with Sedgwick, clergyman and geologist, and he told him one evening how a workman had shown him a tropical fossil shell said to have been found in a gravel pit near Shrewsbury. To his surprise Sedgwick was not at all pleased and said that if this discovery had really been made it would overthrow all that was known about the geological history of that part of the world. The shell must have got there by accident, he added, and this indeed was the case. Darwin was at first surprised but, as he wrote later, "nothing before had ever made me thoroughly realise, though I had read various scientific books, that science consists in grouping facts so that general laws or conclusions may be drawn from them," for Sedgwick's objection to the shell was that it was an isolated fact completely at variance with every other known fact. The incident is worth remembering, for Darwin was about to transform man's picture of the universe quite as much as Galileo did, simply by collecting and grouping multitudes of facts "so that general laws or conclusions may be drawn from them."

On his return from the walking tour he found a letter saying that a Captain Fitzroy about to command a scientific expedition in H.M.S. *Beagle* would give up part of his cabin to a young man who would go without pay as ship's naturalist. The position had been offered to a clergyman, Jenyns, but as he had two livings he had refused it at the very last moment after his bags were packed; another man, Henslow, had decided to go but his wife on hearing of it "looked so miserable" that at once he changed his mind and determined to stop at home. Would Darwin go? Darwin's father was consulted and was utterly opposed to the idea: "My father's objections," wrote Darwin, "are these: the unfitting me to settle down as a clergyman . . ." But Darwin's father was reasonable: "If you can find any man of common sense who advises you to go I will give my consent."

Next day uncle Josiah Wedgwood heard about it: "my father always maintained that he was the most sensible man in the world"; Josiah thought it was a very good chance and not to be missed; "I should not think," he said, "that it would be in any way disreputable to his character as a clergyman. I should on the contrary think the offer honourable to him; and the pursuit of Natural History, though certainly not professional is very suitable to a clergyman." So it was settled that Darwin was to go, and yet one thing very nearly kept him at home—the shape of his nose. Captain Fitzroy had read some treatises on physiognomy and believed himself able to

After a design by Blake. "*The search which in the early days with Kepler had accepted the sun as the centre of the universe because it fitted so well the idea of God as a morning bright Apollo, culminated with Newton seeing him as a super-professor of mechanics, almost worse still . . . a superannuated mechanic.*" (See p. 170.)

judge all character from the face and he did not like the shape of Darwin's nose. Long afterwards he confessed that he had nearly refused to have the young man on this account. Thus Josiah Wedgwood and his nephew's nose were two important factors not in the discovery of evolution, of course, but in the choice of the discoverer. For the progress of human imagination was ripe for the discovery, and the voyage of the *Beagle* put it into Darwin's hands. "The Voyage of the Beagle," wrote Darwin later, "has been by far the most important event in my life: and has determined my whole career; yet it depended on so small a circumstance as my uncle offering to drive me thirty miles to Shrewsbury, which few uncles would have done, and on such a trifle as the shape of my nose. I have always felt that I owe to the voyage the first real training or education of my mind."

§ 2

Once more we see how in any scientific discovery there is the attractive element of accident. Galileo made himself a telescope and looked at Jupiter; then a day later, "guided by I know not what fate," he looked at Jupiter again. He might never have done so, yet only by so doing did he discover that little moons were circling round Jupiter, and thereby get a hint of the real nature of the universe. It is the same sort of story as the old one about Archimedes: he got into his bath and happened to notice that when his body was in it the water spilt over. The simple fact explained the problem he was trying to solve and in his excitement he forgot to put on his clothes before running down the street to his study. It is the same with Newton if he ever did see the apple fall; a happy accident touched a spring and all the ideas and facts in his head began to arrange themselves in orderly array and the secret so long searched for was discovered. Dalton bought scarlet stockings and discovered colour-blindness. We shall see shortly that accidents seem to play a big part in Darwin's framing of the hypothesis of evolution.

Yet this idea of accidents is offensive to the human intelligence, neither is it really a true picture of reality; for though lucky chances single out the man into whose lap the ripe fruit falls, yet we may be quite sure that the fruit would have fallen in any case, though perhaps into another's lap. It is the human imagination which unwraps knowledge, and the individual imagination is purely accidental. Only in the case of a few very great discoveries, perhaps only in the case of Newton and gravitation, does the individual genius so leave its mark on the picture of the universe which results, that we may feel that had the discovery been made by another the road taken by science might have been different; though even then it would have eventually led us to the same place.

In fact Darwin's uncle did not give the world evolution, he merely gave evolution to Darwin; even if Darwin had never used those years of seasickness to gather his vast store of facts, the human imagination could not have failed to stumble on evolution within a very few years. For biological evolution was only the last stage in a series of ideas which was much in the air at the time.

To the modern man it is difficult to put himself in a frame of mind in which evolution has no place: I do not mean that it is hard to eliminate the idea that man is descended from an ape-like animal ancestor, for the idea of evolution goes infinitely deeper than that; the idea of evolution is in fact the idea that orderly change from one form and shape to another is the law of both life and matter: and this idea was already beginning to dominate man's picture of the universe at this time.

Consider for a moment Newton's picture of the universe: it is one of law and machinery but not of change. To Newton the first creation consisted in God constructing things more or less as they are now; with a push of his hand he set the planets going, having at the same time given them the law of gravitation as a guide; and from then until now and on to the Last Judgement no change, save for a stray comet needing to be checked like dust in the works of a watch, could or would happen to the eternal machine. To Newton the proof of God's existence amounted to the necessity of some one starting what we see now. Long before Darwin's day all this had begun to change.

The first sketch of the new picture which Darwin was to complete was the nebular theory of Laplace. This theory threw away the whole idea of a stable machine and suggested that the sun, the planets and their moons, instead of being at the beginning as they are now, were all of them parts of one great cloud of incandescent gas, spinning round and wobbling as it went. In course of time the wobble increased until the cloud broke up into lesser clouds which after ages cooled down to the solid earth and other planets revolving round the still gaseous sun. Such a picture at once destroyed Newton's picture of God as a super-watchmaker: the wheels and parts of the watch had made themselves out of a primordial mist, and the need of God was once more put back further countless millions of years.

It is worth remembering that Laplace was the first of the greater scientists who, in constructing his picture of the universe, was not moved or actuated by any desire to find a place for God in it. With the Nebular Hypothesis the "conflict between science and religion" took a new turn, for the research which with Copernicus and Kepler had begun with the very object of discovering more about God by learning more about the universe, had ended by discovering a universe which could get on very well without any god at all. God is always a mixture of law and love: science had found enough and to spare of the element of law but could give no evidence of the love, so that unless a man had the type of mind which could worship the law of gravitation he had finally to abandon any hope that science would give him anything to worship at all. Of course you could admire the god which presumably was needed to form the original nebula; but you could not really love him; he had ceased to do anything at all so long ago.

In short, the reasons given by Newton for believing in the necessity of a god disappeared when Laplace so signally altered the picture of the universe, and many people refused therefore to accept the nebular hypothesis on what were really theological grounds. Thus as late as 1855 Sir David Brewster, the biographer of Newton, commenting on his letters to Bentley which we have already quoted, says: "In the present day they possess a peculiar interest. They show that the nebular hypothesis, the dull and dangerous heresy of the age, is incompatible with the established laws of the material universe, and that an omnipotent arm was required to give the planets their positions and motions in space, and a presiding intelligence to assign to them the different functions they had to perform." In short, since Laplace upsets the need of God implicit in Newton, let us not examine his theories scientifically but stick to Newton's theology!

On the other hand, men like Whewell accepted the theory and pushed back the moment when God last intervened in the universe a few million years. Even if Newton was wrong in supposing that the motions and forms of the planets required a god to produce them, and even if these followed naturally from the constitution and habit of a vast cloud of gas, without divine intervention, who made the gas? Thus God became the original superintendent of an infinitely distant gasworks. No wonder the god of natural theology became unpopular and what made things worse was that Laplace and his kind did not seem to care. I think it was this which began the gathering storms later to break over biological evolution.

The next step in the establishment of change as a principle governing the universe was the foundation of modern geology. Indeed the position of chief devil in the fundamentalist's demonology today occupied by Darwin was for long occupied by the great geologist Charles Lyall, against whom every sort of abuse was launched. It is quite clear why a new spirit entered into such disputes at this time, for with science coming down from the stars and other realms of mathematical physics to the rocks beneath our feet. its arguments and results became intelligible and disturbing to anyone who could read. Whereas a mere handful of erudite persons could understand Galileo, Newton or Laplace, anyone who could read a cheap tract could discuss fossils and Noah and the testimony of the rocks.

Arguments between theology and science began to assume a vulgar tone for they began to be carried on not by philosophers but by people who certainly had no valid grounds for a tenth of what they believed about theology or science, who believed even the right things for the wrong reasons. In the turmoil which resulted people tried to prove from science what no scientist would dream of attempting to prove, and from theology what any medieval schoolman could have refuted mercilessly. The arguments between the village atheist and the village fundamentalist did as much violence to the dignity of the human mind as the treatment of Galileo by the Inquisition. Fortunately we need not waste our time with these disputes, but may hurry back to the youthful Darwin and to the evolution of a great scientific discovery.

§ 3

Darwin went on board the *Beagle* and spent some years collecting and making notes. The long hours of solitude gave him every opportunity of digesting everything that he saw and he came back home a changed man, or at least a developed one. "During the voyage of the Beagle," he tells us, "I had been deeply impressed by discovering in the Pampean formation great fossil animals covered with armour like that on existing armadillos; secondly, by the manner in which closely allied animals replace one another in proceeding southwards over the continent;

and thirdly, by the South American character of most of the productions of the Galapagos archipelago, and more especially by the manner in which they differ slightly on each island in the group; none of the islands appearing to be very ancient in the geological sense.

"It was evident that such facts as these, as well as many others, could only be explained on the supposition that species gradually became modified; and the subject haunted me. But it was equally evident that neither the action of the surrounding conditions, nor the will of the organisms, (especially in the case of plants) could account for the innumerable cases in which organisms of every kind are beautifully adapted to their habits of life—for instance a woodpecker or a tree frog to climb trees, or a seed for dispersal by hooks or plumes. I had always been much struck by such adaptations, and until these could be explained it seemed to me almost useless to endeavour to prove by indirect evidence that species have been modified.

"After my return to England it appeared to me that by following the example of Lyall in Geology, and by collecting all facts which bore in any way on the variation of animals and plants under domestication and nature, some light might perhaps be thrown on the whole subject. My first note book was opened in July 1837. I worked on true Baconian principles, and without any theory collected facts on a wholesale scale, more especially with respect to domesticated productions, by printed enquiries, by conversation with skilful breeders and gardeners, and by extensive reading—I soon perceived that selection was the keystone of man's success in making useful races of animals and plants. But how selection could be applied to organisms living in a state of nature remained for some time a mystery to me.

"In October 1838, that is fifteen months after I had begun my systematic enquiry, I happened to read for amusement 'Malthus on Population' and being well prepared to appreciate the struggle for existence which everywhere goes on from long continued observation of the habits of animals and plants, it at once struck me that under these circumstances favourable variations would tend to be preserved and unfavourable ones to be destroyed. The result of this would be the formation of new species. Here then I had at last got a theory by which to work; but I was so anxious to avoid prejudice, that I determined not for some time to write even the briefest sketch of it.

"In June 1842 I first allowed myself the satisfaction of writing a very brief abstract of my theory in pencil in 35 pages; and this was enlarged during the summer of 1844 into one of 230 pages which I had fairly copied out and still possess.

"But at that time I overlooked one problem of great importance, and it is astonishing to me, except on the principle of Columbus and his egg, how I could have overlooked it and its solution. This problem is the tendency in organic beings descended from the same stock to diverge in character as they become modified. That they have diverged greatly is obvious from the manner in which species of all kinds can be classed under genera, genera under families, families under sub-orders and so forth; and I can remember the very spot in the road,

whilst in my carriage, when to my joy the solution occurred to me. The solution, as I believe, is that the modified offspring of all dominant and increasing forms tend
to become adapted to many and highly diversified places
in the economy of nature."

Such is the method whereby the *Origin of Species*
came to be written. We see a combination of years of
diligence with moments of inspiration; the facts collected
over long periods suddenly fall into order when *Malthus
on Population* is read. The hidden meaning flashes out
of the obscurity in the midst of a drive in a carriage. It
would seem that every scientific advance comes in this
way; that to a disciplined mind, painstaking and observant, must be added moments which are uncommonly
like the moments of illumination experienced by a mystic.
At least nobody can explain what happened to Darwin
in his carriage, nor to Newton in his orchard; all we
know is that a flash takes place and the night of ignorance
is lit up.

Another statement of Darwin's methods of work is of
great interest: "I had, also," he tells us, "during many
years followed a golden rule, namely, that whenever a
published fact, a new observation or thought came across
me, which was opposed to my general results, to make
a memorandum of it without fail and at once; for I had
found by experience that such facts and thoughts were
far more apt to escape from the memory than favourable
ones. Owing to this habit, very few objections were raised
against my views which I had not at least noticed and
attempted to answer." It is doubtful whether many fundamentalists can claim such honesty of method as this.

§ 4

Now while Darwin was thus elaborating a theory which was to revolutionize the world, Alfred Russel Wallace, a naturalist who had studied and collected in the Malays and elsewhere, was discovering precisely the same theory. Long afterwards he too described how he had come to think out the general ideas of evolution and natural selection. "The idea came to me," he said, "as it had come to Darwin, in a sudden flash of insight: it was thought out in a few hours—was written down with such a sketch of its various applications and developments as occurred to me at the moment—then copied out on thin letter paper and sent off to Darwin—all within a week. I was then the 'young man in a hurry'; he, the painstaking and patient student, seeking ever the full demonstration of the truth that he had discovered, rather than to achieve immediate personal fame."

Wallace in 1908 was still alive to attend a celebration held in honour of the fiftieth anniversary of the joint discovery of evolution by himself and Darwin and we are able once more to get first-hand evidence of how the great revolution in thought came to birth. He described what he thought were some of the reasons why Darwin and he had been led along the same lines to the same result.

"On a careful consideration," he said, "we find a curious series of correspondences, both in mind and in environment, which led Darwin and myself, alone among our contemporaries, to reach identically the same theory.

"First (and most important as I believe) in early life

both Darwin and myself became ardent beetle hunters. Now there is certainly no group of organisms that so impress the collector by the almost infinite number of its specific forms, the endless modifications of structure, shape, colour, and surface markings, that distinguish them from each other, and their innumerable adaptations to diverse environments . . .

"Again, both Darwin and myself had what he terms, 'the mere passion of collecting'—not that of studying the minutiae of structure, either internal or external. I should describe it rather as an intense interest in the mere variety of living things . . .

"Now it is this superficial and almost child-like interest in the outward forms of living things, which, though often despised as unscientific, happened to be *the only one* which would lead us towards a solution of the problem of species . . .

"Then a little later (and with both of us almost accidentally) we became travellers, collectors, and observers, in some of the richest and most interesting portions of the earth; and we thus had forced upon our attention all the strange phenomena of local and geographical distribution, with the numerous problems to which they give rise. Thenceforward our interest in the great mystery of *how* species came into existence was intensified, and—to use Darwin's expression—'haunted us.'

"Finally both Darwin and myself, at the critical period when our minds were freshly stored with a considerable body of personal observation and reflection bearing upon the problem to be solved, had our attention directed to the system of positive checks as expounded by Malthus in his Principles of Population. The effect of this was analogous to that of friction upon the specially prepared match, producing that flash of insight which led us immediately to the simple but universal law of the 'survival of the fittest,' as the long sought *effective* cause of the continuous modification and adaptation of living things. It is an important detail that Darwin read this book *two years after* his return from his voyage, while I had read it *before* I went abroad, and it was a sudden recollection of its teachings that caused the solution to flash upon me.

"I attach much importance, however, to the large amount of solitude we both enjoyed during our travels, which, at the most impressionable period of our lives, gave us ample time for reflection on the phenomena we were daily observing."

We have in these extracts from Charles Darwin and Alfred Russel Wallace a picture which the modern man will do very well to consider deeply. These two men were the vehicles whereby mankind's idea of God and the universe was utterly altered; and how did they come to do this? by studying beetles and reading *Malthus on Population*! Probably the reader regarded my statement that what Forel has to tell us about ants is necessary for our true knowledge of God as paradoxical and flippant and yet who shall say that Darwin's study of beetles has not changed humanity's picture of both the universe and its creator!

§ 5

But the beetles could not have accomplished this un-aided; and to understand why Darwinism was so successful we must look not at Darwin but the world around him. The reason why the hypothesis of evolution became at once so supremely important to the human imagination was that it offered a way out of the evil residue left by the picture of the universe which preceded it. It was not indeed the scientific side of evolution which mattered, it was the overbelief which it made possible. That is why the modern man should ponder well the whole episode of the rise of Darwinism.

Let us turn to the last chapter of the *Origin of Species*; in it Darwin allows himself to speculate over wider fields than usual: "As all the living forms of life," he writes, "are the lineal descendants of those which lived long before the Cambrian epoch, we may feel certain that the ordinary succession by generation has never once been broken, and that no cataclysm has desolated the whole world. Hence we may look with some confidence to a secure future of great length. And as natural selection works solely by and for the good of each being, *all corporeal and mental endowments will tend to progress towards perfection.*

"It is interesting to contemplate a tangled bank, clothed with many plants of many kinds, with birds singing in the bushes, with various insects flitting about, and with worms crawling through the damp earth, and to reflect that these elaborately constructed forms, so different from each other, and dependent upon each other in so complex a manner, have all been produced by laws acting around us. . . . Thus from the war of nature, from famine and death, the most exalted object which we are capable of conceiving, namely the production of the higher animals, directly follows. There is a grandeur in this view of life, with its several powers, having been originally breathed by the Creator into a few forms or into one; and that, whilst this planet has gone cycling on according to the fixed law of gravity, from so simple a beginning endless forms most beautiful and most wonderful have been, *and are being evolved*."

Twenty-two years later Darwin wrote the last words of his second great book and as he completed his survey of the *Descent of Man* exclaimed: "man must be excused for feeling some pride at having risen, though not through his own exertions, to the very summit of the organic scale; and the fact of his having thus risen, instead of having been aboriginally placed there, may give him hope for a still higher destiny in the distant future." Now if we observe the effect of such an attitude, such an over-belief, on the one hand upon the Sedgwick, who years ago had given Darwin his first glimpse of scientific method, and on the other upon a group of eminent Victorians, who achieved high merit in many directions, we shall see very clearly how Darwinism affected an epoch.

The Reverend Adam Sedgwick, Woodwardian Professor of Geology in the University of Cambridge and, as we know, one of Darwin's earliest friends, wrote to him to thank him for a copy of the *Origin of Species*: "lastly then," he concluded his letter, "I greatly dislike the concluding chapter—not as a summary, for in that light it appears good—but I dislike it from the tone of triumphant confidence in which you appeal to the rising generation and prophesy of things not yet in the womb of time, nor, if we are to trust the accumulated experience of human sense and the inferences of its logic, ever likely to be found anywhere but in the fertile womb of man's imagination. And now to say a word about a son of a monkey and an old friend of yours—I find by the loss of activity and memory, and of all productive powers, that my bodily frame is sinking slowly towards the earth. But I have visions of the future. They are as much a part of myself as my stomach and my heart, and these visions are to have their antitype in solid fruition of what is best and greatest. But on one condition only— that I humbly accept God's revelation of Himself both in His works and in His word, and do my best in conformity with that knowledge which He only can give me, and He only can sustain me in doing. If you and I do this, we shall meet in heaven."

And then, on the other hand, let us look at the group of young men who were growing up at the same University of Cambridge while Sedgwick was still an honoured lecturer: the picture is given us by Sir Frederick Pollock. "For two or three years the knot of Cambridge friends of whom Clifford was the leading spirit were carried away by a wave of Darwinian enthusiasm: we seemed to ride triumphant on an ocean of new life and boundless possibilities. Natural Selection was to be the master key of the universe; we expected it to solve all riddles and reconcile all contradictions. Among other things it was to give us a new system of ethics, combining the exactness of the utilitarian with the poetical ideals of the transcendentalists. We were not only to believe joyfully in the survival of the fittest, but to take an active and conscious part in making ourselves fitter. At one time Clifford held that it was worth our while to practise variation of set purpose; not only to avoid being the slaves of custom, but to eschew fixed habits of every kind, and to try the greatest possible number of experiments in living to increase the chances of a really valuable one occurring and being selected for preservation. . . . One practical deduction was that education ought to be directed not to mere instruction, but to making people think and act for themselves; and this Clifford held to be of special importance in the case of women, where cultivation of independent power is too commonly neglected or even purposely discouraged."

At once we see that the assiduous studying of beetles and the fortuitous reading of Malthus has led to the launching of an overbelief repulsive to all those who had lived content with the previously potent overbelief and intoxicating to the young who found in it tangibility and inspiration, qualities of which generations of sleek country livings and the comfortable orthodoxy of the industrial golden age had deprived the older overbeliefs.

Here was something to make life worth living, something altogether more exhilarating than the overbeliefs nurtured by Newtonian mechanical universes, which changelessness loaded with debility and dullness. So long as man and his moods stood outside the picture of the universe to which science had been forced, it was only possible to satisfy the human imagination by keeping beliefs in watertight compartments: now by including man as a cog in the universal machine unity of thought was once more obtainable. True, there were still metaphysical problems as to who made the first nebula, but by simply saying that such things could not be known owing to the nature of the human mind, all other knowledge, emotions, desires could be explained and contained in one formula. Why do we smile? Because of the survival value of a smile. Why do we love beautiful things? Because we see in them things of use in helping us to survive. Why should we try to be good? Because a need to be good, that is to preserve the race future, must exist in any being that has survived. Anything could be put into the formula. Let us not believe in God, seeing that our children will be godlike! Why worry about immortality since our descendants will be perfect and we shall live in them! The continuity of the germplasm was a far better immortality than sitting by a sea of glass twanging a harp.

Even intelligent people like Freud have said that the Darwinian hypothesis was a "trauma" or wound in the imagination of man, that the realisation that he was but an animal hurt man's feelings unbearably: but that is only half the story. It is perfectly true that orthodox men like Sedgwick felt it as an attack upon all they held most dear, and an attempt to overthrow religion; but to the young, the hungry sheep who looked up and were not fed by the current acquisitive, materialistic churches it was a religion in itself.

It came at a time when the natural moral sensibilities of the best in humanity had so grown and progressed that the very ideas of orthodoxy seemed immoral. The idea of a creator who had created all this misery when he might very well have refrained; who had stood by while the serpent tempted Eve, and thereby loaded all mankind for ever with a burden of original sin; who could then think of no better way of neutralizing this sin than by allowing his own son to become a blood sacrifice; who apparently prolonged the existence of this "vale of tears," when at any moment he could bring it to an end; who surrounded human beings with beautiful temptations and punished them if they found the lilies and languors of virtue "not nearly so nice" as the roses and raptures of vice:—this idea could not possibly move any enlightened young man, for it contained neither poetry nor sense.

It is vain to say both that science has nothing to do with such things and that to describe the central doctrines of Christianity in such terms is next door to blasphemy. A Newman or a Manning, a schoolman or a mystic might very well weave these doctrines into a satisfying, if misty, picture, but to the plain man not afraid of thinking for himself, they seemed to be precisely as we have stated them above. Stripped of traditional methods of rousing emotion nothing but an animal fear of the unknown could prevent orthodoxy appearing like this.

Moreover, the young man with a social conscience saw all about him the churches neglecting to protest against social wrong and failing to provide the wealthy with a conscience or the oppressed with a weapon; failing to justify the ways of God to man. In short, though the study of beetles and the reading of Malthus was in a sense the immediate cause, the general cause of the undoing of orthodoxy was its own failure to stand for what was best in the heart of man.

You had to be sufficiently young to accept the change; even a professional rebel like Carlyle, himself the enemy of orthodoxy, was incapable of understanding the meaning of the new picture of the universe: "A good sort of man is this Darwin," he wrote, "and well meaning, but with very little intellect. Ah it's a sad terrible thing to see nigh a whole generation of men and women, professing to be cultivated, looking around in a purblind fashion and finding no God in the universe. I suppose it is a reaction from the reign of cant and hollow pretence, professing to believe what in fact they do not believe. And this is what we have got to. All things from frog spawn: the gospel of dirt the order of the day. The older I grow—and I now stand upon the brink of eternity —the more comes back to me the sentence in the Catechism which I learned when a child, and the fuller and deeper its meaning becomes, 'What is the chief end of man? To glorify God, and enjoy him for ever.' No gospel of dirt, teaching that men have descended from frogs through monkeys, can ever set that aside."

"An ocean of new life and boundless possibilities"— "the gospel of dirt"; one and the same piece of patient scientific research seemed both these things according to the human mind by which it was absorbed. Darwin at once became Antichrist or the giver of a new religion; however much he would have preferred it, never for a moment could he remain a mere entomologist and biologist. No one indeed was more surprised than himself: "I am bewildered," he wrote to the great American botanist, Asa Gray, "I had no intention to write atheistically. But I own that I cannot see as plainly as others do, and as I should wish to do, evidence of design and beneficence on all sides of us. There seems to me too much misery in the world. I cannot persuade myself that a beneficent and omnipotent God would have designedly created the ichneumonidæ with the express intention of their feeding within the living bodies of caterpillars, or that a cat should play with mice. Not believing this, I see no necessity in the belief that the eye was expressly designed."

§ 6

The modern man will do well to examine this remark of Darwin's with more than a passing glance; for in it lies one of the chief secrets about the religion of Darwinism and about the way in which a picture of the universe inevitably affects human ideas of God and religion. He is attacking the chief argument which men have always gleaned from the universe as proof of its creation by a beneficent creator. The argument from design is older than Christianity and it was used extensively by the early Christian fathers. Lactantius, for example, proves God's existence from the shape of the human intestines: "the manifold coils also of the intestines and their length rolled together on themselves, and yet fastened with one band, are a wonderful work of God. . . . It is also a most skilful arrangement, that the bladder which birds do not use, . . . is nevertheless filled and distended with moisture." All sacred literature is full of descriptions of how all nature is a store and larder constructed and stocked for man's use by an all-wise universal provider. Bunyan tells us that God tempers the wind to the shorn lamb; and by noting all the pleasant things in nature a very pretty picture can be drawn of loving-kindness shaping the round world and all that is therein.

But, says Darwin, let us be honest and omit nothing from our survey: consider the ichneumonoidea. These little flies busily seek out the well-fed caterpillars of various butterflies and moths; choosing a victim they sting it, not to death, but to general paralysis; so shooting their darts of poison that each penetrates a nervous centre and in this way they transform the beast into a larder of fresh, because still living, meat, on which their own young may feed. The ichneumon's eggs laid within this helpless caterpillar hatch out and munch their way through the fat tissues, until a dozen little flies emerge from an otherwise empty skin.

Now a religious ichneumon fly has in its life story a most powerful argument from design for the existence of a benevolent creator. "What!" it might say to an infidel fly, "you do not believe in a benevolent God, you to whom He has given a wise mother with great anatomical knowledge to enable her to sting without killing a juicy caterpillar, to whom He has then given this unfailing larder of living flesh, which has been your comfort and stay through youth to maturity; away with you and your gospel of dirt and do not corrupt your fellow flies with such infidelity."

Now the ichneumon infidel would have had no real reply, but we human beings know that the first difficulty about the argument from design is that the benevolent creator of the ichneumons must also be the benevolent creator of the caterpillars; for a god that is god of the one without being god of the other is altogether too partial for human worship or respect.

Moreover, if Darwinism had penetrated into the insect world we can be very sure that it would not have been accepted by the ichneumons, who would remain very well content with the argument from design for the existence of a benevolent creator, but that the caterpillars would have accepted it as an explanation and as a promise of help. "Evolution has put you in your present plight, evolution alone will free you from it: for by enabling you to develop some sort of immunity from the bites of ichneumons, it will fit you to survive." A philosophic caterpillar might go even further; "the argument from design is good enough for the ichneumon," he would teach, "and, rightly from his own point of view, he wishes to impose it on us; it is his weapon to keep us in a place suitable for his own convenience. But we can have no part in the ichneumon's religion, we must be caterpillar-conscious and develop through Darwinism our own philosophy of life and of the universe." What to the ichneumon would seem a "gospel of dirt," to the caterpillar would become "an ocean of new life and boundless possibilities." And though we have no knowledge of Darwinism ever penetrating to the insect world, this is an exact picture of what did happen in the world of human beings, where ichneumons and caterpillars are also to be found.

At least so it seemed to those human beings who in this bisection of humanity felt themselves to be caterpillars. And who were these? The vast army of workers owning nothing but their own children; living in the ghastly conditions of industrial towns; producing a constantly increasing stream of wealth, without ever themselves becoming any more secure or leisured. Just as certainly as communism and socialism, in their present forms, are due to Marx, so is Marxism the direct result of Darwinism. It was largely because an ever-increasing body of humanity had been placed by the industrial revolution in an unsatisfactory position that Darwinism triumphed over the older religion: for Darwinism gave these men a picture of the universe in which there was hope.

Of course this is only one episode, though perhaps the most important, in the evolution of Darwinism from a mere picture of the universe to a religion, and before we trace it a little further we must consider what we have seen so far from the point of view of the modern man in search of a religion. That all attitudes towards life are dependent upon knowledge of the universe has been shown abundantly in our story; but there is another element that is emerging now. Science, beginning as a search after God, has achieved several revolutions in the intelligent man's religion but in every case a little thought suggests to us that the revolution only takes place in the direction where there is already a need for it. In other words scientific discovery can only influence man's imagination in the way that mankind happens to desire at the moment. When the scientific discovery does not bear on any human spiritual needs it just remains a scientific discovery of interest to scientists but ignored by human beings in general. Indeed a scientific picture of the universe only succeeds in getting recognition if the times are ripe for it.

Let us consider once again Copernicus and his theory that the sun, not the earth, is the centre of the planetary system. We have already seen that the idea would never have occurred to Copernicus had it not given him a more æsthetically satisfying picture of God, a picture of a god capable of running the moving spheres by using more economical means than the god of Ptolemy: but why was it possible for intelligent human beings to accept or at least to imagine that such a picture of the universe with the earth tucked away in a corner could be true? It was largely because the economic evolution of society had reached a stage when such a point of view was no longer without its counterparts in human experience.

For hundreds of years all men had felt that to be in the centre of the universe was the only credible thing. Moreover Europe was the centre of the world, Rome the centre of Europe, and present-day Rome the centre of Rome's history. In short, the idea of centrehood was a fixed, unalterable idea in man's mind, very much like a dimension, a thing woven inextricably into the very stuff of thought. Not to be centrally placed was as unthinkable as to be suspended six feet above the ground and to walk on air. And so the various people who had from time to time suggested that the earth was not the centre of the universe had not produced a storm of interest and abuse: their whims had died from general neglect.

But by the time of Copernicus things had changed in many ways. An age of successful exploration and adventure had unveiled America and Africa and left Europe but a patch upon a vastly extended globe: no longer was the Mediterranean the central sea, for the epoch of the Atlantic was fairly begun and with this, centrehood clearly began to be shaken. And then the Renaissance had opened up the learning and romance of the past making the present seem but a point at the end of the long line of history; a line moreover wherein the most exciting point seemed to be a distant golden age long gone by. The Reformation too had brought into being centres of religious thought and general culture which challenged the centrality of Rome, while the break-down of the medieval world state into the rudiments of modern nations also helped to reduce the feeling of centrehood in men's minds. Now when a flight of imagination is too long to be taken by human beings they can be most easily helped by analogies; these shiftings of Europe, Rome, the present, from their former central positions were the analogies which made the greater imaginative flight possible, so that men were able to approach the idea of the earth's banishment without doing violence to their feeling of what was inevitable in thought and reality.

Let us now turn to the Newtonian picture of the universe: it too was fairly smothered with overbeliefs in conformity with the needs of the age. Just as the economic development of the world in Copernicus' day had begun to remove from men's minds the incubus of centrehood; so in Newton's day the economic development seized with avidity the picture of his efficient, business-like God. The world in general was not in a fit state for mysticism; business organisation, commercial expansion, merchandise and banking; these were the things coming into existence in the eighteenth century. You could not have started a crusade to capture the Holy Sepulchre in those days and such a crusade was the last thing Newton's God would ever have desired, and that was precisely why Newton's God was fitting for the age. Again the economic evolution of humanity had something to do with the scientific picture of the universe which became popular.

We must remember that it is not in the least true to suppose that these overbeliefs directly follow from the scientific discoveries, or that Newton or Copernicus believed in or approved the overbeliefs which finally sprouted from the seed they had planted. The great scien-

tific genius makes his discovery, gives it to the world and
the world shapes it anew into the picture which best
serves its purpose. Scientific truth has really little to do
with it, compared with human emotion. It is human
emotion that pays the piper and therefore calls the tune.
Moreover, this is as it should be for science was made for
man, not man for science.

§ 7

Let us now get back to the place from which we set
out and consider what we have learned about it. We
pictured a modern man faced with the inevitable necessity of defining for himself his attitude towards life and
the universe, in brief, his religion. To achieve a satisfying work he must, so we said, know what science is and
what science has discovered, for a man's view of the
universe is dependent on his knowledge of the universe.
We brushed aside the excuse that life is too short and too
full for the ordinary man to learn anything about the
universe and asserted that if this was so then the ordinary
man should have no time to believe. We suggested also
that the ordinary idea of the relations between science
and religion was too simple to be accurate; that scientific
labours have always begun as religious quests so that if
mankind had never had a religious itch there would
never have been any science. We have seen that these
religious quests along scientific lines have always aimed
at the satisfying of human desires, the desire to know
God, to have long life, to be fabulously rich, to know
the future, to live for ever; that without these desires
there would never have been the motive power needed

for such prolonged exercise of reason, such ascetic devotion to the pursuit of knowledge. Moreover, we have seen that although these human desires have never been satisfied by science, science is nevertheless no failure, for it has brought other gifts in their place. Particularly strange has been its dealing with the human desire to know God for it has constantly discovered new gods, while thinking to increase knowledge of the old, and this has led to conflicts with orthodox religion at each succeeding stage, a conflict, it should be remembered between new and old ideas of god, and not between god and godlessness. All this our history has to some small extent illustrated, until it has established in our reader's mind, we hope, the idea of science and of its importance to his personal search laid down in the beginning.

Let the reader, taking heart from memories of his being an intelligent man in 1543 and 1643, imagine himself in his study upon the night when the nineteenth century was breathing its last. The spectral tarsier, the simian ape-man, the savage, the medievalist, the Copernican, the Newtonian contemplates his new form in the looking-glass of his age.

The Victorian epoch is at its height, though the good Queen herself will not long survive the dying century. Unknown to him and to most of the world Einstein was just coming to the end of his schooling at Zurich, where he had had to support himself while he worked. M. Becquerel, four years before, had made a certain lucky discovery, to be mentioned later; and Rutherford had not yet used it to revolutionise science. Freud had five years ago published certain studies of hysteria and had since begun to work out a new therapeutic. Max Planck was just beginning to formulate a theory to be published a year later. But all these things were hidden entirely from the imagination of man, from you as you sat in your study watching 1900 die and thinking of the crowd of people, mostly Scotch, standing outside St. Paul's to greet the new-born century.

What has science done to you and to your picture of the universe in the four hundred and fifty odd years since you fingered the works of Copernicus and Vesalius?

1. First, it has altered the shape of your universe from a series of spheres, the outside ones eternal and unchanging, to a vast space full of galaxies and stretching to vast distances in all directions. In a few years' time you will come to realise that the size of this new universe is such that it takes light 140,000,000 years to get across from one side to the other. This changed opinion, or, if you prefer it, better knowledge about the shape of the universe is especially important because it does away with certain theories you held four hundred years ago about the "perfectness" of its shape; and also because, though its confines are far larger, there is no place left in it which by reason of its changelessness and perfection is fit for you to pass an immortal future existence. Whatever immortality you may imagine for yourself will take place outside, and not inside, not only time, but space.

2. You have altered your mind about the sort of laws this universe obeys: you once imagined each planet, for example, ruled by its private angel; now you see that a few laws quite simple to express in formulæ account for everything that goes on in the sky above. In fact instead of requiring wisdom and conscious will to direct them, the heavens are directed by unconscious necessary rules;

they are not parts of God's body, nor momentarily directed by his mind, but part of a machine which goes mechanically.

3. You have realised that the qualities which you attributed to parts of the universe were non-existent: that to call water better than earth and less noble than air was meaningless. Instead of perfection and imperfection, nobility and baseness, goodness and badness, you must catalogue the parts of the universe by such things as weight, size, velocity: ethical ideas must be given up for a tape measure, and the scales of justice are less useful than those of an apothecary.

4. For a time you were content with a picture of the universe as a machine, once made, perpetually going; but of late you have recognised that change is one of the chief rules of nature. Whatever your idea of creation, it is quite clear that the parts of the universe were not created exactly as they are today, but that they have evolved by just as mechanical a set of laws as those which rule over their motion, out of simpler stuff.

5. These changes have profoundly altered your idea of the relationship existing between you and the universe. To begin with you do not think that it exists chiefly for you yourself. The whole argument from design has disappeared; the universe is a machine which will grind you at last to dust. You are yourself a piece of the machine which will one day be worn out. Once you thought that the stars had secrets about your own affairs which wisdom could discover, that a flower had a purpose and a use for human beings; now you know that if no human being had ever existed there would be just as many stars and flowers, that one day, in all probability, the universe will

exist without human beings and be completely unaware of their non-existence. In short, that the universe has no purpose whatever, from the human or any other point of view, is the overwhelming fact which you pretend to accept with equanimity.

6. So too with your ideas of the relationship between the universe and God. Once you thought that God had his finger in every pie, that he directed every sunrise and every eclipse. But science has shown conclusively that the last time his presence could possibly have been felt in the universe was in nebular days, multimillions of years ago. Since then nothing at all has happened—except possibly a few miracles already jeopardised by higher criticism—beyond what can be explained by natural law. God and the universe have for all practical purposes parted company.

7. Four hundred and fifty years of science have played havoc with your idea of the relationship between God and yourself. Then you lived in a world in which everything that happened was supernatural, or in other words in which God was immanent and all-present. Now you live in a world where nothing at all is supernatural, where God is all-absent. You can choose several gods, all of them unsatisfactory, a god who made the nebula and then went to sleep, a god who deliberately sets traps to mislead all intelligent people, a god made by the human imagination and evolving as humanity evolves, a god which is a personification of what men mean by good. As none of these gods are of the slightest use to the human imagination, you prefer to reject the idea of God altogether as being unnecessary to your picture of the universe. This leaves you as part of a creation created

for no purpose by nothing, and if such a position seems displeasing to you in your weaker moments, you explain that the ideas of creator, purpose, and the rest are drawn from human experience and constitute an infirmity or limitation of the human mind just as centrehood did in the medieval mind.

Or you reject science as a means of knowing anything at all about God and return to older methods; but if you do this you run the risk of constant trouble and probably end by denying the efficacy of science even in its own sphere.

8. A very powerful element in your picture of life comes from the change which science has induced in your idea of the stuff out of which all things are made. Four hundred and fifty years ago you thought of matter as being of four kinds: earth, water, air and fire; and you believed that these four had all sorts of powers and virtues and qualities. Enthusiastically you worked upon them to discover the philosopher's stone and all you did discover was about ninety different kinds of dust. A curiously futile discovery it seemed to be, for in science numbers usually mean something and why did God choose to make his universe of ninety materials?

Now if the medieval idea of matter had still persisted something of the sting might have been taken out of the idea of materialism; it would have been quite bearable to discover that one was made of nothing but dust, but Dalton's dust—that was quite another thing. There is no doubt that the horror with which some people regarded the ideas which they massed together and called materialism, was due to a genteel loathing of common mud and also to the singularly unromantic texture of these ninety elements. If people had said that we were nothing but electricity it would not have sounded half so bad. There is a depressing feeling in the idea that one is nothing but what is scraped off one's boots after a country walk, which particularly upsets the people who reiterate Sunday after Sunday the petition, "Lord, remember that we are but dust"; it is not so depressing to be told that one is nothing but a flash of lightning reverberating through the alleys of eternity: yet the philosophic implications are much the same.

9. The ideas of biological evolution accepted by the mid-nineteenth century have strengthened your newer feelings in all these directions and bound you more tightly to dust and annihilation, at the same time they have banished the careful hand of a paternal god to an even remoter lobby in the halls of time. They have finally annihilated childish dreams about your own future, and they have substituted a dream of a better future for which you can strive, though you will never share it. Energetically and with only the slightest quaver in your voice you proclaim this as a satisfactory view of life and at any rate you refuse to be a coward and fly in the face of irreducible facts. Man is dust and just one whim of a change-loving but meaningless universe.

10. Immortality you have renounced, but not wholeheartedly. You will live again in your children, or in the effects of everything you do, or in the leaves of some second-rate book you have written, or as an atom in the immortal race. The race-future has become a sort of fetish by 1900: just as people denied themselves all sorts of excellent things for a satisfactory life after death, so now they begin to offer human sacrifice to the race-future. You

Blake's "Portrait of Sir Isaac Newton". "Newton measured the stars and regretted his inability to measure a flower or to state the human will in terms of mathematical forces. This was sheer idiocy to Blake. . ." (See p. 181.)

are facing both ways with your double mind in this matter: one half renouncing immortality with fine frenzy for truth, the other half determinedly hanging on to its ghost and proclaiming a vicarious, metaphorical and futile immortality of one sort or another. And all this definitely brought about by the picture of the universe in which you believe. Four hundred and fifty years ago you assumed God and immortality, today you assume a meaningless universe and annihilation. And you pretend too that you like it.

11. But you have learned several invaluable lessons: you have learned, for instance, that wisdom lies in the future rather than in the past. At the same time you must confess that there was a general feeling in the air that most of what is really worth knowing was discovered by about 1885 and that nothing was left but to fill in a few details here and there. You felt quite sure that the search for God was over and that nothing could very much alter the final picture of the universe that you saw about you. Dust was dust, thought was dust, mind was dust; and all that having been satisfactorily settled did it matter very much what sort of dust they were?

It was this feeling that the universe had been found out that produced the atmosphere of decadence which pervaded the civilised world, then *fin-de-siècle,* which inspired poets with all the inspiration of boredom. One of the chief lessons of these four centuries, that wisdom lies in the future, was in danger of being forgotten owing to the very success of science.

12. Another lesson you had learned was to believe your senses and not authority; and never to reason too many steps without making a few observations as well. You

were quite convinced that the limit to possible knowledge was set by the powers of observation possessed by your senses; and since very little remained for you to see, smell, hear or feel it seemed obvious that the limit was approaching. It was of course the most important lesson you could learn, to trust in your senses rather than in Aristotle; but you did not realise that while you were thinking of the dying century new sciences were being born to deal with things no man could ever see or hear; that the senses would be left far behind in the course of a few years. Ignorant of this the knowable universe seemed bound by your senses and if it gave you claustrophobia to be shut into such a narrow space, so much the worse for your nerves.

13. Finally you had made a decision typical of your age about the most important difficulty encountered by science in its long search for God. Descartes had been one of the first people to face the difficulty. The picture of the universe which science was revealing was clearly too restricted to satisfy human emotions, for nearly everything that we love or hate is immeasurable and science was drawing a picture of an altogether measurable universe. How was this insufficiency to be avoided? Descartes did it by imagining two universes, one measurable, with lengths and breadths and speeds and masses; the other without any of these things, a universe of thought without extension in space. It was an excellent theory and has given philosophers ever since plenty to argue about, since it became necessary to explain how these two universes influenced one another, and what their relationships might be.

Now Spencer simply cut the knot: there were certain

things which could be known and measured—far more than Descartes ever guessed of course—and there were certain things that could not be measured or known; because the human mind could not know them by reason of its very construction. With these last things therefore nobody in their senses should concern themselves. Such an attitude left a perfect, though dusty universe, nicely poised on nothing; rather like a motor boat would be on the moon where there is no water on which it could sail. You would be able to understand all the parts of the motor boat, every nut, screw, plank, wheel, but you could not understand the motor boat as a whole. And what is more, according to Spencer you ought not to want to understand it.

And yet this attitude was the right one; for Descartes's dual way of looking at the universe can only be a temporary expedient: sooner or later we must find a way of seeing the universe singly. But as science in 1900 insisted that mind was nothing but measurable matter thrown in almost as an afterthought late in the evolution of the world, it did not seem easy to fit everything into such a scheme.

§ 8

Such a picture of the universe, such an outlook upon life, was the direct result of about five hundred years of scientific search after God. The search had begun by assuming God's existence and had reached the stage of denying it. That nine out of every ten intelligent men had ceased to believe in a personal deity or personal immortality was the last thing that Galileo, Newton or even Darwin would have expected from their labours: but it was the direct result of the picture drawn by their labours: a universe of Dalton's dust cooling and dying; man the product of blind forces, not so much the goal of evolution as the thing which had not chanced to become obsolete.

In considering this picture there is one thing we should not forget, namely, that the object of drawing such pictures at all is to satisfy human emotions. Returning to our description of the human spirit as having a Newton-part and a Blake-part, we may say that on the few occasions upon which the two parts stifled their mutual antipathies to the extent of speaking to one another, the Blake-part could say to the Newton-part, "This picture of yours is not satisfactory, go and draw another one": and the strange thing is that the Newton-part did go and draw another one! What science shows about the universe in 1930 is as different from the picture drawn in 1900 as the latter is from the one drawn in the year Newton published his *Principia*.

The fact is that the picture of the universe drawn by science in 1900 was the vision of a man suffering from claustrophobia, or fear of being shut in restricted places. The savage was a sufferer from agoraphobia; he was frightened of the too vast spaces around him, science calmed his fears and turned the huge expanses of his imagination into a room, almost a cellar or dungeon, surrounded with thick walls called "laws." Although space in 1900 as compared with space known to a savage was as an elephant to an atom, nevertheless it was not open space but a series of dungeons surrounded by laws.

Art and literature which always lag behind science in

their pictures, just as emotion always lags behind knowledge, drew the perfect representation of such a scientific idea of the universe at a time when science was already abandoning it for a new one. It was the Russian Ballet *Petroushka.*

In *Petroushka* we saw a doll surrounded by a vault of blue sky, caged and confined, while an old man with a beard, an inhuman astrologer, sat on a cloud and watched the pain and unhappiness of his creation without an emotion of any kind. The doll paces out the boundaries of its prison, frenziedly beats upon the blue walls, finally tears away a piece of heaven to find it blue paper splashed with painted stars and revealing nothing behind, and falls half in the world and half hidden in this paper heaven. That was where the spirit of man had found itself by 1900. It was a step in the right direction as compared with the savage starting point or the medieval lodging for the night, but it was not the goal.

And even while the century was dying there were to be seen at various points the first flickering signs of the New Renaissance.

CHAPTER SEVEN

>>>>>>>>>>>>>>>>>>>>>><<<<<<<<<<<<<<<<<<<<<

The New Renaissance

A. The Universe

§ 1

WITH the overbeliefs inspired by Darwin's followers
closes the Old Testament of the modern man's Bible. And
often enough it is the Old Testament which is all that
he reads. Not only in the minds of ordinary people, but
also in the minds of those who write books explaining
science to them, the thoughts of 1900 are too often still
uppermost.

And yet in the quarter of a century, more or less, that
has intervened, there has been enough new thought, new
observation, and new philosophy to transform all that
went before. What we have so far had of the twentieth
century can only be compared with the seventeenth for
the enlargement which has come to man's view. Our picture of the universe has changed once more and with it
there is bound to be sooner or later a new religion, in the
sense in which we have learned to use the term in these
pages.

It is curious to find all sorts of people imagining themselves very up to date because a reading of Haeckel and
Spencer has in 1930 at last produced in them a state of
mind which might have been a little advanced in 1900.

⌒256⌒

Very often a young man, brought up in a religious atmosphere, which would have been almost reasonable in 1600, "revolts"; but he only revolts as far as 1900 and is absolutely unable to stay the last lap of his self-imposed course. A sort of love for intellectual martyrdom makes him crucify his emotions on the phantom of a cross taken down and thrown away long ago.

It must be admitted by any scientist that in spite of the enthusiasms made possible by what we may call the Darwinian picture of the universe there was something a little cramping about its proportions. It was like coming in from a vast plain lit by a colourful twilight into a room impeccably bright, but in consequence apparently too full of walls. Victorian self-satisfaction smiled possessively at all the ornaments, but sooner or later the human imagination was sure to crave for the vague shapes in the night outside.

William Blake had long ago suggested that every bird "that cuts the airy way is an immense world of delight, clos'd by your senses five." Consider what an effect upon the human imagination it would have made if science instead of showing that the bird was a mass of matter in a state of motion forced into its actual shape by the vicissitudes of a blind evolution, had revealed a living creature fit for a midsummer night's dream or a fairy palace garden; with more in it than imagination could invent, instead of less. One feels that if the human mind, looking through the glass of science, had discovered this, then Victorian architecture would have been more attractive and the age would not have had to commit suicide in that most typical product of Victorianism, the Great World War.

But, the reader will say, that is going back to the nursery; we have done away with just this very fairy-tale mysticism and the "fact" of evolution is far more exciting than childishness about "worlds of delight" hidden by our five senses. And of course the reader is perfectly right; as we are dust we had better remember that we are but dust, and no ethereal star. But let us wait a moment.

Let us consider a small incident which happened in 1896. M. Becquerel, distinguished French chemist, was making a series of experiments in Paris. They were rather haphazard experiments in a way, and designed to see what might chance to turn up rather than to illustrate a deeply conceived theory. Something did turn up.

The year before, a German named Röntgen had noticed that if he passed an electric discharge through a glass tube out of which the air had been pumped, a glowing light was produced with very peculiar properties. When he put a plate of phosphorescent material near the tube, it began to glow as well, and if a coin was put up against the plate it could be seen as a strong black shadow from the other side. If a piece of wood were placed against the plate a paler shadow could be seen. Now here was something quite new in the history of the world, for it meant that, whatever the substance was which could produce the glow in the tube, it was able to pass through certain opaque objects so that you could see the shadow of other objects lying against them. The light passed through the phosphorescent plate, but was partly stopped by a piece of wood and altogether stopped by a thick metal coin.

If there was one thing that had seemed certain hitherto,

it was that light could not pass through opaque objects, and here was a kind of light which most certainly did. Let us note in passing the value of the strict training which science had given to the human imagination: in Galileo's day the fact that two weights fell from the Leaning Tower at Pisa in equal times could not be seen, because the human minds of the professors had been trained to believe Aristotle and not to use their eyes. To them it was impossible to imagine that anything could happen except as Aristotle had said and it took many generations before the human mind could change so far as to use its senses. Imagine Röntgen describing his discovery in seventeenth century Pisa: he would have been indicted for sorcery and heresy. But by 1895, though humanity had not really advanced very far, it was able to accept the facts as Röntgen's experiments revealed them. Whatever had been hitherto thought, clearly here was a light which penetrated opaque bodies; and as it penetrated bodies made of light atoms more easily than bodies made of heavy ones, and as human bones are made of heavier atoms than human flesh, it could be used for seeing a broken arm in a living man, and for many other useful purposes. The newspapers of the world were full of Röntgen and his rays: they were useful; but they were more than useful, they were the beginning of a new picture of the universe and therefore of a new religious outlook.

To see this we must return to M. Becquerel. It occurred to him that as these discoveries of Röntgen involved the use of a phosphorescent plate, perhaps ordinary phosphorescent light could penetrate through opaque substances in the same manner as Röntgen rays. In order to find out if this were so, he selected a substance which was phosphorescent when exposed to sunlight and which contained, as it happened, as one of its ingredients, the heavy and rather rare element uranium.

He took this substance and, after putting it in the sun, wrapped it up with a photographic plate protected by a covering of black paper. After a while he took out the plate, unwrapped it, and developed it: it was fogged. Thus the phosphorescent light had passed through the black paper and affected the photographic plate hidden within.

M. Becquerel repeated the experiment on successive mornings and then one day just as he had wrapped up the plate and was about to expose his uranium compound to the sun, the sun went behind a cloud and stopped there. Being a busy man, M. Becquerel put his materials away in a drawer and turned to other things. Some days later he happened to open the drawer and saw the package lying there: I wonder, he said to himself, if this phosphorescent ray can penetrate through the wrapper, even in the dark. So he developed the plate, and found it fogged all over, just as much as if he had exposed his preparation in the sun for hours so as to stimulate the phosphorescence.

This was not in the least what M. Becquerel had expected, and he began to wonder if after all it was the phosphorescence which produced the fogging. He made experiments with other phosphorescent substances: neither in the dark nor in the sun did they penetrate the black wrapper at all. Only when there was uranium in the preparation did the photographic plate darken, and when there was uranium it darkened, whether the preparation was phosphorescent or not. Uranium was the cause then and possessed a property, hitherto quite unsuspected, of shooting out rays which could pass through opaque matter. M. Becquerel hardly realised how pleased he ought to be with himself: by putting away a photographic plate with a piece of uranium in a dark drawer, he had begun one phase of the new renaissance; for his accident was to turn Dalton's dull dust into "an immense world of delight, closed by our senses five."

We cannot follow the succeeding discoveries in detail: how it was shown that beside uranium and often to be found with it was the far more violently active element, radium: how these elements, and especially radium, are constantly pouring out part of themselves into space: how vast results come from this and yet the part dissipated is so minute that the process of giving out goes on for thousands of years. But we must try to show what a world of delight the discovery has opened to us.

Chemistry had discovered in the eighteenth and nine-teenth centuries a series of brutally final facts: somehow their very statement seems to depress the imagination. Thus such laws as the conservation of matter and the conservation of energy tell us things of a fundamental nature that we can*not* do. We burn a piece of coal: if we could weigh the ashes and the smoke that has gone up the chimney and all the other products solid or gas-eous of the burning, the total weight of these would be exactly the same as that of the piece of coal: nothing that we can do can destroy the least tittle of matter. If we push a great boulder over a precipice we have neither produced nor destroyed any energy at all: we have merely changed the energy latent in the food we ate for dinner into muscle and nerve, that into heat and motion, the boulder fell to earth, the earth rose up to meet the boulder and the total result of all that has happened is as if nothing had happened at all. What a picture of human endeavour it suggests: a million years of activity, frenzied, exhausting, and at the end of it all there will be exactly as much energy in the universe as there was at the beginning; only much of it that was once "useful" will have changed into a useless form. Or take the truth about heat: watch a cup of coffee cooling: you cannot warm it by taking heat from the surrounding room and putting it into the coffee unless the room is hotter than the coffee to begin with. Things tend to cool to the temperature of their surroundings and what is true of a cup of coffee is true of the universe as a whole: everything in it will cool down until everything is uniformly cold: and very chilly our bones will be then. Finally consider the nature of matter; the table at which I write is an enormous mass of minute particles of dust. It is all very depressing indeed.

But now look at the change that has taken place in everything since M. Becquerel put away the uranium with the photographic plate: we cannot explain the process whereby the new picture of matter has grown but here are some of the details as they appear to us now:

1. The lump of earth which has been scraped off our boot after the muddy country walk is not a mass of minute pieces of lifeless, motionless dust. If we could inspect an atom of it enlarged to a size which would let us see it in detail, we would find something very like a solar system: round a central speck, at distances vast for the size of the various specks, would be circulating in

circles or ellipses a number of other little particles, planets moving round their central sun. Just as practically all the space occupied by the solar system is made up of the space between the various members of the solar system, so practically all the space occupied by an atom is empty space between its constituent particles. Indeed, the chair upon which the reader sits is in reality, as Bertrand Russell puts it, "much more like the Irishman's definition of a net, 'a number of holes tied together with pieces of string.' Only it would be necessary to imagine the strings cut away until only the knots were left." Moreover, this is true not only of the reader's chair, but of the reader himself: he is emptiness punctuated with a multitude of lonely and isolated dots. And if the dots could be squeezed together and the emptiness removed the whole world would be reduced to the size of an orange.

2. All these atoms are in a state of eternal movement and change and just as the planets pass round the sun according to strict laws of motion, so do the various particles within the atom whirl obediently about their central body. But the atomic system is far more complicated than the solar system, at any rate in the heavier elements: for example, the "sun" of the uranium atom consists of two hundred and thirty-eight bodies, exactly like the "sun" of a hydrogen atom, and one hundred and forty-six electrons; while the "planets" consist of ninety-two electrons revolving round this highly complicated central body in a series of rings. The outer rings of electrons are subject to changes: their numbers vary or their speeds and orbits change, and when this happens we have something which is apparent to us as a chemical change.

Certain elements have exactly the right number of electrons in their outer rings and these never combine with any other element to form compounds; other elements are deficient in electrons and rush at other elements so as to rearrange their outer rings by capturing electrons from them or by balancing their electrons in a new way, and this is what is happening whenever two or more elements combine to make a substance with new chemical properties.

The rays which Röntgen discovered come from the inner rings of electrons and are caused by the shooting out of a few electrons from these rings into outer space. Finally, when the nucleus or "sun" breaks off a part and shoots it into outer space we have radio-activity. Thus radium and uranium have the property of penetrating through opaque substances because they are constantly and according to rigid laws shooting out part of their central particles far away from the atom into surrounding space. It is as if one of the planets in the solar system suddenly sped off into interstellar regions, or as if the sun itself launched a limb at incredible speed to regions beyond the Milky Way.

3. Every element is built up of complicated atoms such as these, but in most cases the atomic system goes on without change in its sun for indefinite periods. If the simplest atom there is, hydrogen, is charged with positive electricity it becomes a "sun" or nucleus without any "planet" at all, for the process deprives it of its only electron, which returns to it directly it ceases to be electrified; but nothing ever happens to the hydrogen nucleus itself. It is only because some of the more complicated elements suffer violent changes in the nuclei, changes

that reveal themselves to us by radio-activity, that we are able to realise what goes on inside the atom. Thus M. Becquerel can claim to have made the first step towards discovering that the ultimate particles of matter are not dead dust at all but violently agitated systems of incredible energy. In radium and other radio-active elements we are able to see and study the nature of this energy because some of its results get outside the atom, and from them we can reason out what the other atoms are like.

4. When a radium atom shoots out a part of its nucleus it becomes something different from what it was before: it becomes, in fact, another element. Thus the idea of the alchemists, the human desire which as we have seen began the science of chemistry, is in a sense found to be true. Dalton's eighty or so kinds of dust can be transmuted one into another and are in their own way subject to growth and change.

Now if we consider these facts about the new picture of the universe it is hardly possible any longer to feel about matter as a person could feel about it in 1900. Matter then seemed to be the kingdom of death; now it seems to have a greater abundance of life than life in the ordinary sense itself. The sting seems to have been extracted from the very word "materialism." Inevitably such an idea of matter produces a new set of emotional reactions, a new type of overbelief. We cannot face the universe in the same spirit now as then, for, to begin with, instead of feeling a contempt for the raw material of earth and stars we may legitimately wonder if we are as much alive as an atom of radium. We do not emanate energy at such a pace; the atoms of which we are composed are sluggish compared with the atoms whose violent life we can study in the stars and nebulæ. Are we imprisoned sparks of life in a dead universe? Or are we only half alive in a universe the intensity of whose life we are at present too comatose to realise to the full? To such questions as these we can return when we have investigated some other parts of this new picture of the universe.

§ 2

In 1901 Max Planck was working to explain certain facts about the way in which a hot body pours out its heat into surrounding space. He found that if, as everybody supposed, this outpouring was a steady continuous stream of heat waves, it was impossible to explain what observation reported to be happening. If, however, instead of continuous, unbroken oozing out of heat, there was a series of jerks of heat, each small indeed and each followed almost at once by the next jerk, then the facts of observation could be explained. This was the first indication of something about the nature of the universe which had never been suspected hitherto and which, if true, must cause an upheaval in everything that we know about the nature of things.

Let us try to see what this idea of jerks, or packets, of heat-radiation really means. Suppose somebody says to you that a line is not just a continuous thing, but a series of infinitely minute dots, infinitely close together, your idea of a line remains much as it has always been. The dots are infinitely small and infinitely close and therefore you can always put another dot between any two dots which have already been made. You are at liberty to say

A chemical experiment conducted with due attention to the influence of the stars. "Some stars sulphurised the atmosphere while others made it arsenical, saline or mercurial." (See p. 195.)

that the line you draw continuously is just the same as this series of dots and that the only difference is in the more common-sense way you choose for describing it. But suppose some one was to say that the line was made up of dots of the minutest size but nevertheless not infinitely small, and exceedingly close together but not infinitely close, so that there were two dots very close together but not touching one another between which there was no room to put another; then your whole idea of lines and of space itself would have to be revolutionised. It is hard enough to imagine that you can always put a further dot between any two however close they may be, but it is much harder to imagine that you cannot; for this would mean that space itself is not a continuous thing but has holes in it in exactly the same way as we have seen is true of matter. If this were true all sorts of strange things would follow. A pen drawing a straight line would be jumping from point to point a measurable distance apart with no space between; it would get to the second point in no time and without traversing the space between, because although the points are separated from one another yet there is a gap in space equal to the distance. In fact everything would become paradoxical and apparently meaningless. Yet in a sense Max Planck's work on heat suggests very much this picture of the universe, although the illustration of the straight line that we have given is only an analogy of what has actually been found.

Let us imagine a drop of water tremendously magnified: if we could magnify it several times as much as the most powerful microscopes of today can accomplish we should see it as a mottled substance and each of the mot-

tles would be a molecule. Greater magnification still
would show that these molecules were an arrangement
of two atoms of hydrogen and one of oxygen. Enormously greater magnification still would reveal that each
hydrogen atom was a nucleus with one electron rushing
round it. Of course, even if we could succeed in building
a super-microscope capable of seeing such minute objects, we should in practice see nothing since the molecules, the atoms, and the electrons would all be rushing
about at incredible speeds which we could not stop without smashing the drop of water into something quite different. But if only we could annihilate the motions and
enlarge the sizes that is what we should see.

Let us now suppose that we are observing a dozen
hydrogen atoms at once; in some ways they would all
look more or less the same; they would all have a nucleus
or sun, and one electron planet moving round. But the
orbits of these electrons would differ from one atom to
another; some would be bigger than others, some would
be circular and others elliptic. In certain conditions we
could see an electron change from one sized orbit to
another, very much as if Jupiter suddenly left its orbit
and began to move in the orbit of Mars. When this
happened the first thing that would be noticed would
be a flash of light; for we would learn that when an atom
gives out light it means that one of its electrons, if it
has several, has suddenly shot in from one orbit to another nearer the nucleus or sun; a change which releases
energy which we see as light. Thus when a lump of coal
begins to be red-hot, it means that first the molecules
in it have been banging about so violently owing to
the increasing heat, that with the co-operation of oxygen

atoms in the air the chemical state which we call burning
has been set up and then the electrons in the atoms have
started to jump from one orbit to another, an action
made known to us as light. Only atoms thrown into
agitation by some such means as this give out light because otherwise the electrons do not change their orbits.

The second thing we would notice is of even greater
interest than how light is produced, for it upsets a great
deal of what we have always taken for granted. Suppose we were constructing a model of an atom; we
would put a sun in the middle and electron-planets revolving round it. How big would we make the orbits?
We would of course make a scale model of the original
atom and place the electrons in accordance with what
we saw. We should do exactly the same if we were
making a scale model of the solar system. Now suppose
we were making a scale model of an imaginary solar
system; and suppose we wanted it to be a *possible* system
though not one actually in existence. We would be guided
by the laws which Newton discovered in our own system
and we would find nothing in those laws to prevent us
from making the size of our planets' orbits anything we
liked. Once we had chosen an orbit we would know
various things about the speeds and times which would
be possessed by a planet with that orbit, but we should
be at liberty to make the orbit bigger or smaller by any
fraction: we could not think of an orbit in which no
planet could possibly move provided the shape were
right. In short, the Newtonian laws governing solar systems dictate to us the shape of the orbit but not the size.

If we then decided to make a model of a *possible*
though not necessarily an actual atom, we would find

ourselves in a totally different situation; for the laws which govern atom-systems dictate not only the shape of the electron's orbit, but also its size. There are possible sizes, and an infinitely greater number of impossible sizes. A little consideration shows us how upsetting this fact must be.

Imagine what would happen if Jupiter suddenly decided to go round the sun in the orbit occupied by Mars. Suppose that all the forces which exist today continued to exercise their strength on the planet, but that a new force pushed it inwards to the new orbit. The process would of course take time and at each successive moment Jupiter would be going round the sun in a gradually smaller ellipse; its path would consist of little pieces of all the infinite successive ellipses lying between the ellipse of Jupiter's original orbit and the ellipse of Mars' orbit. We could imagine this path, or draw it and measure it. There would be nothing surprising about it and no untoward incident connected with it. Though the event is certain not to happen, there would be nothing puzzling about it if it did.

Now consider an electron leaving one orbit and going to another nearer to the nucleus: observation assures us of the following facts: (1) that electrons do change their orbits; (2) that there are only a very few orbits not only that they *do* occupy but that they *can* occupy; (3) that the size of these is always a multiple of the smallest orbit ever occupied by an electron going round a hydrogen nucleus; (4) that an electron leaves one orbit and reaches the next not in a very small space of time but in no time at all.

Let us consider the difference between what happens

to an electron and what would happen to Jupiter. Every inch of the way from Jupiter's orbit to that of Mars is a point on a perfectly possible orbit round the sun; between two points separated by an inch there is an infinite number of points all on possible orbits round the sun. We have the same sort of thing as we saw in the line made up of infinitely close dots. But between one orbit of an electron and the next there are no possible orbits at all; there are no points on any possible orbits, so that the path of the electron is not, as was Jupiter's, a continuous succession of ellipses each occupied for an infinitesimal moment before going on to the next: it has to get from one place to another without traversing the space between.

Here we have something so unexpected that we cannot see at all what it can mean. We have seen earlier in our history how for a time the idea of "centrehood" was so woven into the very fabric of human thought that nobody could release his imagination from it: in the same way the idea of "continuity" is so much a part of our mind that this new picture of a universe where things jump from one place to another without passing through any space on the way sounds nonsensical. Yet so real is it that we can measure this distance between one electron orbit and another, which does not seem to be occupied by space as we have imagined it, with a considerable degree of accuracy. It we multiply the circumference of the smallest orbit possible for a hydrogen electron to occupy by the velocity of that electron and its mass we get a quantity always called h, or Planck's constant, which is 6.55×10^{-27}, a quantity which, as Bertrand Russell says, is a million million million million times smaller than the smallest dot one could see, but a quantity which is nevertheless quite definite and not just "infinitely small." The distance between one orbit and another is such that this product is h for the first orbit, twice h for the second, three times h for the third, and so on. Nothing lies between these orbits which can be occupied by an electron for an instant.

At this point the modern man is likely to raise some definite objections: chief of them is that he cannot see that these things can affect his religion even if they do mean anything at all; and, second, that in fact they seem to be meaningless. Thirdly, who can possibly say what goes on inside the atom, considering no atom has ever been seen?

Let us take the third objection first. It is true that none of these things have ever been or will ever be seen through any microscope: but everything that has been said about them has been deduced from ascertainable facts. The brilliance of modern physics is largely a matter of correlating observed phenomena with invisible causes. Thus, when the light from hydrogen atoms is passed through a spectroscope a band is seen with a number of lines crossing it: these lines can be shown to be caused by electrons jumping from one orbit to another inside the atom and the orbits to and from which they are jumping can be calculated from the position of the lines. These lines only appear in certain fixed places and nowhere else and these places each correspond to one of the orbits. If there could be any orbit whatever for each electron, the lines would appear haphazard. The picture of the atom at which we have hinted is composed of inferences from such facts as these.

As to the complaint that some of the statements we have made are meaningless; that, for example, it means nothing at all to say that an electron gets from one place to another without going through the intervening space; this is a much more serious objection, and its consideration will at the same time dispose of the question as to what all this has to do with religion.

In the first place, what was the situation when science set out to examine the universe? There was a number of common-sense, easily defined things lying ready to hand, such as the earth, the moon, the sun. Science had to clear away many ideas as to their nature and their relations with one another. "The greatest service that one can render to science," said Cuvier, "is to make the ground clear before constructing anything there"; and we have watched how science had to clear away medievalism before it could construct anything; clear away "centrehood" from the stuff of men's thoughts, clear away Aristotle from the schools, clear away authority to make room for experience and experiment. When all the clearance had been accomplished there were the sun, moon, and planets, perfectly recognisable bodies about which there could be no dispute, but nothing was known about their interrelations. Science proceeded to discover these, until with Newton all the bodies of the universe were bound together by a set of quite simple relations. Meanwhile other sciences investigated the parts of each body and their relations to one another and the whole. Most of these relations had to do with speeds and sizes, and indeed most that science found out about the universe whether of the stars, or of chemical substances or even of biological substances, was in terms of speed and size. Everything fitted astonishingly well; there seemed to be a few general rules which always held good.

Now simply because they always worked and because science has always believed to a certain extent that "a truth is a truth if it works," science admitted certain laws which were really overbeliefs and could not be scientifically proved. One of these is the simple assumption that effects have causes which can be understood and that if you can once prophesy something from a group of known facts you can prophesy it again from the same group of facts. If, for example, you know that two billiard balls hitting one another with a certain velocity in a certain way from a certain direction will be once moved to certain positions, then you can prophesy that this will happen again and again. So long as science did not deal with very great speeds or very small sizes, everything went well; so well that the overbeliefs, accepted just because they worked, got established as necessary truths in everybody's mind. But when very high speeds like the speed of light or very small things like an electron began to be studied everything went wrong.

Two things especially seem to have gone wrong: first, with minute bodies like electrons it is not at all certain now that similar effects can always be prophesied from similar causes. If you could never be certain that the train to Brighton might not land you at Glasgow, you would feel distinctly dissatisfied with the railway companies; and if it really means that perhaps he cannot prophesy that what has happened once will always happen, given the same causes, then the scientist will, so to speak, feel dissatisfied with the universe. In the second place, whereas science started with known, common-sense things—suns, stars, lumps of matter—and unknown formulæ relating them; it has ended with a number of wonderful mathematical formulæ, but the things which are related by them to one another can neither be imagined nor understood. A given formula will tell you what an electron will do inside the atom, but the electron has become something which nobody can conceive, namely, something which goes from one place to another without passing through the space between.

Now if, as scientists seem to believe, these two things are true, it means that the universe is essentially meaningless. We are all of us made up of atoms and electrons and, though we are big enough to behave properly, as it were, our parts are wayward and unreliable. Before considering what this means to the modern man's outlook on the universe we must pass on for a moment elsewhere.

§ 3

Newton's picture of the universe and especially his law of gravitation had that element of æsthetic beauty which had been the desire of men like Kepler and every great scientist. A single principle, one mathematical formula, explained every movement that man could see going on in the universe. We must remember that a scientific law is true if it "saves the phenomena," that is, explains everything it ought to explain, and that if two laws equally succeed in this task, then the more simple is the truer. It is possible that there is no better reason for this last rule than that man's imagination likes the simple and economic more than the complicated and extravagant; but that does not matter.

Now there were certain observed phenomena in the universe which needed to be fitted into the general law of gravitation; and in course of time most of them were explained. Moreover, whenever any refinement of observation discovered a new motion, of the moon for example, it was soon found to be amply explained by Newtonian laws, to be in fact just what one would have expected. Only one really troublesome exception continued to defy analysis in terms of the law of gravitation as expressed by Newton: time after time when the planet Mercury reached the spot in its orbit nearest to the sun, it proved to be unpunctual. Newtonian gravitation gave no explanation of this: it was indeed a phenomenon which steadily refused to be "saved" by the law which ought to save it. Some people invented a planet Vulcan, nearer the sun, which was interfering with Mercury's movements, but Vulcan refused to be seen.

In the second place, as the science of spectroscopy grew, it became noticeable that certain lines in the spectra—lines caused, as we have seen, by the behaviour of electrons within the atom—were not exactly where they ought to have been, if they were the consequence of Newtonian laws. Finally, careful measurement revealed that the rays of light from stars near the sun during a total eclipse were bent towards the sun in a way not satisfied by Newtonian laws. These three little exceptions spoiled the perfect applicability of the laws which had explained so much. To explain them satisfactorily it has been found necessary to destroy utterly Newton's picture of the universe.

Before we see how this has happened we will make a preliminary digression. In the town of Kazan so long ago as 1826 Nicholas Lobatchewsky expounded in a paper read to the University certain ideas about geometry. Euclid had written a postulate about parallel straight lines which is familiar to every schoolboy: "If a straight line falling on two straight lines make the angles, internal and on the same side, less than two right angles, the two straight lines being produced indefinitely, meet on the side on which are the angles less than two right angles"; on the other hand, if the said angles equal two right angles, then the two lines are parallel and meet at infinity; moreover, there is only one line parallel to another through any given point. All this Lobatchewsky changed to another postulate: "All straight lines which, in a plane, radiate from a given point, can, with respect to any other straight line in the same plane, be divided into two classes, the intersecting and the non-intersecting. The boundary line of the one and the other class is called parallel to the given line"; from which it follows that there are two parallel lines through any given point.

Nine out of every ten readers have skipped most of the last paragraph and are now clamouring for some justification of its existence. Here it is in the words of W. K. Clifford: "Copernicus and Lobatchewsky both brought about a revolution in scientific ideas so great that it can only be compared with that wrought by the other. And the reason of the transcendent importance of these two changes is that they are changes in the conception of the Cosmos.

"Before the time of Copernicus men knew all about the Universe. They could tell you in the schools, pat off by heart, all that it was, and what it had been, and what it would be. There was the flat earth, with the blue vault of heaven resting on it like the dome of a cathedral, and the bright cold stars stuck into it; while the sun and planets moved in crystal spheres between. Or, among the better informed, the earth was a globe in the centre of the universe, heaven a sphere concentric with it; intermediate machinery as before. At any rate, if there was anything beyond heaven, it was a void space that needed no further history. Its future could be predicted in general terms as far forward as a certain epoch, about the precise determination of which there were, indeed, differences among the learned. But after that would come a changeless eternity, which was fully accounted for and described. But in any case the Universe was a known thing.

"Now the enormous effect of the Copernican system, and of the astronomical discoveries that have followed it, is that, in place of this knowledge of a little, which was called knowledge of the Universe, of Eternity, and Immensity, we have now got knowledge of a great deal more; but we only call it knowledge of Here and Now. We can tell a great deal about the solar system; but after all, it is our house, and not the city. . . .

"This then was the change effected by Copernicus in the idea of the Universe. But there was left another to be made. For the laws of space and motion implied an infinite space and an infinite duration, about whose properties as space and time everything was accurately known. The very constitution of those parts of it which are at an infinite distance from us is just as well known, if the Euclidean assumptions are true, as the geometry of any portion of this room. In this infinite and thoroughly well-known space the Universe is situated during at least some portion of an infinite and thoroughly well-known time. So that here we have real knowledge of something at least that concerns the Cosmos, something that is true throughout the Immensities and the Eternities.

"That something Lobatchewsky and his successors have taken away."

What does all this mean in a few words? Human beings began to draw a geometrical picture of the universe under the very natural impression that geometry begins at home. Measure the room you occupy and you will find out certain undoubted things about it; it has length, breadth, and height; it is a box with three dimensions, in fact; if you want to measure the shortest distance from door to window you will have to measure a straight line; if your foot rule exactly measures a length in your dining-room and another length in your bedroom, then you assume that these two lengths are the same. Equally these rules apply to measurements extended over the garden, the parish, the county, England, and, common sense adds, the Universe as a whole; you can go up, along or across the universe, and you can go on for ever in a straight line, for the universe is made up of a multitude of spaces into which you could put boxes of any height, breadth, or length; you would never have to fit in boxes of a different shape or size so as not to leave gaps, and you could always cut out of the universe a bigger and bigger straight sided cube whose sides would never meet because they would be parallel.

All these things assumed from common sense and from practical experience in measuring houses and land were made by Euclid necessary truths about the universe. By a group of "self-evident truths" he laid the basis of a geometry which not only assumed that the universe can be measured like a room, but seemed to prove that this assumption must be so. It was something which need not be doubted and could not be doubted. Lobatchewsky's importance lies in having shown that some of Euclid's "self-evident truths" were not self-evident at all, and possibly not even true; that, in fact, the human imagination was not in the least bound to suppose that lengths and lines behave everywhere in the universe as they do at home; that the one thing that people had always supposed to be above suspicion, namely, the geometry of the universe, was capable of being gravely suspected.

Simply by supposing that things, which Euclid had taken for granted on false grounds, are not true, you can invent as many pictures of the universe as you like. It may be curved in all sorts of ways; straight lines may not in the long run be the shortest way from place to place; space may not be even and uniform so that a foot in the bedroom and in the dining-room may be different lengths; only you cannot know because the foot rule changes length on being taken from one room to the other; it may be that there are more dimensions than merely up, along, and across,—four, five, six, or n dimensions perhaps. He does not say that these things are so, he merely says that there is no reason inherent in the nature of things which prevents them from being so and that as we have no experience of the universe in the big, but only of minute corners of it, there is no knowing whether they are so or not.

Very few people outside the ranks of mathematicians realised at the time how important these ideas were, and even the mathematicians regarded them as abstruse intellectual games; Clifford realised, but he died too young to pursue them far. Huxley, though no mathematician, had some vision of their importance, but the wrong vision: "Let us suppose," he says, "that a telescope powerful enough to show us what is going on in the nebula of the sword of Orion, should reveal a world in which stones fell upwards, parallel lines met, and the fourth dimension of space was quite obvious. Men of science would have only two alternatives before them. Either the terrestrial and the nebular facts must be brought into harmony by such feats of subtle sophistry as the human mind is always capable of performing when driven into a corner; or science must throw down its arms in despair, and commit suicide, either by the admission that the universe is, after all, irrational, in as much as that which is truth in one corner of it is absurdity in another, or by a declaration of incompetency."

Now very nearly a hundred years after Lobatchewsky a man showed that the Universe did not behave as Euclid's common sense geometry assumed, and did behave according to one of the non-Euclidean geometries, invented by rejecting what Euclid had to say about parallel straight lines. In fact the shape, dimensions, and geometrical truths of the universe are such that we can never see them with our eyes nor even imagine them pictorially with our minds, because our eyes and minds can only answer to our experience, which is of rooms and pieces of the universe too small to know the truth as a whole. What we thought were self-evident necessary geometrical truths are really only the rough approximations which are all we need for our practical everyday life. Just as "centrehood" was a necessary part of human thought until practical discoveries dislodged Rome,

Europe, the earth from their central positions, so three
dimensions and straight lines as the shortest distance
between two points are of the very stuff of our thought;
but as with centrehood they are not of the very stuff of
reality.

If the modern man has found it difficult to imagine
that space is in any way different from what his senses
insist on feeling about it, let him remember that that was
exactly how intelligent people felt when Copernicus or
Galileo challenged "centrehood." The pictures of the
universe suggested by Copernicus must have seemed a
piece of fantastic intellectual foolery and people went
about making jokes, no doubt, about the absurd practical
consequences of such a theory.

We have seen, by the way, how they thought that it
would do away with God: that was because the old beliefs about the universe accepted God: in exactly the same
way today, since the old-beliefs of 1900 more or less re-
jected God, we find him slipping in once more by way
of Relativity, ever present, though ever hidden in the
fourth dimension.

But how has Einstein been able to prove that the universe is formed in a way which the human senses can
never directly detect? By the most convincing of all
scientific methods: namely, by showing that, if the universe is so formed, then his explanation of motions and
behaviour explains not only all that Newton's law of
gravitation explained, but also the three phenomena that
could not be "saved" by Newton's law. Moreover, he
was able to predict certain results from his law which
have since been verified. This has shown that so long as
we look at the universe with our imaginations in exactly

the same way as we do with our eyes, as Newton did, we cannot explain certain things, but that these things can be explained directly we see that our eyes deceive us. Fortunately the behaviour of Mercury and one or two other little facts are just of a nature to show up the falsity of the old way of thinking about the universe and to indicate a truer picture.

To the modern man trying to discover his place in the universe the first importance of Einstein and of relativity is that they show him a new relationship between his senses and the world of fact; once more we are thrown back on quotations from William Blake: "Man has no body," he wrote, "distinct from his soul, for that call'd body is a portion of the soul discern'd by the five senses, the chief inlets of soul in this age," and, as we have already seen more than once, "how do you know but ev'ry bird that cuts the airy way is an immense world of delight, clos'd by your senses five"? Probably Blake meant something quite different from what we mean, but his words can be construed as an excellent description of what the modern man must feel about his senses and the universe. True, the senses are the chief inlets of soul, or knowledge, in this age, but they are also by their very nature veils between us and the immense world of delight which is reality. Through them alone can we learn that to them reality is always closed.

How different is this point of view from any which would have seemed reasonable to Herbert Spencer or to any Victorian scientist; and how different must a man's attitude to the universe become when his imagination has played upon the changed idea.

In the second place, there is another way in which

one's whole outlook on the universe is influenced by relativity; and that is in what it has to say about Time. It is of course impossible for us to enter into the mathematics, or indeed the physics, of the new intellectual revolution; our concern is with the general attitudes towards the universe, likely to be produced in men's minds by these discoveries, and the sort of overbelief which will be derived from them. Attempts to popularise such ideas as space-curvature or four-dimensional space-time frames probably lead to more confusion than they are worth; but there is an idea about time, which we owe to Einstein, and may assume likely to influence the human imagination greatly. Suppose two different people observing an event: common sense says that there will never be any difficulty in their agreeing as to the correct time at which it took place; and if two things happen according to one observer at the same moment, then common sense says that the other observer will always agree that the two events are simultaneous. Now mathematical physics can show that this is by no means necessarily true. If the observers are moving in certain ways relative to one another they will not agree as to the time at which an event has taken place, and two events may very well seem simultaneous to one but not to the other. We need not discuss why this is so, but we must take it on trust.

Now what has happened, as a result of Einstein and relativity, is that, whereas, before them, a scientist would say: although the two observers cannot agree about the times owing to the nature of things, nevertheless one of them will get the time right and one of them will get it wrong; nowadays he would say: the two observers will not agree about the time, but one will not be wrong and the other right; both of them will be right.

It is probably by way of overbeliefs based on this attitude that relativity will first percolate into the ordinary human mind, an extension of the principle that "whatever is is right" that Pope certainly never dreamed of; for what it means in the world of common sense is that absolute ideas of rightness and wrongness are apt to be overstressed while the search for the good had better be given up in a realisation of a multiplicity of goods.

Here then are some of the elements which have brought about a new renaissance based on a totally different picture of the universe from that current in 1900; but before we put the pieces together we must take a look at certain equally radical changes in the scientific attitude towards life and man himself.

B. Man

§ 1

In 1900 the science of biology was absolutely dominated by a series of ideas formulated by Wallace and Darwin and developed by men like Huxley, Haeckel, Weismann, Spencer. Everybody knows what those ideas are and we have seen how they produced overbeliefs and roused human enthusiasm because they freed man from so many false and crippling ideas about life and himself. But as in human political history a liberator may first raise enthusiasm because he frees men, and then produce discontent because he sets up new curtailments of liberty, so in science a theory is first received because of all it explains and then doubted because of all that it leaves unexplained.

Darwinian biology in the New Renaissance is in the second of these two stages: and if Darwin is the Newton of biology, its Einstein is still unborn and everybody feels the need of his coming. Only whereas in physics it was merely a few things like Mercury's unpunctuality that suggested the need of an Einstein, in biology the gaps and difficulties are far more apparent; they even enter into the consciousness of the man in the street.

Now in considering this part of our subject we shall be able to adopt a quite different approach from that adopted in the preceding section of this chapter; for whereas the content of the new physical picture of the universe can only be really understood by physicists and mathematicians, any intelligent person can understand the new doubts and prophecies which make up the present state of biology, the science of life. The best way to approach the changing ideas about life in the New Renaissance will be to make a long digression and to invite our readers to consider with us certain biological facts about the loves of the orchids. Nor will he be unprepared for finding that such material also is very distinctly part of the biography of humanity.

Unlike most animals, flowers usually possess both sexes and could therefore reproduce their kind without assistance from any other plant. But the enriching of the individual by giving it the varying qualities of two distinct parents is so important in nature's economy that we find the most elaborate precautions against self-fertilising, and the most ingenious schemes to secure cross-fertilising adopted by nearly every flower in the world's garden.

Every child knows that since a plant cannot go a-walking to meet its mate it is dependent very often upon the assistance of insects so that pollen can be carried to and fro and the necessary mating achieved. Bees, butterflies, moths, flies sipping nectar and gathering honey, are, all unknown to themselves, making the continuance of the vegetable world a possibility; for while they are busy with the sweet drink provided for them, their heads bruise against the pollen grains or their hairy legs get entangled in yellow dust to be dropped later into the heart of another waiting flower.

Thus a flower is at least three different things: first, it is a mass of colour and scent delighting human beings; second, it is a barrel of good liquor delighting insects; and third, it is a being fulfilling the duty of all life by securing the survival of the species. The biologist studying a primrose has to explain how, in the course of ages, these three things have come about. It is not true to say of him

> Primroses by the river's brim
> Dicotyledons were to him
> And they were nothing more.

He may not find it necessary, as do most poetasters, to turn all flowers into pretty but brainless young women; but he uses them to stimulate his imagination to far more exciting things. The reason why the flower delights human beings he will probably leave to the psychologist and even so he has left himself a difficult enough task.

In the first place, he has only two little clues to guide him on his way: he knows that all living beings reproduce their kind, but that the offspring always vary in all sorts of ways from their parents; and in the second place, he knows that there are always a great many more individuals born into the world than there is room for or food for. A dandelion or a daisy or a thistle could cover the earth in a very few years if all their offspring lived and reproduced, but lack of space and food and the competition of other forms of life restrain them.

With these two clues he looks at a bank of flowers as a detective looks at the evidence of a crime and he asks himself if he can reconstruct the history through countless ages of those masses of colour, those delicate forms. Here, he says to himself, is a flower; for ages back it has had parents more or less like it but never exactly like it; for ages there were always too many children, so that most of them starved to death, pushed off the earth by weeds and waste places.

Clearly, he thinks, this may be the explanation: millions of years ago very simple plants lived; they had offspring, too many of them for comfort, like the old woman who lived in a shoe; and only those best fitted to live could find a way of continuing to live. And so of the offspring of these simple plants, all rather like their parents, but all varying in one way or another, only those which varied fortunately lived; the others died. The survivors had offspring in their turn, the successful varieties lived, the others died; and so on for countless generations. Probably the simple plants fertilised themselves; a lucky chance enabled some of their progeny to attract insects; cross-fertilisation, thus accidentally discovered, was such a success, that these survived still more frequently; more lucky chances improved the machinery until today the most complicated and subtle plans, traps, devices summon the insects, all unknown to themselves, to the office of entrepreneur for the loves of the flowers.

Everyone knows that this is the Darwinian hypothesis of natural selection as a means of evolution. It is an explanation which is only valuable if it explains all the facts, if it "saves the phenomena" as the medieval scientist would say. Does it "save the phenomena"? Some people think that it does not.

To begin with there are the fundamentalists; they do not think that Darwinism explains the facts. It does not, for example, explain the fact that the Word of God says that Creation took place in six days according to the Book of Genesis; and they are perfectly right, this fact is not explained by Darwinism. And it is therefore no use to argue about evolution and fundamentalism as if it were a scientific problem; for the dispute depends entirely on whether the fact of the fundamentalists is a fact at all, and that is clearly a matter of theology and not of science. In passing, one may observe that neither Augustine nor Aquinas ever believed in the literal interpretation of Genesis and that no Catholic in later times would ever in all likelihood have done so but for a Spanish Jesuit named Suarez; while Anglo-Saxon Protestants probably derived the true strength of their belief from the overwhelming force on the Anglo-Saxon imagination of Milton's *Paradise Lost*.

But, fundamentalists aside, there are those who feel that Darwinism and its more orthodox relatives do not "save the phenomena"; and that other clues must be added before a reasonable picture can be constructed. It is in order to understand their doubts, that we must examine for a while the loves of the orchids.

§ 2

Besides his best known books, Darwin wrote a fascinating study of the *Fertilisation of Orchids*, wherein he described minutely the way in which all their structure is adapted to attract insects and to ensure the carrying of pollen from one flower to another.

Take a typical common orchid, not one of those fantastic almost obscenely shaped objects which wealthy men give to idle women, but a simple variety to be found in any June meadow. To us it is quaintly pretty, a worthy thing for a vase, something to look at and admire. To itself it is very different, it is an elaborate machine without a superfluous part, without a useless member or patch of colour. Everything that it has is an invention for securing the attention of insects.

The extravagant lower lip, pouting sensually and seductively, is a platform on which the visitor may alight; the spurlike extremity hanging down behind is a nectary down which he must thrust his head in order to suck up the nectar. In a position which makes it certain that the insect's head must knock against it, as it noses down for the nectar, is the seat of the pollen grains. An insect alights on the landing stage and probes into the spur for nectar; the top of its head touches the pollen and these become attached. Thus while going about its own business the insect is coaxed into transacting the flower's.

All this has come about, according to the most reasonable scientific explanation, by countless generations of plants varying haphazard and without plan; some of these lucky chance variations were in the direction of a better platform for insects, or a more certain position of the pollen to ensure it being carried away and these had "survival value"; that is, being more useful to the plant which had them, than the chance variations of other plants, enabled it to survive and have offspring inheriting them. Let us make this quite clear: there must have been ancestors of the orchid which had no way of attracting insects, and these must have fertilised themselves or increased by growing more roots, and then one day a "mutation," a change, took place, nobody knows why; a seedling grew to maturity with a longer lip on which an insect alighted, carrying away pollen to another flower; and this new way of fertilising was so superior that the offspring of that seedling and others like it pushed the self-fertilisers off the face of the earth.

That is remarkable enough in itself but we are only at the beginning of the loves of the orchids. It is not a question merely of providing an insect with a landing stage and letting it go off with a pollen grain: the machinery is far more subtle. Let us look for a moment at the pollen. It is seated, as we have seen, in the ceiling of the spur in such a position that the head of the insect must strike against it. It is a very complicated affair, moreover. At the end of the stick containing the pollen grain is a little knob so formed that when the insect touches it, its covering breaks in pieces, revealing a lump of liquid cement, which hardens on contact with the outside air. In the course of ages, says Darwinism, chance variations have brought it about that certain plants, by luck and not by cunning, have developed a spot of cement, which has the property of hardening when its cover is split by a visiting insect's head. Even that is not all: let us suppose that this insect, with a pollen stalk firmly cemented to its head, goes off to another orchid and thrusts down its head for nectar; what good can that do to the second plant? All that will happen is that the pollen brought from abroad will be pushed against the pollen already possessed by this flower and no good can clearly come of two male elements being brought into contact. If what we have so far said has seemed altogether credible, what will the reader make of what follows?

Just as the male pollen hangs from the ceiling of the spur so does the female ovary, but from a spot rather lower down. How does the pollen brought by the insect come into contact with it? If we could have seen the insect as it left the first orchid, we would have found the pollen on its stalk standing erect and stiff, but, by the time it has reached the second flower, a special hinge has come into operation bending the grain through an angle of ninety degrees forward over the insect's nose. In this new position it is ready to touch not the pollen but the ovary of the next flower visited and fertilisation takes place.

Nor is that all; as we have seen, successful fertilisation requires that the pollen shall stick to exactly the right spot on the insect's head; supposing it thrusts its nose down into the nectary sideways everything will be void. And so we find that orchids have special revolving shutters, which, when the insect visits the flower, twist round and hold its head in exactly the right position.

We could easily elaborate the picture still more, but enough has been said to show that the orchid is a complicated mass of machinery for inducing an insect to carry pollen from one plant to another. Darwinism asks us to believe that this machinery consists of many parts which arose by chance and were assembled by chance; that they just "happened" and, proving useful, continued. It is as if motor cars, instead of being intelligently made, resulted from nuts, screws, pipes, tanks, pieces of steel of every shape, all in infinite variety, being fitted together haphazard for countless years by some one who had never seen a motor car and had no idea of a use for one, until finally one such fitting together happened to work.

§ 3

The orchid has not yet revealed all its secrets, however, and we may use it to stimulate our imagination a little further. Darwin, whose patient observation enriched us with all these wonders, was sorely puzzled by one difficulty. Here was a marvellous, indeed an incredible machine for securing the visits of insects, a perfect trap in every particular but one—many kinds of orchids seem to have forgotten to give the insects any inducement at all to come to them. In fact Darwin, try how he would, could not find the least drop of nectar in the nectary. Honey, the *quid pro quo*, which any insect would demand was altogether lacking. That was a fact which needed a great deal of explanation.

A German botanist solved the matter by giving the flowers a magnificent name, "Scheinsaftblumen" or sham-nectar-producers, and suggested that they grew false nectaries in order to get the insects there on false pretences; "that is," said Darwin, "he believes, for he

well knows that the visits of insects are indispensable
for their fertilisation, that these plants exist by an organised system of deception. But when we reflect on the
incalculable number of plants which have existed for
enormous periods of time, all absolutely requiring for
each generation insect agency; when we think of the
special contrivances clearly showing that, after an insect
has visited one flower and has been cheated, it must almost immediately go to a second flower, in order that
impregnation may be affected, we cannot believe in so
gigantic an imposture." In short the insects are surely
not such fools as this!

In some cases the mystery has been solved since Darwin's day by the discovery that the insects bored into
a closed bag and sipped the liquor which they found
there; but only a year or so ago a far more surprising
discovery was made, which may be guaranteed to aston-
ish even those readers who have not been astonished
by the facts so far described. The discoverer was a Frenchman and when we have heard the nature of his discovery
everybody will agree that it is the sort of thing poetic
justice requires that a Frenchman should discover.

This Frenchman spent many patient days observing
certain North African orchids and trying to find out
what insects visited them and why. These particular
plants were of the type which so closely resembles an
insect that popularly they are known as "Bee Orchis"
or "Fly Orchis." The whole flower at first sight is easily
mistaken for an insect at rest.

Careful observation showed that these orchids resemble
the female of a certain kind of insect and that every year
the males of this kind of insect emerge from their

chrysalis state two weeks before the females; that finding themselves in a he-infested world they buzz about blindly looking for their unborn better halves, until they see a flower, which deceives them into thinking it is the lady love for whom they seek. The passionate bachelor races off and embraces the phantom; then, disappointed, zig-zags through the glade; again he sees the lady of his dreams, only, when clasped, to prove a second phantom. This sort of thing goes on for two weeks until the right-ful brides are ready; meanwhile the bachelors, sowing their wild oats, serve the orchids' purpose by transferring pollen from one flower to another. Put in terms of ortho-dox biology this means that some plant, by blind chance, varied sufficiently from its parent to become like a female insect and thereby survives by attracting insects under false pretences. Blindly and entirely by chance this varia-tion took the form of an insect, whose females always appear two weeks after the males; and a final stroke of luck is that during the millions of years that must have passed before this particular piece of luck happened to turn up, the insect in question did not happen to become extinct.

These facts, sufficiently wonderful in themselves to interest the layman, become doubly important for the light they throw on recent biological thought; but before we consider their general importance to scientific theory we must add one or two further details to an already complicated picture.

§ 4

When Darwin made his great attempt to "save the phe-nomena" by his theory of natural selection he assumed that all the little varieties he saw around him, in shape of leaf, or colour, or time of flowering, or whatever else in plant or beast did vary, could add up in course of time to become a valuable variation and a new form of life. But it was soon found that most of these variations never added up to anything, that, for example, a plant with a slightly longer leaf than its parents did not have offspring with longer leaves still, but that the length oscillated backwards and forwards around a mean which was always more or less the same.

In the second place, it is quite clear that little variations gradually adding up to something important could not possibly result in a plant resembling an insect; it would have been useless for a plant to be rather like an insect, and for its offspring to have been a little more like and so on: it had to be all or nothing. Once the plant was sufficiently like an insect to induce insects to come on visits, there would have been no sense in becoming more like an insect still; and until the plant was sufficiently like, no insect would have come. In either case the variation would have had no "survival value" and the plant would not have survived any better for its chance existence. It had to be "all or nothing" because just "some" would not have served any useful purpose.

And so we are to believe that quite by chance one bright morning an orchid bud "just growed" into a flower so completely unlike its parents as not to be recognisable as their offspring, and so like an insect as to be mistaken by one for its bride. As a matter of fact such "mutations" or sudden big changes do occur in nature, but infrequently, and never in a significant way.

But a final point must be considered in this strange

story: the whole assumption of Darwinism is that these great changes, these brilliant but chance adaptations which reach the last word in complicated invention by the orchid, have come about because they are valuable to the plant or animal as making them fitter to survive. And yet it would seem that the orchid's astounding adaptations are failures, so much so that orchids are rare compared with many simpler plants; and that those which do exist, more often than not, increase their numbers, not by fertilised seed at all, but by division of their roots. The whole thing is love's labour lost and a flower like the dandelion which simply fertilises itself and lets the wind blow the seed where it lists gets a far wider place in the sun, than the too clever or too lucky orchid.

Bluntly, all these facts would not give any reasonable man a favourable view of evolution and natural selection as a means of explaining them; rather they seem more simply solved by assuming a special creation, but then—lest I give comfort to the fundamentalists—the creator could not have been the God of the fundamentalists, but a cheery sort of individual with a Gallic sense of humour.

§ 5

Modern biology is said to be in revolt from Darwinism, and it is true that old-fashioned Darwinism is nearly dead. But this does not mean a return to Genesis or to any mythological reading of creation; it means that, just as the physics of Newton do not completely "save the phenomena" of celestial motions, so the biology of Darwin does not save such phenomena as those we have considered about the loves of the orchids. And if the old ideas no longer seem quite sufficient, it is interesting to know what is being put in their place. It is interesting, but not wholly possible, for the sufficient reason that the Einstein of biology is not yet born.

To see the sort of approach which this unborn co-ordinator will take is not so very difficult. What we have been considering about the loves of the orchids can give us the clue, for it is an example of the kind of phenomenon that is not saved by Darwinism and we can ask ourselves what kind of additions to Darwin's underlying ideas would be necessary in order to explain it.

We have seen that Darwin used two clues: first, that the offspring of plants and animals, although like their parents, vary in different ways from them; and, second, that as there are always too many living things born for the food supply, any varieties which make their owners more able to snatch their share will survive and be transmitted. The value of such a scheme was precisely that it got rid of the current ideas of a supernatural creator creating all sorts of things with a definite purpose, namely to help and comfort his pet creation, mankind. For all sorts of reasons this older theory of special creation did not "save the phenomena" and Darwinism was important and took the form it did because it "saved the phenomena" left out by it. And Darwinism did this admirably; it explained all sorts of things hitherto not capable of explanation; it got rid of a "purpose" in the universe, which had become unpopular for reasons many of which had nothing to do with science; it substituted blind chance and showed that nothing more was needed to explain the facts of evolution as they were then known;

CHARLES DARWIN, BY THE HON. JOHN COLLIER.

"'An ocean of new life and boundless possibilities'—'the gospel of dirt'—
one and the same piece of patient scientific research seemed both these things
according to the human mind by which it was absorbed. Darwin at once
became Antichrist or the giver of a new religion; however much he would
have preferred it, never for a moment could he remain a mere entomologist
and biologist. No one indeed was more surprised than himself." (See
p. 237.)

it banished mind from the multitude of living things and merely put it in as a sort of afterthought which has begun to emerge late in the evolution of animals. But it was only because of its valuable results that men could blind themselves to its deficiencies; such an advance was it in man's struggle for freedom from medievalism that these were unnoticed for a time.

Now there is one curious thing about Darwinism and it is this: that, although it is a theory about life and living things, you could construct the whole of it from visits to a museum and from the pages of a collection of dried plants; that is, from entirely dead material. Put in another way we can say that the whole trend of modern biology has laid more stress on what a thing is than on what a thing does, on its structure rather than on its function; and this has led to the logical assumption that what a thing is, its structure, is the important thing; and that what a thing does is dependent on it.

It may just as well be assumed that the opposite is true; that, to put it technically, function determines organism and not organism function; and if this were true it would mean that the variations of offspring from their parents, instead of being the product of blind chance, are in some way or other dependent on how the parents' organism functioned; that is, on something which was in some way in the control of the living being. If this is true, it means that mind has more to do with evolution, and chance less, than Darwinism teaches, although it is quite probable that we will have to enlarge our definition of mind before we can understand exactly what this new idea involves.

§ 6

We can see to what an important revolution in biological ideas this leads if we leave the orchid for a moment and follow the bee, which has unconsciously been acting as our orchid's "best man." Let us watch it wandering among the various flowers on the bank, not only orchids, but flowers of many other varieties as well. Sooner or later it finds a particularly good supply of nectar, takes what it can carry, and returns to the hive. What does it do there?

Whatever it does, we soon see the result of it; for, whenever a bee finds a particularly good hunting ground, very soon a swarm of other bees will arrive to profit by the discovery. We might assume that the first bee guides them back personally; but actually this does not prove to be the case. On arrival at the hive it settles on the comb and proceeds to waltz round in a circle performing an unvarying dance. When the other bees see this, they immediately approach their comrade, smell it in order to get an idea of the sort of scent to look for and then go off to look for flowers with the same scent. When the flowers do not happen to be scented, they are led to the right spot by the scent left by the first bee in the flower itself; for whenever a really good store of nectar is found the bee squirts it all over with a special scent-producing organ, thereby making the scene of its discovery perfectly clear to the scent-detecting organs of the others. After a time the treasure has all been garnered and then the returning bees do not perform their dance, a signal to the rest not to sally forth any more from the hive. Apparently Professor K. von Frisch, the painstaking observer of these facts, has also been able to prove that a quite different dance is executed to inform the hive of the discovery of a valuable store of pollen. In short there is a nectar-dance and a pollen-dance and unless one or the other is performed, no bee issues forth on a food-gathering quest.

Let us apply orthodox Darwinism to this: the dance, the spraying of scent, the recognition of scent, the whole astonishing behaviour of these bees, are habits which happen to have come into existence purely through chance; a bee one day danced for the first time and since it proved helpful it had survival value and the next generation of bees also danced—a complicated matter since the bees being neuters could not directly influence any offspring, could not pass on their habits themselves, so that we have really to assume that a queen bee suddenly developed a tendency to have offspring which danced, or understood when one of their number danced, and that this proving valuable in the struggle for existence, that particular queen bee's hive and her offsprings' hives survived.

But the dance which one must assume was caused by the action of the nectar on the body of the bee, although nectar had never had that effect upon the body of any other bee, was not the only new thing suddenly arriving at the same time; an ability to search out flowers and to compare scents, to refrain from dancing when the nectar was gathered and all sorts of other things all rushed together by mistake and produced a complicated instinctive behaviour, inheritable by other bees, without purpose, mind or memory. It is impossible to pretend that it is any easier to believe this than to believe in special creation.

How then are we to "save the phenomena"? There is only one way and that is by limiting the power of "blind chance" and assuming the dominance of "mind" and memory in all these strange happenings; in believing, in short, that an animal has the organism and uses it in the way it does because it *remembers* from past experience, when, instead of being itself, it was its ancestors, that just that organism is useful, and just that way of using it the best.

The first man who popularised this idea that mind and memory are clues which have to be assumed as well as the other two clues before the phenomena of evolution can be explained, was, as we have seen, Samuel Butler. We already know how he pointed out that a day-old baby can do a great many things which it obviously has not learnt in its present twenty-four hours' existence: "shall we say," he wrote, "that a baby of a day old sucks (which involves the whole principle of the pump, and hence a profound knowledge of the laws of pneumatics and hydrostatics), digests, oxygenises its blood (millions of years before Sir Humphry Davy discovered Oxygen), sees and hears—all most difficult and complicated operations, involving a knowledge of the facts concerning optics and acoustics, compared with which the discoveries of Newton sink into utter insignificance—shall we say that a baby can do all these things at once, doing them so well and so regularly, without even being able to direct attention to them, and without a mistake, and at the same time not know how to do them and never have done them before?"

The baby does them "instinctively," that is it knows how to do them so well because it has done them such countless numbers of times before, when it was its father, grandfather and so on back to Adam. And so with all living beings; the bees dance and spray scent, not because they have been taught, but because they already knew how before they were born. When the living being is faced with a given situation it behaves as it did when it last found itself in that situation. What happens when it meets a new situation? Either it dies because it cannot think of anything to do, or it makes some necessary alteration in its organism to meet the new situation. Its offspring remember in their turn what to do and change their organism in the same way and we have what we call an inherited variation, the product of mind and memory working out sensible solutions to the problems of life. The existence of some sort of unconscious memory would account for the fact that, although there is so much variety about in nature, yet species do remain fixed—a fact just as surprising as that new and different forms arise out of old ones; the living being is forced to behave as it remembers behaving before, except when a new line of conduct becomes necessary. And to memory must be added the ability to think for itself, that is to vary, and to act upon its thought so far as environment will permit. The orchids then are not lucky, but cunning, and the story of their loves is a story of a million years of intrigue rather than of blind throws of dice or spinnings of the wheel of fortune. It happens also, as we have seen, that the orchids have been too clever by half, and wasted much ingenuity with no result worth having.

§ 7

It is probable that the future Einstein of biology will look at the loves of orchids somewhat along these lines and that by including memory and mind among his clues he will succeed in "saving the phenomena"; but a good deal will have to be done before such a view can become scientifically satisfactory. In the first place, psychology will have to show us the machinery whereby the living being remembers what its own ancestors did. We already know that every living cell of a man alive today is actually part of the cells in his earliest ancestor's body; are these cells stamped with the memory of everything that has happened since Adam? If so, not until demonstrable evidence is found proving it, can it be accepted scientifically. This does not, of course, mean that we must be able to *see* the evidence, any more than a physicist is expected to see an electron, but we must be able to test it by controlling its results and prophesying future results; for the only way of proving the "truth" of a scientific hypothesis is by using it to produce correct prophecies.

Hitherto biologists have been in a peculiar position; their labours have been rather contemptuously regarded by those who work in physics or one of the other "exact" sciences, and yet they certainly have not allowed themselves the flights of imagination which are everyday occurrences among the physicists. While the exact scientist has proved the futility of the human senses, biologists are determined only to see what lies in front of their noses. They are perfectly right not to risk the fundamentalist God slipping in by a back entrance or a weakly fastened shutter; but sooner or later they will have to be bold and advance a hypothesis which may be misunderstood and misused, namely, that whether or not the universe has a purpose, life most certainly has, and that life in the present is bound by memory of a sort to life in the past, and by forethought to life in the future. Mere faith in blindness cannot lead us far enough.

It is, of course, no part of our present task to follow biology into the future, but it will be clear to the reader that already ideas about man and life are in the melting pot. We know that the materialism of a Haeckel does not solve all sorts of biological problems, and yet we had got into the habit of letting it solve philosophical problems into the bargain! Sooner or later biologists are going to give us even greater shocks than the physicists and our overbeliefs will change in consequence; at present we can only say that Darwin seems almost as far away as Newton, and that we have not found a way of supplementing him yet. The mere knowledge that there is so much more to be found than we realised fifty years ago has freed the atmosphere from a certain Victorian stuffiness and is exhilarating and stimulating us even though our picture of the universe on the biological side seems little more than an empty canvas. At least we have the painting before us and the hope that the picture will be excellent, rather than the regret that it has not turned out as well as we hoped.

§ 8

The New Renaissance comes then from the scientific picture of a new universe and a new man within it. The modern man would have to explain to the self which stopped growing intellectually in 1900 that physics has destroyed utterly the universe in which he believed, painting in its stead a far more exciting and stimulating canvas. He would further have to explain that biology has begun to rub out its nineteenth century picture of man, and is hard at work thinking out the sort of picture to put in its place. But there is one other element in the New Renaissance, which, in a way, has produced a greater change in man's attitude to life than the scarcely understood revolutions of physics or the embryonic novelties of biology. It is the element brought into our lives since 1900 and inevitably crystallised about one name, the name of Sigmund Freud.

Our survey of the New Renaissance would be grossly inadequate if we were to say nothing of Freud and his effect upon the human outlook on life: and yet it is not necessary to describe to the reader what he cannot fail to know already, seeing that psychoanalysis, its truths, its half-truths, its jargon have penetrated to every drawing-room in the civilised world.

The science of psychology differs from the other sciences only in having been for a rather longer period than they a mere branch of theology. We have seen how astronomy, even, began as a search for God, that is, as theology. Not until the time of Laplace could it be said to have a quite separate existence. Only with Freud did psychology cease altogether to be a search into the human soul regarded as free from all the ordinary laws of matter and machinery. In 1900 the intelligent man would argue: "I quite agree with Darwin that the human body obeys the same laws of evolution as an animal; but not his soul. We read in Genesis that God breathed into man *a living soul* and that I regard as the distinction between him and all other living beings." In 1930 this line of argument is less popular.

Because Freud has been the destructor for many people of the last ditches of supernatural theology he has been called a materialist; and yet the whole of modern psychology is a revolt from anything which the nineteenth century would have called materialism. It lays stress upon thought and not on the machinery which produces it. One instance will suffice to show this: during the war many soldiers suffered from "shell-shock," a terrible complaint as a result of which they had hallucinations and delusions of many kinds. Representatives of the old psychology examined some of the victims and found that their brains were covered with little dots of blood: they therefore attributed these delusions and other mental symptoms to "punctiform hæmorrhages," a purely material cause. The adherents of the newer psychology said that under the strain of war, feelings, thoughts, emotions long buried, repressed beneath the threshold of consciousness, had broken out and insisted upon the attention of the sufferer, who in his delusions acted out his desires and lived in a world of imagination where he could achieve what was impossible of achievement in the world of reality.

Whether such an attitude is right or wrong does not here and now matter to us: the overbeliefs which Freud has made possible may be wise or foolish, correct or mistaken, it does not alter the fact that they have captured our imaginations and altered our attitude towards life. And their chief effects are to be found in the most practical parts of our everyday philosophy, in questions of conduct and behaviour. The picture of the universe which includes a Freudian tinge can never inspire the same attitude towards moral questions as a picture without it.

There is something peculiarly attractive to the man who finds himself cramped by the spirit of 1900, in being told that although it is perfectly true that the chemical condition of his blood may affect his thoughts, nevertheless his thoughts are just as able to affect the makeup of his blood. It gives him a sense of freedom and an emotion of exaltation which, though they may not be scientifically justified, lead to the building of a different sort of over-belief from the previous one. Why the average man regards his thoughts as being more remarkable than his blood and prefers them to rule the other, we need not consider, but that this is so we must all admit. We do not see our thoughts die and we have all seen clotted blood; which probably helps to explain our attitude. A non-materialistic psychology such as that of Freud, therefore, comes as a messenger of freedom.

It is moreover noteworthy that the fact that the new psychology seems to give more than it takes away shows that men do not necessarily want the things which theologians have made them think that they want. The sort of things which have been destroyed completely are inspiration, intuition, survival of personality—for the personality which emerges from the new psychology makes the thought of its survival an absurdity—all the things which made life seem bearable to monks, nuns, ascetics and puritans; and the things which have been given instead are the elimination of the old idea of sin, temptation, the devil, and a justification of joy in life and every healthy desire. Of course everybody must decide exactly what this means in their own lives for themselves, and their is room for disagreement and the building of conflicting codes; but all that we need say here is that the overbeliefs which arise from the new idea of man's soul, added to the new ideas of his body and his dwelling place, the universe, will necessitate a new and happier morality and an increased capacity for enjoying this life.

C. Man and His Universe

§ 1

Here then is a new picture of the universe and here too for all intents is the making of a new man. What will the new man do with the universe he has created anew? At present, of course, the implications of the revolution going on about us ever since 1900 have not sunk into our imagination: we go on with our general ideas about life in a mixture of medievalism and nineteenth century science: we have not grown up with the more recent science, we did not drink it in with our mother's milk and so it is not yet part of our nature. But already certain elements are beginning to cause rearrangements in our mind, to alter the emphasis here and there and to prepare us for fresh adventures to be undertaken soon.

As so often happens we first of all accept the magic of a word: just as in 1900 the word "evolution" struck the imagination of the epoch and was wrested from the hands of the biologist to become the darling of the plain man; so today the word which seems most full of magic is undoubtedly "relativity." The history of those two words is almost identical; they began as names for highly significant rearrangements of ideas in limited fields of science; they spread from their original contexts until they became the symbol of the attitude of an age towards the biggest problems of life. Evolution was the watchword of rebels against social injustice; relativity is becoming the watchword of rebels against the tyrannies of obsolete moral judgements and too inflexible rules of life. In neither case were the facts and ideas which became grouped under the magic word particularly new, but the word illuminated them and added force. It is a wise father that knows his own children and certainly Darwin and Einstein must have been surprised at what their labours have brought forth.

Relativity has the great advantage over evolution as a magic word in that it is more mysterious: the number of people who know that relativity theory is vastly important and vastly beyond their grasp adds to the strength of the desire to use relativity as a symbol; to get a vicarious pleasure by way of analogy. Nor is this an altogether regrettable thing, for, as we have seen again and again, it is the overbelief that science gives mankind that really justifies science.

The idea of relativity has come as an inspiration to all those who find themselves in revolt, emotionally and spiritually, against the ideas about human nature which have been accepted by Western civilisation for centuries. Of course Einstein's relativity has nothing at all to do with human nature, but the mere fact that he has shown that the ideas we have of time and space and of the very stuff of the universe are not as absolute in their nature as everyone supposed leads by a natural gradation to the focusing of attention upon the far greater relativity of human nature.

"As things have been, they remain," and "you cannot get away from human nature"; these two platitudes, though they may still represent the outlook of most un-imaginative folk, no longer contain any meaning or threat for those who have extracted the new overbelief, the new philosophy of life, which arises naturally out of the new picture of the universe wherein relativity is a reigning principle.

Thus relativity soon ceases to be merely a doctrine of the higher physics and becomes a way of looking at things which is valuable in the age-long fight of the younger generation of the moment against the tyranny of tradition. This current tradition of western Europe is to a large extent Platonic in its main outlines and rests on a belief, unconscious at least, in absolute existences apart from time and space; but in the new picture of the universe Plato has been largely left out, as we must now proceed to show.

The orthodox outlook on human nature—that thing from which you cannot get away—included a belief in the Economic Man. Men, we were told, were always selfish, nor could anybody be expected to work unless hunger and elementary needs forced him to work. The last scientific picture of the universe rather encouraged this particular overbelief by adapting the idea of the survival of the fittest and the struggle for existence to such questions as the value of private enterprise as an

inducement to work; and in this way biology found itself
used as a means of short circuiting all sorts of generous
hopes of changing social conditions for the better; such
changes cannot be successful, for man is limited by his
selfishness and laziness; "you cannot get away from
human nature"; competition is the breath of life. Thus
the same scientific picture of the universe which gave
revolutionary socialists a rational basis for their overbelief, supplied an overbelief for their opponents; while
Prince Kropotkin, the great Russian anarchist, hit back
by writing a book to show that "mutual aid" was as great
a factor in evolution as the struggle for existence, and
that animals survive as much by helping one another as
by being red in tooth and claw.

This theory of man's essential laziness except under the
scourge of necessity was, and indeed still is, held as an
article of faith by most men, just as all medieval scientists
believed that a spider surrounded by a circle of powdered
unicorn's horn could not escape. The Royal Society investigated the matter of the spider in 1650 and exploded
it by the simple method of experiment; as the minutes
of the meeting say, "a circle was made withe powder
of a unicorn's horn and a spider set in the middle of
it, but it immediately ran out." Now the question as
to whether the economic man exists and is essentially lazy
could very well be proved or disproved in precisely the
same way, namely, by looking about for evidence and
approaching in a scientific spirit the question: does human nature everywhere satisfy the conditions by which
such a belief is justified?

It is here that the magic of words like evolution and
relativity can be seen most clearly. There are always

sufficient facts lying about to prove or disprove anything about human conduct; one set of facts is drawn as by a magnet to evolution, another set to relativity; evolution supported the overbelief in the necessity of a struggle for existence; relativity, though it originally is concerned with a four-dimensional space-time frame, lends itself to the discovery of opposite tendencies in human nature, and magnetises facts hitherto neglected. It becomes the general who deploys the multifarious knowledge of the anthropologist.

For it is to the anthropologist that we owe the knowledge that the economic man is a fiction, since he is able to show us that many communities do not act as they should, were the economic man a reality. Let us glance at his facts.

To begin with, there is the idea that at all times and in all places men will work only to gain their daily bread. Let us look at the behaviour of a native of the Trobriand Islands, off the coast of New Guinea. The Trobrianders are great cultivators of gardens in which they produce yams. The believer in the economic man will assume that in this task each man will cultivate the garden in the most labour-saving way known to him; that he will work to produce only as much as he requires for his family to eat; that in order to do his work well he must have the inducement of enjoying the fruits of his labour; in short, that he works, rather than idles, from motives of enlightened self-interest.

In actual fact none of these assumptions is correct: the gardener spends much time on unproductive labour, decorating his garden and using better quality materials than are needed for the proper growth of the plants; he grows far more yams than he can use, and cheerfully leaves half the harvest, if it is abundant, to rot; and finally, he is content with a social convention which allows him only one-quarter of his harvest for his own use and makes him give away the rest chiefly to his relations-in-law. "The Trobriander," says Malinowski, "works in a round about way, to a large extent for the sake of the work itself, and puts a great deal of æsthetic polish into the arrangement and general appearance of his garden. He is not guided primarily by a desire to satisfy his wants, but by a complex set of traditional forces, duties and obligations, beliefs in magic, social ambitions and vanities. He wants, if he is a man, to achieve social distinction as a good gardener and a good worker in general." In fact the Trobriander has got very far away from human nature as represented by the economic man.

It is worth while pointing out that such facts as these could be used just as effectively to support an opposite overbelief when evolution was the keynote to man's picture of the universe: the mere fact that Trobrianders have remained savages instead of mounting in the social scale to a position such as industrial Britain occupies—we can hear the Victorian scientist speaking—shows where such anti-economic conduct will lead a people; their failure to accept the rules of the struggle for existence has found them out. But under the reign of relativity the moral is quite different.

Let us take another example: competition is, we are told, the breath of life; human nature must be given the chance of beating rivals or the motive for industry will be removed. In fact many people represent money making—which is what they mean by industry—as

A. Einstein

"Thus it comes about, fantastic though it may sound, that men lie with their neighbours' wives denuded of the last shred of guilty conscience because observations of Mercury's perihelion enabled Einstein to alter our ideas about space-time!" (See p. 319.)

a great game. Now if there is one place in which we might expect competition to be an absolute necessity it is in sport: it is certainly human nature, we may assume, to want to win. Let us look for a moment, however, at the Nicobar Islanders and their sporting habits.

The Nicobarese delight in regattas, and an observer has described a race between two village crews and his conversation before the race with the chief of one of the competing villages. "I wanted to know which he considered the stronger team. 'They are both excellent,' he replied. In answer to my further inquiries I was told that there was no difference in skill between the two teams— neither party could be bettered. I also found out that there is no starting point and no winning post; and that whilst they competed side by side, struggling for all they were worth, if one side begins to find that it is getting a little ahead of the other it will very soon slacken off a bit and let the others get ahead, that neither the hosts nor the guests may shame one another." There will be no disputing that human nature among the Nicobarese is different as far as boat races are concerned from human nature in America or England; the activity is the same, but the motive has been changed beyond recognition.

Or consider the New Zealand Maori as eaters of poultry. Certain of these natives, whose food is almost exclusively vegetarian, become obsessed from time to time with a craving for flesh and, to satisfy it, they organise bird-snaring expeditions; but again they do not behave like the economic man: the snares used to catch the birds are not made with the minimum of labour but are decorated with exquisite and laborious carving; when in the forest the Maori does not economise in time but spends hours

315

gathering up and burying the least little feather; on his return it does not for a moment occur to him that his bag is his own, but all birds are placed together in a common heap and shared out according to convention among the whole populace. "It is clear," says Raymond Firth, "that self interest alone is not the driving force in native industry, and that each man is also actuated to some degree by the wish to promote the welfare of the community of which he is a member."

Or let us examine certain of man's reactions to the incidents of his sex-life. Nothing seems so absolute and unchanging as sexual jealousy; at least no one would dispute the statement that it is part of human nature for a man to desire his betrothed to be chaste, and for a woman to resent having to share her husband with another. Nor is this last supposition altered by our knowledge that polygamy has existed in many communities: that happens, we explain, not by the consent of the women, but by their more degraded state of subjection.

Human nature in Nigeria, however, does not seem to strengthen either of these convictions. Among some communities there, we are told, betrothed couples may live together, but far from it being disgraceful for the girl to have a child, such an event increases her value and the bridegroom has to pay an extra bride price for her. In other tribes, if a girl betrothed to one man has a child by another, her betrothed does not break the engagement; far from it, he claims the infant as his own property into the bargain. In other cases "no stigma attaches to the girl who bears a child before marriage. The child is claimed by the girl's family unless the father of the child was the girl's betrothed and had paid the

bride price in full. As to the woman's point of view
towards polygamy, the wealthy man has more than one
wife, for it is commonly the woman who incites her husband to add to the number of his wives, no doubt with
a view to lightening her domestic burdens." In other
words, we are forced to assume that so basic a part of
human nature as human jealousy is not absolute, but relative to the accidents of particular circumstances.

With the assistance of the magic word "relativity" such
facts as these can be woven together to form a practical
philosophy of life of the greatest significance; and the
name of a physical theory becomes a dogma which alters
that part of religion which is concerned with a man's
duty towards his neighbour. The medieval picture of
the universe with its insistence that stones and stars alike
were made of things having the quality of good and evil;
that smoke, flame and mist could be measured in terms
of angelic and demonic power suggested that man was a
theatre where good and evil played their eternal drama
and mankind judged human conduct accordingly. A bad
act was a victory for the devil and a defeat for humanity
in general. The Newtonian picture with its emphasis on
law coincided with the raising of codes and conventions
to the highest place in the sphere of morality. Under the
magic word "evolution" crimes and sins were judged
by their effect upon the race, and individuals guilty of
them were unworthy of compassion since their actions
showed them to be unfit to survive. Relativity once more
shifts the emphasis: conduct must be judged not as an
incident in the eternal war between contending good
and evil; not as a breach or an observance of the one and
only sovereign code; not as a step forward or backward

in the evolution of the one and only superman; but as the result of a particular time and space, the product of a given environment, to be judged by standards dependent upon the context, and not upon eternal truth.

Why is the Trobriander actuated by different motives from those which actuate the ordinary working man of today in England or America? Clearly because his social milieu calls forth a different set of responses. He can stamp his individuality upon his work, whereas an age of standardisation deprives the worker of that possibility; and if we ask why the idea that man works for bread alone is more true with us today than with the Maori or Trobriander, the answer is to be found in the effect of our institutions upon human nature. Put the son of a bricklayer in infancy with the family of a Trobriand gardener, he will grow up with the traditional outlook towards yam culture of his foster parents. And from this it follows logically that a different set of institutions in the future may alter the human motives behind action and work, just as they have been so frequently altered in the past.

So too with our attitude towards the criminal. Evolution encouraged the idea that he was one of nature's failures doomed to extinction and artificially kept alive to the great danger of the human future; that the main problem with regard to him is how to protect the community from his depredations. Relativity lays the emphasis on the cause of his conduct being his environment: given all the factors of the case he had to act as he did, and whether or not society has to be protected from him, nevertheless, it must treat him with the consideration due to his having acted on compulsion.

Questions of morality follow the same changing course, for the idea, which Einstein's physics expresses by saying that two observers moving with certain velocities relative to one another will believe that a single event took place at two different times and will both be right, is the same idea which poetry expresses in the sentence "one law for the lion and the ox is oppression." Thus it comes about, fantastic though it may sound, that men lie with their neighbour's wives denuded of the last shred of a guilty conscience because observations of the changes of Mercury's perihelion enabled Einstein to alter our ideas about space-time! It is true, because although in one generation men first do what they want and afterwards invoke Einstein as an excuse, in the next Einstein becomes the philosophy which encourages the act. One generation's rationalisation becomes the next generation's example. It is because of this that all inquisitors and censors are perfectly right from their point of view in trying to thwart all new sciences, for the moral code of an age is a function of its picture of the universe and when this picture changes so does the moral code.

§ 2

So far we have considered only the most superficial effect of the new picture of the universe on man's religion and morals. Relativity as a magic word is a heading beneath which a number of facts can be arranged to give strength to a certain kind of overbelief. With its help an orthodox view of man's duty towards his neighbour and of right and wrong in human conduct is attacked. Well schooled by the age of Darwin to regard the laws

governing scientific phenomena as models for those governing moral phenomena, rebellious youth sees the sword
which wounded it bent back against the body of its
oppressor.

But we must hurry on to the more profound aspects
of the coming change: are these to be found in new
answers to the old questions? What does the new picture
of the universe offer us by way of immortality? Science
limits the possible overbeliefs, as we have seen, by de-
manding that they shall not be nonsensical when equated
with its picture of the universe; for the facts we know
about the universe are as food which our mind swallows
and digests: just as we cannot tell that the food our
stomach digests will become leg tissue rather than arm
tissue, but can tell that it will not become wing tissue, so
with the produce of our mental digestion of the universe;
we can rule out certain things and reduce the choice,
though we can perhaps do no more.

What then may the modern man think about
immortality?

One thing is certain, that our ideas about our own
immortality are to some extent limited by whether or
not the universe as a whole is immortal. Suppose we are
at a village fair and go for a ride on the merry-go-round:
when the merry-go-round stops, three possible things
may happen to us. Either we wait until the merry-go-
round begins again and repeat our past experiences once
or many times more, or we leave the merry-go-round and
sit down at a table in a gaudy tent to tea and light refresh-
ments, or the lights go out, the sounds and movements
cease and night blots out the closed and completed fair.
So with the universe and ourselves: when our little round

has ended we may begin all over again as Buddhists believe, or we may sit down to tea elsewhere, or all may be finished.

Now Aristotle and medieval Christians believed that whereas the earth and all that happens on it are evanescent, imperfect and temporary, the spheres above know no change; their life and motion are perfect and eternal. The great hope which lay at the bottom of all dogmatic intricacies for medieval and later Christians was that Christ's teaching and action were promises that after life on earth a remnant of the faithful would be transferred from the temporary earthly sphere to the permanent, infinitely lasting celestial spheres. That is why when Galileo showed that the new star which blazed forth where no star had been before was in the regions of the fixed stars, all his contemporaries were offended and infuriated: for if there could be change up there, what could be said for the chances of an unchanging immortality above the bright blue sky! To deny the crucifixion of Christ was scarcely a greater challenge to their hope of immortality than to suggest that change and impermanence could be found in the region of the stars. In short, the idea of immortality taught for so long by orthodox Christianity depended upon the idea of the universe in which Christians believed. Galileo's new star upset not only the idea of the universe but the idea of immortality.

Science has shown quite conclusively that there is no other place in the universe to which we can hope to be transferred out of this, so as to escape change and to discover changelessness. The modern man therefore gives up the kind of picture of immortality which seemed quite natural to anyone who imagined the universe consisting of the earth in the centre and outside it a succession of eternal spheres.

Now let us look at the Newtonian universe and consider what sort of immortality could be imagined in that. Here we have a machine, a watch, constructed by a definite watchmaker, almost perfect, but requiring now and then little adjustments. Since the watchmaker is proud of his watch he will keep it well adjusted and so make it go on for ever just as it is now. Many people having the Newtonian picture of the universe still keep the medieval picture of immortality, but there is a great difference in their reason for keeping it. They imagine God taking them out of the watch and therefore out of time and space into an existence which has nothing to do with time or space. Medieval immortality went on in another part of space, Newtonian immortality must go on out of space altogether. Therefore all that part of us which occupies space must disappear and that does not only mean our bodies, but our ideas about people or things indiscriminately, if they involve space. If you can think of anything at all in your feelings, desires, knowledge, ideas of your neighbours or of yourself, which does not involve space, that you can hope to keep in an immortality outside space.

But, of course, there might be an immortality within the Newtonian universe: you might start all over again on Jupiter or elsewhere in a better climate and among more agreeable people, or alternatively, of course, somewhere where climate at any rate was worse. If this repetition was endless it would be immortality and with a Newtonian god carefully superintending a Newtonian

universe there is no reason why it should ever end. Thus
the Newtonian picture of the universe gives us a chance
of an intelligible picture of immortality—after all is said
and done no picture of immortality *outside space* is intelligible—although it is obviously not as satisfactory as that
given by the medieval picture of the universe. But the
Newtonian picture of the universe has been shown, in one
important particular especially, to be utterly wrong. The
universe as a whole is not a machine, which, once constructed and completed, works perfectly as long as it is
adjusted and carefully overhauled; it is far more like an
animal which is born, grows, declines and dies.

The modern man, who will inevitably see his picture
of immortality in the light of his picture of the universe,
must realise that, whatever he may think about himself,
the universe as a whole seems to be moving very slowly,
but very surely, towards complete annihilation. In about
one million million years the universe will have changed
into a state which will practically mean non-existence:
instead of stars and planets and nebulæ, lumps of matter
all of them, there will be no matter left but only a uniform mist of radiation, a huge spherical ghost of matter
filling the place of the earth, moon, stars and interstellar
chasms at a temperature of more than two hundred and
fifty degrees below freezing point.

A million million years may seem a long time but it
is short compared with the time that has already elapsed.
"We can estimate," says Jeans, "the future life of the
present matter of the universe from the rate at which it
is transforming itself into radiation, but we can only fix
a lower limit to its past life. Even so, this lower limit is
so long as to create a suspicion that we may have appeared

on the scene rather late in the history of the universe; possibly the main drama of the universe is over, and our lot is merely to watch the unwanted ends of lighted candles burning themselves out on an empty stage." It is in a universe such as this that the modern man finds himself puzzling about his own immortality.

Let us fill in the picture with a few more details. It is believed by astronomical physicists that about two thousand million years ago another star passed near enough to our sun to produce a huge tide of matter by its gravitational pull; and this rendered the sun unstable, so that it split up into smaller masses rotating round the biggest mass. This was the beginning of the earth and other planets as separate bodies moving round the sun. This sort of accident is rare in the universe and indeed can only have happened to about one star in every hundred thousand and only at intervals of about five thousand million years. In other words, we can calculate from the number of the stars and their distances from one another that once in five thousand million years two stars come near enough to inaugurate a planetary system; that is, to produce the only condition which makes life a possibility, since no life is possible except upon a solid cooled-down fragment warmed by the rays of a still luminous sun. Since it is only two thousand million years since our particular accident took place we are probably the youngest solar system in the universe. "If," says Jeans, "each planetary system in the universe contain ten planets, and life and civilisation appear in due course on each, then civilisations appear in the galactic system at an average rate of one per 500 million years. It follows that we should have to visit 50,000 galaxies before finding a civilisation as young as our own. And as we have only studied cosmogony for 200 years, we should have to search through about 25 million galaxies, if they exist, before encountering cosmogonists as primitive as ourselves. We may well be the most ignorant cosmogonists in the whole of space."

To these words let us add the concluding paragraph of Jeans' great book [1] in which we see the scientist asking himself those very questions which the modern man must ask if he seeks to find the value for his imagination, for his humanity, of the picture of the universe drawn in such a work: "What is the significance of the vast processes it portrays? What is the meaning, if any there be which is intelligible to us, of the vast accumulations of matter, which appear, on our present interpretations of space and time, to have been created only in order that they may destroy themselves? What is the relation of life to the universe, of which, if we are right, it can occupy only so small a corner? What if any, is our relation to the remote nebulæ, for surely there must be some more direct contact than that light can travel between them and us in a hundred million years? Do their colossal incomprehending masses come nearer to representing the main ultimate reality of the universe, or do we? Are we merely part of the same picture as they, or is it possible that we are part of the artist? Are they perchance only a dream, while we are braincells in the mind of the dreamer? Or is our importance measured solely by the fractions of space and time we occupy?"

And so once more, what does the modern picture of the universe do to the modern man's belief in his own

[1] J. H. Jeans, *Astronomy and Cosmogony*, Cambridge, 1928.

immortality? Does it take away all possibility of existence after death? It does not. Does it hold out any probability of such existence? No. It does something far more revolutionary, it suggests raw material for the human imagination far more stimulating, far more satisfying than any speculation about biological death and its results; so that anyone embarking upon a study of the universe in the hopes of finding hints about his personal destiny therein, soon forgets his quest in the infinitely more exciting question of the destiny of the universe.

The truth is that desire for immortality is not a natural desire in the least; it is the artificial by-product of a certain picture of the universe; a habit like smoking, drug taking or gambling which grows on one, but had to be consciously stimulated at first: the savage desired it because his ideas about death and his conception of the world in which he lived required it; much as fairies and Santa Claus and witches and guardian angels are of value to the child. In the Middle Ages a belief in immortality fitted perfectly into the cosmology of orthodox scholarship and the lengthy reign of medievalism made us so deeply accustomed to the thought, that we have allowed ourselves to be convinced that without hope of immortality we should be wretched indeed. And yet children, who have not been accustomed to the idea from the cradle, and scientists, who have better things to think about, are certainly not in any way less happy as a class than the orthodox believers.

Far from being the natural instinct of a healthy mind, the desire for immortality is the symptom of a disease; of the worst of all diseases, that of unhappiness coming from starved ways of living. For those who lead empty lives another life is needed as recompense and the cure for an itch for immortality is to live this life more abundantly. After all immortality is but an exaggerated degree of "length of days": you can imagine a man living to be a hundred by wrapping himself up in cotton wool, eating synthetic food and never worrying about anything; but his life would be shorter in true enjoyment than that of many a man dead at fifty. Length of days is intensive rather than extensive, and so is immortality. Fill every hour with all that can stimulate the imagination, and immortality will be remembered as little as death. The free man's meditation, said Spinoza, is of life and not of death, and the free man is he whose fears and envies and covetousness have been liquidated in the fires of imagination. That is why science today is a liberator, because it is far more exciting even than music and poetry, since the picture it draws of the universe exceeds anything invented by mythologies. That is why it is the ignorant stunted fear-ridden man and not the scientist who bothers about immortality.

But, you say, there are more Babbitts than scientists in the world and they have a right to be served. This is true enough, but every Babbitt is at liberty to flood his mind with the pleasure of science and to make himself free of fear by knowing the truth, for just as ordinary poetry pleases the reader as well as the poet, so too the superlative kind of poetry which the scientist translates from the language of the stars can be the property of all men alike.

The modern man then can get no knowledge of his destiny from knowledge of the universe; if he is to be immortal it is in spite of rather than because of the universe, as modern science sees it; but he will find that if he allows himself to be disciplined into thinking clearly, he will derive that tranquillity of emotion that all the high priests of the world have tried in vain to give; for science is the putting way of childish things and the finding of adult forms of longing. It is an emancipation from useless obsessions which occupy the minds of most unfortunate men; how useless we realise when we see one half humanity embracing religions like Christianity because of their terror lest they should not be immortal, and the other half seeking in religions like Buddhism the means of escaping the immortality which they fear.

To all these science says that since time does not seem to be in the least what one had supposed, it is as absurd to think one wants to stretch for ever through time as it would be to think one wanted to stretch for ever through space. In fact immortality is not a thing to be looked for in the future, but in the present where by living to the full one can experience eternity in an hour.

We may say then that the new picture of the universe neither gives men hope of immortality as did the medieval picture, nor takes it away as did the picture of 1900; it simply says that the idea has no kind of meaning and that one might as well hope for the square root of minus one. When people realise this they will very naturally stop thinking about immortality altogether, just as scientists have already done. Then instead of allowing themselves to be obsessed with death and its consequences they will be free men preoccupied with life.

§ 3

We have mentioned that time and space according to the new picture of the universe are regarded as parts of the same thing which the human mind has separated into very different ideas and accompanied with very different feelings. How it can be that what seems to one person a year may seem to another a billion miles is obviously incomprehensible to ordinary mortals, yet scientific reasoning based upon observations of actual phenomena makes it as certain as any proposition in Euclid, and far more certain than some of his axioms. "Space in itself and time in itself," says Minskowski, "sink to mere shadows, and only a kind of union of the two retains an independent existence."

That this makes a desire to live for ever as unintelligent as a desire to stretch from the earth to Sirius and beyond the farthest nebula seems quite inevitable; and it is typical of what the new picture of the universe is likely to do to all such human desires. For you must be able to imagine a thing to want it, and in the long run it is reality which stimulates imagination. If then the questions which human beings have habitually asked of the universe are shown to be meaningless, clearly no one will continue to ask them; but since man is habitually inquisitive other questions will be asked instead. Indeed the real importance of the new picture of the universe is not the answers it gives to old questions, but the new questions which it stimulates mankind to ask.

We all know a certain type of question which children sometimes ask and of which these are two typical examples: "What is that?" "That is a cow." "Why?"; and "Why is there only one Pope?" "Because the Pope is the head of the Church of Rome." "Why not of the cathedral?" Since the questions are altogether outside the plane of meaning, they are not answered and when the child matures they are not even asked. That is what has happened, or will happen to adults when the new knowledge of the universe produces a new outlook on life as a whole. People will begin to see that certain questions which they believed vital are just nonsense.

We must remember too that we are at the very beginning of the revolution: yesterday the newspaper announced that hydrogen had been split into two separate and distinct substances, which if true will administer a shock to chemistry; today a book of Jeans is reviewed which says that two nebulæ seen in one part of the sky may very well be the backs of the same bodies as can be seen in the opposite part of the sky, their light having gone all round the spherical universe and come back to us. Every day produces its first-class sensation and questions, not answers, are the most exciting things of all. In this turmoil one or two things stand out.

First, the picture of the universe against which the modern man must see himself contains a large number of subtle mathematical truths about the relations of things, but the things themselves are of such a nature that the human mind cannot imagine them. It would be hard to determine which is the less difficult to imagine, the Trinity or an electron. Moreover, some scientists, Eddington for example, go so far as to say that the laws which we understand are not laws at all but conventions erected by our minds to satisfy themselves and that the laws of quantum physics are the first real laws and may be known for such by the very fact that they do not satisfy the mind's craving for intelligibility. It is as if the universe had hitherto only explained itself in baby language to suit our infantile brains and was only just beginning to use proper conversational methods. This amounts to saying that the universe is really nonsense and that we cannot see this except with difficulty because of our inherent craving for sense. If this is so the modern scientist is taking the "I believe, because it is absurd" of the Christian schoolman and applying it to his own interests.

Now if scientists insist upon talking like this the modern man may feel himself entitled to say: "away with all your subtleties, I do not see that they can in any way affect my outlook on life in the same way as earlier pictures of the universe did whenever they were intelligible." But that also would be a mistake; apart from the fact that knowledge of these meaningless things like electrons cures him of cancer, reveals broken bones, lights his house and gives him telephony, wireless and television, the very suspicion of their existence and their nature affects his imagination in general ways. Moreover, it is quite possible that sooner or later we shall make an even greater use of the irrational things within the atom in everyday life and that will familiarize us with irrationality.

After all size is an unimportant thing: it so happens that the human body is almost as much bigger than an atom as it is smaller than an average star; owing to the nature of his senses man sees things enormously bigger than himself much more easily than things enormously smaller than himself; and of course custom makes him

partial to the particular scale to which he happens to be
made. But suppose that a particular atom was not only
like the solar system in having a nucleus or sun and
planets running round it, but also in size; and that man
was on one of the electrons studying the behaviour of
his atomic system. Instead of expecting a rigid deter-
minism which would make the future prophesiable from
observation of natural laws, he would assume that anything might happen; instead of wondering if he was a
creature with free will caught in a deterministic universe,
he might even wonder if his own actions were determined while observation showed that the parts of his
universe had free will. Only an accident of size makes
us accept as normal what we see in the solar system and
jib at what we see in the atom; and perhaps some day
now, that the curtain is down, our infra-atomic life will
become more conscious and we shall take for granted
the reasonableness not only of the mechanics of the solar
system but of that of the atom. We may even learn to
be denizens of the solar system when we want to be
reasonable and, when we do not, retire within the atom!

In the second place, the new picture of the universe,
as we have seen, makes a totally different use of man's
senses. It will probably influence the modern man's view
of life considerably when his imagination grasps the
fact that things are never what they seem. Even if the
difference becomes important only when things are going
at speeds approximating to that of light or when things
are as small as electrons, it is disconcerting to find that
William Blake was in some measure perfectly right.

We shall have to get used to the fact that though
Euclid is good enough for practical purposes like laying

railway lines, and that the two rails will never meet all the way from New York to Los Angeles, nevertheless for the vast distances and velocities of our cosmic dreams, Euclid is of no use to us whatever. There is something in the realisation that our senses are at once the windows and the blinds revealing and obscuring the universe that adds a new tang of adventure to the joy of hunting for reality.

But there is something else besides our senses of which it could be said equally that it is at once the windows and the blinds revealing and obscuring the universe: and that is our language. When you say "what is the time?" or "I feel cold" you know perfectly well what you mean by time and cold and you assume that the scientist has the decency to mean the same thing. Probably he did start off with honest intentions and not realising that the circumstances of his search would lead him astray. But what are we to make of such a sentence as this: "the final fate of the white dwarf (a star like the companion of Sirius) is to become at the same time the hottest and the coldest matter in the universe. Because the star is intensely hot it has enough energy to cool down if it wants to; because it is so intensely cold it has stopped radiating and no longer wants to grow any colder." Clearly it only means something once we agree that coldness and heat are not to be taken to mean what we usually mean by them. Thus if we are to understand the universe at all the first step is to learn a new language: that will reduce the amount of apparent meaninglessness in what scientists have to tell us.

When we are impatient about some of these nonsensical statements let us remember that in the mathematical language invented by physicists for the study of the universe they are perfectly sensible, it is when they are translated into English that the trouble begins.

§ 4

In 1543, 1643 and 1900 we invited the modern man to seat himself at his study table and consider the knowledge of the universe which lay about him and from the cosmic picture that resulted to construct his outlook upon life. In 1930 we will ask him to do something a little different: let him walk out into the winter night and let his imagination run freely to and from the stars above his head. Low down on the horizon he will see Sirius flashing: when he was a savage, Sirius was his timepiece by which he reckoned the passage of the year; when he was a medieval philosopher, Sirius the dog-star seemed to have serious effects upon those whose births it was able to influence; Galen whose art cured or sought to cure mankind for a thousand years, recommends a sick man to make medicine by burning a live river crab on a plate of red bronze after the Dog-star has risen and when the sun is in the constellation Leo. On this night of 1930 the modern man knows that hidden in the rays of Sirius is a faint companion star made up of matter so closely packed together that it is sixty thousand times denser than water, so that a cubic inch of it weighs about a ton.

Not far away from Sirius is the constellation of Orion; so called because in savage days human imagination could do no better than think of these scattered stars as the figure of a great hunter, shooting and slaying in the sky, as once he had hunted on the earth below. Now in

334

1930 the modern man knows that the brightest of these stars, Betelgeuse, is far bigger than the whole orbit of the earth about the sun. Here matter is only one-millionth as dense as water. Of this star Eddington says: "According to the modern theory of gravitation, a globe of the size of Betelgeuse and of the same mean density as the sun would have some remarkable properties: owing to the great intensity of its gravitation, light would be unable to escape; and any rays shot out would fall back again to the star by their own weight. . . . Mass produces a curvature of space, and in this case the curvature would be so great that space would close up round the star, leaving us outside—that is to say, *nowhere*."

Among the constellations he can make out one or two planets, wandering stars, shining, he thinks, with a steadier light; once upon a time, when he was still one of his ancestors, he was convinced that these stars, Venus, Jupiter, Saturn and the rest, were actively employed in wrecking or making his fortune. So as to predict the future he made elaborate observations and calculations, invented eccentrics and epicycles, and from these found whether or not next year was propitious for his business. Now he knows that these planets have never given him a thought; that they wander round the sun according to the laws of gravitation; that he has nothing whatever to hope or fear from them or any other star.

If he had a telescope he could see nebulæ which were themselves great stellar systems, often bigger than all the galaxy of bright points he sees about him. In such a universe there is room to think and to feel expansively!

But above everything he knows that his own body is composed of atoms and electrons of extraordinary vigour and of precisely the same nature as those crushed close together in the companion star of Sirius, or nodding distantly to each other across vast interatomic distances in Betelgeuse. He will be left wondering how it has come about that whereas most atoms throughout the universe have simply joined one another to form masses at which he can look, a few here and there have coalesced to form far smaller masses, like himself, which can do the looking! He and the universe are reduced to electrons and atoms seeing and being seen.

This must for ever remain the main mystery, how some atoms have developed the quality of thinking about the rest; and the more we know of the universe, its vast extent, its minute structure, the more we realise how much there is to see, the more surprising it will be that we, atoms and electrons as we are, are here to see it. Would Betelgeuse exist, if we had not learned to know of its existence? Does Betelgeuse see us? Who that is alive to the questions that can be asked can dare to pretend that science has destroyed the splendour of the heavens, or the glory of the universe? The truth is that nobody has yet been able to imagine a God splendid enough or glorious enough, æsthetically or ethically, to capture the imagination of man once it has become alive to what modern science can show it lying about its feet or hanging overhead. There is certainly as much beauty in the music of the spheres discovered to us by modern physics as in the greatest earthly music, if we can use our brains to capture it; and since, where man finds the greatest beauty, there will his reverence be, the modern man worships the human intellect which has drawn a picture of the universe infinitely more beautiful than any system of theology has disclosed. Science has increased the æsthetic value of the night sky.

And as these thoughts occur to the modern man standing under the frosty stars, the sound of people enjoying themselves comes to him from somewhere near by. These people will probably never read a book of science in their lives and will never realise whence comes their greatest pieces of good fortune. But we are able to judge what the New Renaissance with its new picture of the universe has done for them; and we can sum up its chief gift in a phrase—it has eliminated from their lives nine-tenths of the fear which dominated the lives of their ancestors.

Let us think the worst of these night revellers: let us assume that they are breaking the law and the commandments; it is the fashion to think and speak ill of the younger generation! Fifty years ago they would have been making illicit love just as much as they may be now; but then whatever beauty might have been in their emotions would have been destroyed by fear; fear of venereal disease, fear of pregnancy, fear of a curiously mean avenging God. Perhaps these fears kept them "good": but it is surely better to be bad because of Freud and Margaret Sanger than good because of that trinity of fears! The new picture of the universe has certainly altered our attitude towards morals and only a hypocrite can pretend that the Ten Commandments mean what they did.

It is not necessary to inquire too closely what these revellers are doing. It is true that a chorus comes from certain quarters that jazz, cheap cars, hip flasks, the movies, psychoanalysis, birth control and modernism are wrecking the home, marriage, love, innocence, purity and many other high-sounding things; and there can be no doubt that great changes are taking place in what people regard as "moral" for them to do. We have seen in an earlier chapter that science and conscience are linked together; all that we have been studying leads us to believe that the picture of the universe which dominates an epoch will mould the outlook on life and morals, the religion and the God of the epoch; and that explains why in the forge of the New Renaissance people are no longer ashamed of doing what shocked their grandmothers.

What if the revellers do not possess the desire for ritual purity, the horror of certain physical defilements, the respect for biological virginity which suited the shuddering superstitions of the Middle Ages! They have shed with these muddy garments another garment, covered not only with mud but with human blood and tears, the garment of fear. The revellers are not afraid and the importance of that is that perhaps lack of fear will bring lack of cruelty. Cruelty has usually been the result of fear and the picture of the universe which has lessened the one may, we hope, in time lessen the other.

Science by destroying the old sanctions of morality has destroyed the old morality as well; inevitably however a new morality, a new overbelief comes to take its place. The trouble with the revellers is not that they are immoral—whether they are or not is a matter of opinion—it is that possibly they are vulgar. How is that? It is because, though science determines morality, science without art can do nothing against vulgarity. If then there is legitimate ground for complaint against the revellers, it is not because science has made them lose their fear of what frightened their parents, but because poetry has not yet built up a lovely structure of emotions and ideals in which they may live. All that has ever separated us from the cats on the garden wall has been the words of the Shelleys, Shakespeares, Donnes, Brownings, who have covered the animal core with imaginative dreams. In so doing they have had to use what science had to give them; and now science gives them more than ever by taking away fear.

Somewhere too in this night of stars a man, once a reveller, has died. What has the new picture of the universe done for him? A few weeks ago the English newspapers published the will of an old gentleman of seventy-seven who had died as a result of an accident in the hunting field. In the will there occur the following paragraphs:

"At death my body shall be placed in the cheapest decent receptacle and taken in my own trailer and car to the most convenient crematorium and cremated—my gardener William Gittes and my chauffeur will accompany my body and no one else, taking a small box (deal of about twelve inches each way) to bring back the ashes, which are to be broken up and scattered in my wood at Breinton Court, as were my daughter Alice's ashes in 1901.

"I believe (and some of the leading scientific men of the day assure me that I believe rightly) that at my death the organic constituents of my body will be quickly converted into carbonic acid and ammonia, and that these gases will by the law of diffusion be at once distributed over the whole world, and will help to build other plants, and in their turn animals, so that in the future every plant and animal in the world will contain an infinitesimal portion of my body.

"The inorganic parts of my body, the phosphates of lime, etc., will also be dissolved, and by the agency of rains, rivers and ocean currents will also be distributed, but more slowly. The energy left in my body at death, degraded to heat, will quickly leave it and form part of the energy of the universe. This I believe to be the true Resurrection of the Dead and the Life Everlasting.

"I believe in God, but, like the God of St. Paul's Greeks, it is an unknown God, as in our present state of development we are incapable of understanding Him, His origin and some of His laws."

The writer had probably stuck fast in the Darwinian picture of the universe; and his opinions are only moderately important; but what is really interesting is that nobody any longer seems to care at all that he should dare to express such feelings. Though the majority of people still believe in some sort of immortality they are not terrified at the idea of anyone denying what they believe. In short, science has in course of the ages brought humanity the gift of tolerance: it remains for the New Renaissance to extend this gift further than ever before.

The modern man's Bible has its own commandments, "be tolerant" among them, and its own spiritual gifts including the abolition of fear: it is probable that the ancient commandment, the most valuable thing to be found in the Christian Bible, to love one's neighbour as oneself, will become easier to obey in consequence. But if the modern man desires to be good—and all human beings always do—and if he desires spiritual comfort, he can get it in only one way, by studying and trying to understand the best picture of the universe which his epoch can afford. A good conscience is the key to happiness and conscience ever waits on science.